FOREWORD

Trigonometry: Functions and Applications is designed for a two-quarter course at the high school level or a one-semester course at the college level. As an instructor with degrees and experience in both mathematics and chemical engineering, I have learned that a thorough understanding of theory is a prerequisite for the intelligent application of mathematics. Over the past 27 years I have evolved an approach to trigonometry that both imparts the theory and handles the applications in a realistic way. This approach allows each topic to be related to the study of a particular class of function. The students must

1. Define the function,
2. Draw representative graphs,
3. Figure out properties of the class of function,
4. Use that kind of function as a mathematical model.

The resulting ability to use functions as models allows the students to pay more than just lip service to applications. Rather than simply *seeing* graphs of periodic phenomena, the students are expected to draw the graphs *themselves*. Then they must *write equations* for the graphs, and *use* the equations to make predictions and interpretations about the real-world situation they are modeling. Since answers to real-world problems seldom come out "nicely," a calculator or computer is called for, where appropriate. Studied this way, mathematics is certainly not a "spectator sport!"

The materials are designed to interface well with algebra studied from the functions standpoint. However, since many students have studied algebra from more traditional texts, it has *not* been assumed that the students have used this approach before the present trigonometry course. It is assumed that the students have studied geometry, and at least one semester of high school second year algebra.

Since all educators share the responsibility of teaching students to read and write, discovery exercises are included so that students may wrestle with a concept before it is reinforced by classroom discussion. The students are helped with this reading by the fact that much of the wording came from the mouths of my own students. Special thanks go to Brad Foster and Nancy Carnes, whose good class notes supplied input for certain sections.

The third edition differs from the first and second editions in two respects. First, the computer, while not absolutely essential to the text, is considered to be a normal part of the students' repertoire, not just a novelty. For that reason, students concentrate on *using* the computer, rather than on writing programs for it. The primary area of computer use is graphics. Graphics are used to convey concepts rather than simply to draw pretty pictures. For instance, the meaning of trig identities becomes clear as students consider the left and right members to be functions, and those functions turn out to have identical graphs. In this way students learn that the sum-and-product properties of the trig functions explain why AM and FM transmitters broadcast radio waves with the same pattern. Concepts such as asymptotic behavior, negative radius in polar coordinates, and intersections of polar curves that do not correspond to solutions of the two equations make sense due to the fact that students see them dynamically rather than statically.

Programs written by the author, adequate for this text, are contained on a disk that accompanies the Teacher's Resource Book. You are urged to look for commercial software that produces the desired results quicker, more accurately, and in a more user-friendly way.

The second major difference is in the presentation of review materials. Most problem sets now have review problems. The problems usually appear at the end of the problem set. But they are deliberately *not* labeled as review. For the instructor, these problems make it easier to assign review along with regular homework, without having to search back through the book to find problems students have not yet worked. For the student, these problems make a more effective review. He or she must work the problem based on what is asked rather than based on the section in which it appears.

The only new topic introduced in the third edition is computation of the intersection points of polar graphs. Computer graphics makes this topic accessible to students in a mathematically honest way without an exorbitant expenditure of time.

As was true with the second edition, it is assumed that students will use scientific calculators rather than tables. Sinusoidal model problems and triangle problems thus can have answers that use "real" data. As a result, students must check their answers based on whether or not they are reasonable rather than on whether or not the answer came out a small, whole number. The use of the calculator also necessitates an early introduction to the reciprocal properties and to the inverse trig functions so that students will know what keys to press. The ambiguous case for triangles can be handled efficiently using the Law of Cosines and the Quadratic Formula to get both solutions at once. The tables and brief directions on their use are still included for those instructors who choose to teach them.

The third edition retains starting with general angles in degrees, then moving into arc length and radians as they are needed for real-world applications.

Thanks to the many collegues who have supplied input for the second and third editions. These people include Gay Anderson, Carole Arnott, Lou Baker, E. G. Bearden, Darrell Boyd, Anne Brassell, Jeri Chatfield, Melody Gann, Joan Gell, Hector Hirigoyen, Rosalind James, Wayne Johnson, Michael Keyton, Diane McGowan, Carolyn Rankin, Carol Sue Reed, Grady Roe, Ann Singleton, Susan Thomas, Huronica Walker, and Mercille Wisakowsky.

Thanks also go to those who pilot tested and supplied input for the first edition. These include Charley Brown, Pat Causey, Loyce Collenback, Bob Davies, Walter DeBill, Rich Dubsky, Michelle Edge, Sandra Frasier, Byron Gill, Pat Johnson, Pat Juelg, Bill McNabb, Sharon Sasch, Shirley Scheiner, Chuck Straley, Rhetta Tatsch, Kay Thompson, Jim Wieboldt, Marv Wielard, and Martha Zelinka. Calvin Butterball and Phoebe Small appear with permission of their parents, Dr. and Mrs. R. V. Andree.

Paul A. Foerster

CONTENTS

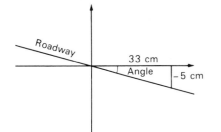

Trigonometry is a study of functions described by angles and distances. By measuring horizontal and vertical distances along the wall, you can calculate the angle that measures how steep the hill is.

In the real world there are many situations in which the values of two or more variable quantities are related to each other. For example, there is a relationship between your weight and how much food you eat. It can be said that your weight *depends* on the amount of food. Weight is the dependent variable and amount of food is the independent variable. In mathematics, equations such as $y = 3x + 5$ are used to express the relationship between two variables. You should recall that the set of ordered pairs (x, y) that satisfies such an equation is called a *function*.

In this chapter you will refresh your memory about the graphs of certain familiar functions. Then you will encounter the *trigonometric* functions whose independent variables are measures of angles. The word *trigonometry* comes from *trigon*, another name for triangle, and *—metry*, meaning measurement. As has happened with many mathematical inventions, the newer uses of trigonometric functions, such as the description of periodic motion, are now more important than the original uses.

Specific objectives for this chapter are listed below. You may not yet understand all the words in these objectives. But they are listed here for your future reference.

1. Given the equation for a function, name it and plot its graph.
2. Given a situation in the real world involving two variable quantities, sketch a reasonable graph showing how these quantities are related to each other.
3. Given information about the sides of an angle, use the definitions of the trigonometric functions to find exact values of the functions.
4. Given the degree of measure of an angle, find approximate values of the six trigonometric functions by calculator.
5. Given a value of a trigonometric function, find the measure of the angle.
6. Given information about a right triangle, use the definitions of the trigonometric functions to find measures of sides and angles.

1–1 REVIEW OF FUNCTIONS

You have probably learned the names of various parts of a function in previous mathematics courses. Some of the more important names are listed here to refresh your memory.

1. *Ordered pair:* A pair of numbers such as (6, 200), in which the first number is a value of the independent variable and the second number is the corresponding value of the dependent variable.

2. *Relation:* Any set
   of ordered pairs.

3. *Graph:* A picture
   of the ordered
   pairs in a relation
   (see sketch).

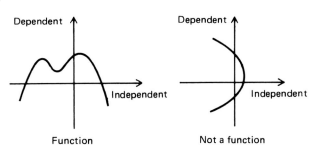

Function   Not a function

4. *Domain:* The set
   of all possible
   values of the in-
   dependent variable.

5. *Range:* The set of those values of the dependent variable corresponding to values of the independent variable which are in the
   domain.

6. *Function:* A relation that has exactly *one* value for the dependent
   variable whenever you put in a value of the independent variable
   that is in the domain (see sketch).

A function is given a name according to the equation that defines it.
For example, if the equation were $x = 3x^2 + 5x - 7$, the function would be
called a "quadratic function," the word *quadratic* being another name for
"second degree." Below are some types of functions and their names.

1. *Linear Function*
   Equation: $y = mx + b$
   Words: y varies linearly with x.

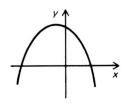

2. *Direct Variation Function*
   Equation: $y = mx$
   Words: y varies directly with x.
   y is directly proportional to x.

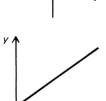

3. *Quadratic Function*
   Equation: $y = ax^2 + bx + c$
   Words: y varies quadratically with x.

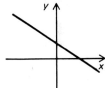

4. *Higher Degree Variation Function*
    Equation: $y = ax^2$, $y = ax^3$, etc.
    Words: y varies directly with the
            square of x.
            y varies directly with the
            cube of x, etc.

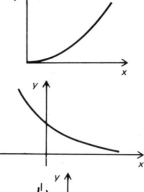

5. *Exponential Function*
    Equation: $y = a \times b^x$ or
              $y = a \times 10^{kx}$
    Words: y varies exponentially with x.

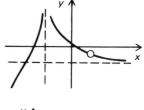

6. *Rational Algebraic Function*
    Equation: $y = \dfrac{\text{polynomial}}{\text{polynomial}}$
    Words: (No special words.)

7. *Inverse Variation Function*
    Equation: $y = \dfrac{a}{x}$, $y = \dfrac{a}{x^n}$
    Words: y varies inversely with x.
            y is inversely proportional
              to x.
            y varies inversely with the nth power of x.

In this section you will name and plot graphs of functions whose equations are given.

Objective:

Given the equation of a function, name it and plot its graph.

Example: For the function $y = 3x^2 - 12x + 7$,

a. Name the function.
b. Calculate values of y for $x = -1, 0, 1, 2, 3, 4$, and 5.
c. Plot the points on graph paper and connect them with a smooth curve.

   a. This is a *quadratic function* because the equation has the form
       $y = ax^2 + bx + c$.

   b. The first thing to do is substitute -1 for x. You get

       $$y = 3(-1)^2 - 12(-1) + 7$$

Doing the arithmetic gives

$$y = 22.$$

By repeating the calculation you get the following table of values.

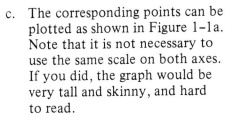

x	y
-1	22
0	7
1	-2
2	-5
3	-2
4	7
5	22

c.   The corresponding points can be plotted as shown in Figure 1-1a. Note that it is not necessary to use the same scale on both axes. If you did, the graph would be very tall and skinny, and hard to read.

The following exercise gives you practice identifying and plotting graphs of functions.

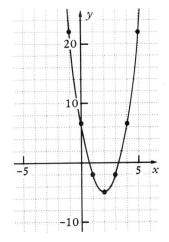

$y = 3x^2 - 12x + 7$

Figure 1-1a

Exercise 1-1

For problems 1 through 14,

a.   Name the function.
b.   Calculate the values of y for the given values of x.
c.   Plot the graph. It is not necessary to use the same scales for both axes. You may use the program PLOT FUNCTION or PLOT RATIONAL on the accompanying disk, or a similar plotting program.

1. $y = 2x + 3$; $x = -4, -2, 0, 2, 4$

2. $y = -\frac{3}{5}x + 1$; $x = -2, -1, 0, 1, 2, 3, 4, 5$

3. $y = \frac{2}{3}x$; $x = 0, 3, 6, 9, 12$

4. $y = 50x$; $x = 0, 1, 2, 3$

5. $y = x^2 - 5x + 4$; $x = -1, 0, 1, 2, 3, 4, 5, 6$

6. $y = -16x^2 + 80x + 3$; $x = 0, 1, 2, 3, 4, 5$

7. $y = 0.3x^3$; $x = 0, 1, 2, 3, 4$

8. $y = 0.2x^4$; $x = 0, 1, 2, 3, 4$

9. $y = \dfrac{12}{x}$; $x = 1, 2, 3, 4, 6, 12$

10. $y = \dfrac{36}{x^2}$; $x = 1, 2, 3, 6, 12$

11. $y = 2^x$; $x = 3, 2, 1, 0, -1, -2$ (Don't forget the definition of negative and zero exponents!)

12. $y = 20 + 80 \cdot 2^{-x}$; $x = 0, 1, 2, 3, 4$

13. $y = \dfrac{x + 1}{x - 2}$; $x = -2, -1, 0, 1, 1.9, 2.1, 3, 4$ (What happens at $x = 2$?)

14. $y = \dfrac{x^2 - x - 2}{x - 2}$; $x = -2, -1, 0, 1, 1.9, 2.1, 3, 4$

   (Simplify the fraction first. What happens at $x = 2$?)

Problems 15 through 17 will refresh your memory about things you have learned in previous courses that you will be using soon in this course.

15. A right triangle has legs 7 cm and 13 cm long. How long is the hypotenuse?

16. A right triangle has a hypotenuse 50 inches long and one leg 32 inches long. Is the other leg shorter or longer than 32 inches? By how much?

17. Name the geometry theorem that is used to work Problems 15 and 16.

1–2 MATHEMATICAL MODELS AND PERIODIC FUNCTIONS

People who apply mathematics want to be able to calculate values of a dependent variable for given values of the independent variable. In this way mathematics can be used to make predictions about things in the real world. For instance, astronauts returning to Earth must fire the retro rockets when they are at exactly the right position. For this purpose they must know equations expressing position as a function of time. When the right time comes, the rockets are fired.

   Functions used in this manner are called *mathematical models*. In this section you will sketch graphs of functions that could represent relationships in the real world.

Objective:

Given a real-world situation in which there are two variable quantities, sketch a reasonable graph showing how these variables are related to each other.

Example 1:   The time it takes you to get home from a football game is related to how fast you drive. Sketch a reasonable graph showing how this time and speed are related.

It seems reasonable to assume that the time *depends* on the speed. This assumption means that you must plot the time on the *vertical* axis and the speed on the *horizontal* axis. You must now decide what the graph looks like, and what the domain and range are.

You decide what the graph looks like by thinking about what happens to the time as your speed varies. For example, at some moderate speed it will take you a moderate amount of time to get home. So you put a point somewhere in the first quadrant (Figure 1–2a). If you go *faster,* it will take you *less* time. So there will be another point to the *right* of and *below* the first one (Figure 1–2b). If you go *slower,* it will take *more* time. So there will be a point to the *left* of and *above* the first point (Figure 1–2c).

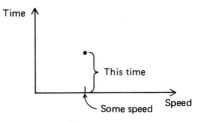

Figure 1–2a

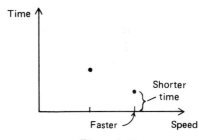

Figure 1–2b

When you have enough points to tell what the graph looks like, you connect them with a line or curve. Figure 1–2d shows the completed graph. Since it always takes you *some* amount of time no matter *how* fast you drive, the graph never touches the horizontal axis. It never touches the vertical axis, either. Any point on that axis has speed = 0, and you would *never* get home if you remained stopped!

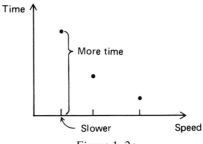

Figure 1–2c

A line that a graph gets closer and closer to but never touches as x or y gets very large is called an *asymptote.* The time and speed axes in Figure 1-2d are both asymptotes.

This graph looks like an inverse variation function, as in Section 1-1.

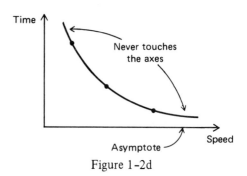

Figure 1-2d

Example 2:   As a child goes up and down on a seesaw, his or her distance from the ground depends on time. Sketch a reasonable graph of this function.

When the child first climbs on, the distance from the ground is zero. So you show the graph starting at the origin. As time goes on, the distance gets higher and lower, higher and lower, at more or less regular intervals. A reasonable graph is shown in Figure 1-2e.

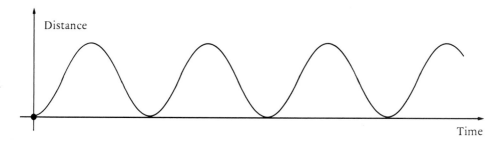

Figure 1-2e

Functions whose graphs behave like Figure 1–2e are called *periodic functions.* The dependent variable has values that repeat themselves as the independent variable changes. You will find that the trigonometric functions which are the subject of this course have graphs that are periodic.

In the following exercise you will sketch reasonable graphs of some other real-world situations.

Exercise 1–2

For problems 1 through 10,

a.   sketch a reasonable graph,

b.   identify the type of function it could be (quadratic, exponential, periodic, etc.)

1. The depth of the water at the beach depends on the time of day due to the motion of the tides.

2. The distance required to stop your car depends on how fast you were going when you applied the brakes.

3. The temperature of a cup of coffee depends on how long it has been since the coffee was poured.

4. As you breathe, the volume of air in your lungs depends on time.

5. A gymnast is jumping up and down on a trampoline. Her distance from the floor depends on time.

6. The distance you go depends on how long you have been going (at a constant speed).

7. As you ride the Ferris wheel at the amusement park, your distance from the ground depends on how long you have been riding.

8. The average temperature for any particular day of the year (averaged over many years) depends on the day of the year.

9. A pendulum swings back and forth in a grandfather clock. The distance from the end of the pendulum to the left side of the clock depends on time.

10. A straight line starts along the positive *x*-axis and rotates counterclockwise around and around the origin of a coordinate system. The *slope* of the line depends on the number of degrees through which the line has rotated.

Problems 11 through 16 will refresh your memory about things you have learned in previous courses or in this course.

11. Construct a right triangle with acute angles of 30° and 60°. If you use graph paper, make the leg opposite the shorter leg 40 cm long. If you use computer software, make it some convenient length.

    a. Confirm that the hypotenuse is *twice* as long as the shorter leg.
    b. Use the Pythagorean Theorem to calculate the *exact* length of the longer leg.
    c. Measure the longer leg, thus confirming the conclusion of the Pythagorean Theorem.

12. Construct an isosceles right triangle. Make the legs each 40 cm long if you use graph paper, or some convenient length if you use computer software.

    a. What are the measures of the acute angles?

     b. Use the Pythagorean Theorem to calculate the *exact* length of the hypotenuse.

     c. Measure the hypotenuse, thus confirming the conclusion of the Pythagorean Theorem.

13. *Reflex Angle Problem:* A reflex angle is defined to be an angle whose measure is between 180° and 360°. Draw reflex angles of the following sizes

     a. 210°   b. 270°   c. 300°   d. 350°

14. *Negative Angle Problem:* If an angle of measure 30° is used to designate rotation in the counterclockwise direction, what would an angle of measure −30° represent? Show your conclusion in a sketch.

15. Write the general equation for a quadratic function.

16. Write an equation for the particular linear function whose graph contains the points (3, 5) and (7, 16).

1–3 MEASUREMENT OF ROTATION

In the last section you sketched graphs of functions which repeat themselves at regular intervals. For example, the time of sunrise is late in the winter, early in the summer, late the next winter, early the next summer, and so forth. Figure 1–3a is a reasonable sketch showing the relationship between the time of sunrise and the day of the year.

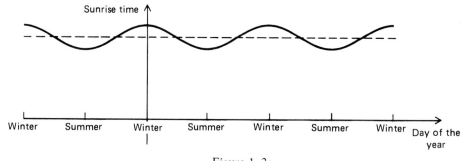

Figure 1–3a

    In this section you will begin to develop the mathematics needed to analyze such *periodic* functions. You will start by generalizing the concept of an angle to angles having measures that are more than 180°, or are negative.

Objective:

Given the measure of an angle, be able to draw a picture of the angle.

An angle is used to measure an amount of *rotation.* For example, it makes sense to say "I rotated 180°" to describe what you did when you turned around backwards. As a measure of rotation, an angle can be as large as you like. For example, a figure skater in a spin turns through an angle of thousands of degrees. To distinguish between clockwise and counterclock-wise rotation, you can use positive angles for one direction and negative angles for the other.

To put these ideas into familiar mathematical terms, consider a ray in some initial position with its end-point kept in a fixed position. Let the ray rotate through a certain num-ber of degrees and come to rest in a terminal position (Figure 1–3b). So that the terminal position will be *uniquely* determined by the measure of the angle, a "standard position" is defined.

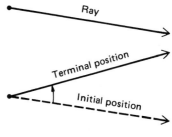

Figure 1–3b

DEFINITION

An angle is in *standard position* in a Cartesian coordinate system if
1. its initial side is along the positive *x*-axis,
2. its vertex is at the origin, and
3. it is measured *counterclockwise* from the *x*-axis if its measure is positive, and *clockwise* if its measure is negative.

Several angles in standard position are shown in Figure 1–3c.

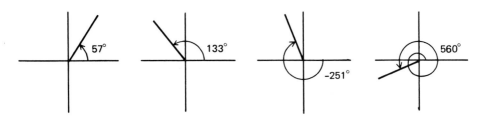

Figure 1–3c

It is possible for angles with *different* measures to terminate at the *same* place. For example, $493°$ terminates at the same place as $133°$ after going through one more complete revolution. So does $-227°$, by rotating clockwise instead of counterclockwise. These "coterminal" angles are shown in Figure 1-3d.

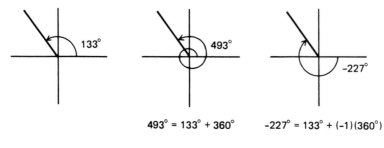

$$493° = 133° + 360° \qquad -227° = 133° + (-1)(360°)$$

Figure 1-3d

DEFINITION

Two angles in standard position are *coterminal* if they terminate at the *same* place (i.e., the terminal rays coincide).

Since coterminal angles differ by an integral number of revolutions, and one revolution is $360°$, the measures of coterminal angles will differ by an integral multiple of $360°$.

Conclusion: The measures of two coterminal angles differ by an integral multiple of $360°$. In other words, angles θ and ϕ are coterminal if and only if

$$\boxed{\phi = \theta + 360n°}$$

where n is an integer.

Notes:

1.   The symbol θ is the Greek letter "theta." Greek letters are often used for angles. Some more frequently used ones are:

α alpha θ theta
β beta ϕ phi
γ gamma ω omega

2. The letter θ may be used for the *angle itself* rather than the measure of the angle. In this case the measure of θ in degrees would be written

$$m°(\theta).$$

For the sake of brevity, the symbol θ is often used interchangeably for the angle or for its measure, provided no confusion will result.

In order to accomplish the objective of drawing an angle in standard position, you can find the measure of the acute angle between the x-axis and the terminal side. This angle is called the reference angle.

DEFINITION

The *reference angle* of an angle in standard position is the *positive, acute* angle (or right angle) between the x-axis and the terminal side of the angle.

Angles terminating in each quadrant are shown in Figure 1–3e with their reference angles.

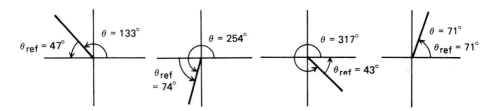

Figure 1–3e

From these sketches you should be able to figure out that if θ is the degree measure of an angle between $0°$ and $360°$, then the measure of its reference angle θ_{ref} can be calculated as follows:

If θ terminates in Quadrant I, $\theta_{ref} = \theta$.
If θ terminates in Quadrant II, $\theta_{ref} = 180° - \theta$.
If θ terminates in Quadrant III, $\theta_{ref} = \theta - 180°$.
If θ terminates in Quadrant IV, $\theta_{ref} = 360° - \theta$.
If θ terminates on a quadrant boundary, $\theta_{ref} = 0°$ or $90°$.

Note: It is usually easier to draw a picture and *figure out* a formula than it is to memorize the formula.

The objective of drawing a picture of an angle in standard position re-duces to the following sequence of steps:

Technique: To sketch an angle in standard position:
1. If the angle is not between 0° and 360°, find a coterminal angle which *is* between 0° and 360°.
2. Find the measure of the reference angle.
3. Sketch the angle in the appropriate quadrant, using the reference angle to tell where in that quadrant it belongs.

Example: Sketch $\theta = 4897°$.
First, you should find a coterminal angle between 0° and 360°. Dividing 4897 by 360 gives

$$\frac{4897}{360} = 13.602777 \dots .$$

This number tells you that the terminal side makes 13 complete revolutions, then another 0.602777 . . . revolution. So you subtract 13 from the original number in the calculator to get 0.602777 . . . , then multiply by 360 to trans-form back to degrees.

$$(0.602777 \dots)(360) = 217$$

Because of round-off in the calculator, it might display a number such as 217.0000008, or 216.99997. These should be rounded off to integers if you start with an integral number of degrees.

So 4897° is coterminal with an angle of 217°, which terminates in the third quadrant. Hence, $\theta_{ref} = 217° - 180° = 37°$. To draw a picture of θ, then, just go 37° below the *x*-axis in the third quadrant, as shown in Figure 1–3f.

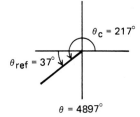

Figure 1–3f

The exercise which follows is designed to give you practice in finding coterminal angles and reference angles and in using these to sketch graphs of various angles in standard position.

Exercise 1–3

For each angle given, find the measure of the reference angle, then draw the angle in standard position. Mark the reference angle on your sketch.

1. 137°	2. 198°	3. 259°	4. 147°
5. 342°	6. 21°	7. 54°	8. 283°
9. −160°	10. −220°	11. −295°	12. −86°
13. 98.6°	14. 57.3°	15. −154.1°	16. −273.2°
17. 5481°	18. 7321°	19. −2746°	20. −3614°

The following angles have measures in degrees and minutes, or in degrees, minutes, and seconds. There are 60 minutes in a degree, and 60 seconds in a minute. To find the difference $180° − 137°24'$, for instance, you "borrow" a degree from 180° and convert it to 60 minutes.

$$\begin{array}{r} 179°60' \\ -137°24' \\ \hline 42°36' \end{array}$$

21. 154°37'	22. 268°29'	23. 213°16'	24. 121°43'
25. 291°44'	26. 352°16'	27. 1066°9'	28. 2001°34'
29. 7321°46'	30. 9007°10'	31. 242°19'27"	32. 146°57'12"
33. 112°48'13"	34. 345°11'59"		

The following problems are for review, either of things you will be needing soon in this course or of things you should know to be mathematically "literate."

35. *Similar Triangles Problem:* Construct a right triangle with a horizontal leg 10 cm long and a vertical leg 6 cm long, as shown in Figure 1−3g.

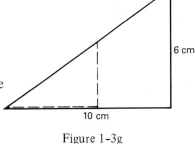

Figure 1-3g

a. Measure the smaller acute angle in the triangle.

b. If you construct a vertical line at the midpoint of the 10 cm leg, thus forming a smaller triangle to the left, would the ratio

(vertical leg)/(horizontal leg)

be smaller or larger for the small triangle than for the original triangle? What theorem from geometry tells you this?

c. Confirm your conclusion in part (c) by actual measurement.

36. Use the Pythagorean Theorem to find the distance between the origin and the point (−5, 2) in a Cartesian coordinate system.

37. A ray with its end at the origin starts pointing along the positive *y*-axis. As it rotates clockwise, its slope depends on the number of degrees through which the line has rotated. Sketch a reasonable graph of this function.

1–4   DEFINITION OF THE TRIGONOMETRIC FUNCTIONS

The position of the terminal side of an angle in standard position is uniquely determined by the measure of the angle. That is, given the measure of an angle in standard position, there is one and only one position of its terminal side. So the position of the terminal side is the *dependent* variable in a function whose independent variable is the measure of the angle. The six trigono-metric functions provide numerical ways of describing the position of the terminal side of an angle in standard position.

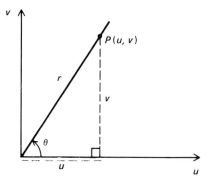

Figure 1–4a

Let θ be an angle in standard posi-tion in a Cartesian coordinate system, as in Figure 1–4a. The variables *u* and *v* are used here because *x* and *y* will be reserved for independent and dependent variables of functions later on. Let *P* with coordinates (*u*, *v*) be a point on the terminal side. Thus, *u* and *v* can be considered to be measures of sides of the right triangle formed by drawing a per-pendicular from *P* to the *u*-axis. By the properties of similar triangles, the ratio *v*/*u* will depend only on the measure of θ, and not on the particular position picked for *P* (Figure 1–4b). The ratio *v*/*u* is called the *tangent of* θ, abbre-viated tan θ. If you designate the dis-tance from the origin to the point *P* by *r* (for radius), there are *six* such trigo-nometric ratios which can be made among *u*, *v*, and *r*. The six trigonometric functions each have θ as the independent variable and one of the trigonometric ratios as the dependent variable.

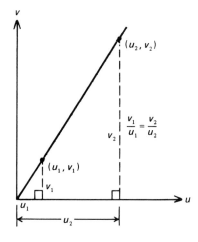

Figure 1–4b

DEFINITION

The six trigonometric functions–tan, cot, sin, cos, sec, and csc–are defined as follows:

$$\tan \theta = v/u \quad \text{(abbreviation for "tangent of } \theta \text{")}$$
$$\cot \theta = u/v \quad \text{(abbreviation for "cotangent of } \theta \text{")}$$
$$\sin \theta = v/r \quad \text{(abbreviation for "sine of } \theta \text{")}$$
$$\cos \theta = u/r \quad \text{(abbreviation for "cosine of } \theta \text{")}$$
$$\sec \theta = r/u \quad \text{(abbreviation for "secant of } \theta \text{")}$$
$$\csc \theta = r/v \quad \text{(abbreviation for "cosecant of } \theta \text{")}$$

Note: The symbol $\tan \theta$, etc., is a form of $f(x)$ terminology where the function's name is tan and the independent variable is θ. The parentheses are omitted unless they are needed for other reasons. As with the logarithm function, $\log x$, the independent variable of the trigonometric functions is often called the *argument.*

Agreement: For the present, r will be assumed to be *positive.*

You have defined six new functions. The first thing you must be able to do is find values of the functions for various values of θ.

Objectives:

Be able to use the definitions to find *exact* values of the six trigonometric functions given

1. the coordinates of a point on the terminal side,
2. the value of one function and the quadrant in which the angle terminates,
3. a "special angle" whose measure is a multiple of $30°$ or $45°$.

The same technique is used for all three of these kinds of given information.

Technique:
1. Draw a picture of θ in standard position.
2. Pick a convenient point (u, v) on the terminal side.
3. Draw a perpendicular from (u, v) to the u-axis.
4. Fill in values for u, v, and r on the diagram.
5. Use the definitions to write values of the six functions.

Example for Objective 1: Find the six trigonometric functions of θ if the terminal side passes through $(-5, 2)$.

Figure 1-4c shows a sketch of θ. The point to pick is obviously $(-5, 2)$. By Pythagoras, you can find r,

$$r = \sqrt{(-5)^2 + 2^2} = \sqrt{29}.$$

The values of the functions are thus

$$\tan \theta = \frac{v}{u} = \frac{2}{-5} = -\frac{2}{5},$$

$$\cot \theta = \frac{u}{v} = \frac{-5}{2} = -\frac{5}{2},$$

$$\sin \theta = \frac{v}{r} = \frac{2}{\sqrt{29}} = \frac{2\sqrt{29}}{29},$$

$$\cos \theta = \frac{u}{r} = \frac{-5}{\sqrt{29}} = -\frac{5\sqrt{29}}{29},$$

$$\sec \theta = \frac{r}{u} = \frac{\sqrt{29}}{-5} = -\frac{\sqrt{29}}{5},$$

$$\csc \theta = \frac{r}{v} = \frac{\sqrt{29}}{2}.$$

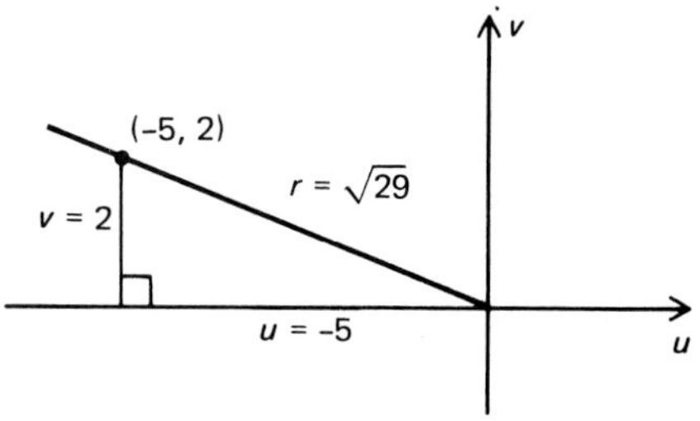

Figure 1-4c

Example for Objective 2: Find the six trigonometric functions of θ if θ terminates in Quadrant III and $\sin \theta = -2/3$.

Figure 1-4d is a picture of a third-quadrant angle. Since $\sin \theta = -2/3 = v/r$, the convenient point to pick on the terminal side has $v = -2$ and $r = 3$. By Pythagoras,

$$u = -\sqrt{3^2 - (-2)^2} = -\sqrt{5},$$

where the "$-$" sign is selected because u is negative in Quadrant III. The values of the other five functions may now be written by inspection.

$$\tan \theta = \frac{v}{u} = \frac{-2}{-\sqrt{5}} = \frac{2\sqrt{5}}{5}$$

$$\cot \theta = \frac{u}{v} = \frac{-\sqrt{5}}{-2} = \frac{\sqrt{5}}{2}$$

$$\sin \theta = \frac{v}{r} = -\frac{2}{3} \text{ (given)}$$

$$\cos \theta = \frac{u}{r} = \frac{-\sqrt{5}}{3} = -\frac{\sqrt{5}}{3}$$

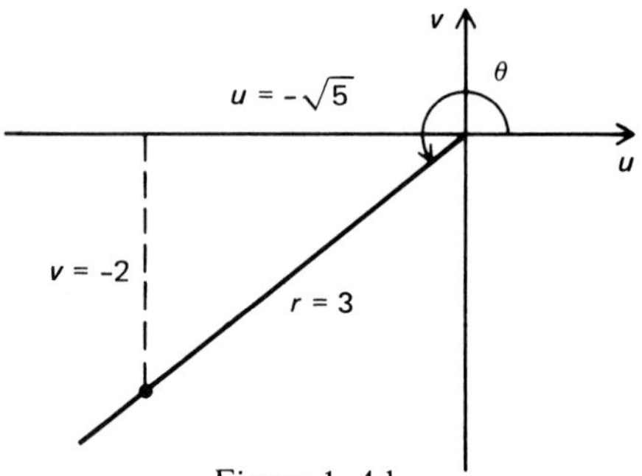

Figure 1-4d

$$\sec \theta \;=\; \frac{r}{u} \;=\; \frac{3}{-\sqrt{5}} \;=\; -\frac{3\sqrt{5}}{5}$$

$$\csc \theta \;=\; \frac{r}{v} \;=\; \frac{3}{-2} \;=\; -\frac{3}{2}$$

Examples for Objective 3:

a.   Find the six trigonometric functions of $300°$.

A sketch of a $300°$ angle is shown in Figure 1–4e. Notice that the reference angle of $300°$ is $60°$. This $60°$ angle is an angle of the triangle formed when a perpendicular is drawn from the point (u, v) to the u-axis. From geometry, you recall that a $30°–60°$ right triangle has sides in the ratio $1:2:\sqrt{3}$. So the most convenient point (u, v) to pick is $(1, -\sqrt{3})$, as shown in Figure 1–4e, the negative sign being picked for v since v is negative in Quadrant IV. The values of the functions can now be written by inspection.

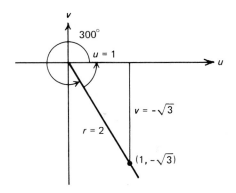

Figure 1–4e

$$\tan 300° \;=\; \frac{v}{u} \;=\; \frac{-\sqrt{3}}{1} \;=\; -\sqrt{3}$$

$$\cot 300° \;=\; \frac{u}{v} \;=\; \frac{1}{-\sqrt{3}} \;=\; -\frac{\sqrt{3}}{3}$$

$$\sin 300° \;=\; \frac{v}{r} \;=\; \frac{-\sqrt{3}}{2} \;=\; -\frac{\sqrt{3}}{2}$$

$$\cos 300° \;=\; \frac{u}{r} \;=\; \frac{1}{2}$$

$$\sec 300° \;=\; \frac{r}{u} \;=\; \frac{2}{1} \;=\; 2$$

$$\csc 300° \;=\; \frac{r}{v} \;=\; \frac{2}{-\sqrt{3}} \;=\; -\frac{2\sqrt{3}}{3}$$

b.   Find the six trigonometric functions of $45°$.

Figure 1–4f shows a $45°$ angle in standard position. A perpendicular from the terminal side to the u-axis forms a $45°–45°$ (isosceles) right triangle. Therefore, its legs have equal length. A convenient point to pick is $(u, v) = (1, 1)$. By Pythagoras, you can find that $r = \sqrt{2}$. The values of the six functions can now be written by inspection.

$$\tan 45° \; = \; \frac{v}{u} \; = \; \frac{1}{1} \; = \; 1,$$

$$\cot 45° \; = \; \frac{u}{v} \; = \; \frac{1}{1} \; = \; 1,$$

$$\sin 45° \; = \; \frac{v}{r} \; = \; \frac{1}{\sqrt{2}} \; = \; \frac{\sqrt{2}}{2},$$

$$\cos 45° \; = \; \frac{u}{r} \; = \; \frac{1}{\sqrt{2}} \; = \; \frac{\sqrt{2}}{2},$$

$$\sec 45° \; = \; \frac{r}{u} \; = \; \frac{\sqrt{2}}{1} \; = \; \sqrt{2},$$

$$\csc 45° \; = \; \frac{r}{v} \; = \; \frac{\sqrt{2}}{1} \; = \; \sqrt{2}.$$

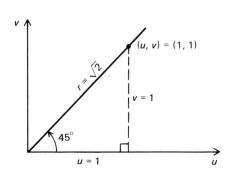

Figure 1–4f

c.   Find the six trigonometric functions of 180°.

An angle of measure 180° terminates on the negative side of the u-axis, as shown in Figure 1–4g. *Any* point on the terminal side is convenient. If $(u, v) = (-3, 0)$, then $r = 3$. It has been agreed that r will always be a *positive* number equaling the distance from the origin to the point (u, v). By inspection,

$$\tan 180° \; = \; \frac{v}{u} \; = \; \frac{0}{-3} \; = \; 0, \qquad\qquad \csc 180° \; = \; \frac{r}{v} \; = \; \frac{3}{0}, \text{ which}$$

$$\cot 180° \; = \; \frac{u}{v} \; = \; \frac{-3}{0}, \text{ which} \qquad\qquad \text{is also undefined because}$$

is undefined because of
division by zero,   (center: of division by zero.)

$$\sin 180° \; = \; \frac{v}{r} \; = \; \frac{0}{3} \; = \; 0,$$

$$\cos 180° \; = \; \frac{u}{r} \; = \; \frac{-3}{3} \; = \; -1,$$

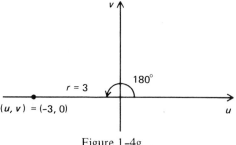

$$\sec 180° \; = \; \frac{r}{u} \; = \; \frac{3}{-3} \; = \; -1,$$

Figure 1–4g

The exercise that follows is designed to give you practice finding exact values of the six trigonometric functions using the definitions. Problem 49 will lead you to discover why three of the functions have the prefix "co–" in their names.

Exercise 1-4

For Problems 1 through 4, find exact values of the six trigonometric functions of an angle θ whose terminal side passes through the given point.

  1. $(4, -3)$ 2. $(-12, 5)$ 3. $(-5, -7)$ 4. $(2, 3)$

For Problems 5 through 8, find exact values of the six trigonometric functions of θ if θ terminates in the given quadrant and has the given function value.

  5. Quadrant II, $\sin \theta = \dfrac{4}{5}$ 6. Quadrant III, $\cos \theta = -\dfrac{1}{3}$

  7. Quadrant IV, $\sec \theta = 4$ 8. Quadrant I, $\csc \theta = \dfrac{13}{12}$

For Problems 9 through 14, find exact values of the six trigonometric functions of the given angle.

  9. $60°$ 10. $135°$ 11. $-315°$ 12. $330°$
  13. $180°$ 14. $-270°$

For Problems 15 through 26, find the exact value of the given trigonometric function. You should try to do this *quickly*, either from memory or by visualizing the diagram in your head.

  15. $\sin 180°$ 16. $\sin 225°$ 17. $\cos 240°$ 18. $\cos 120°$
  19. $\tan 315°$ 20. $\tan 270°$ 21. $\cot 0°$ 22. $\cot 300°$
  23. $\sec 150°$ 24. $\sec 0°$ 25. $\csc 45°$ 26. $\csc 330°$

For Problems 27 through 46, evaluate the given expression. Leave the answer in simple radical form, that is, with no radicals in denominators. Note that the expression $\sin^2 \theta$ means $(\sin \theta)^2$.

  27. $\sin 30° + \cos 60°$ 28. $\tan 120° + \cot (-30°)$
  29. $\tan 300° \sec 300°$ 30. $\sin 300° \csc 300°$
  31. $12 \sin 45° \cos 45°$ 32. $20 \sin 60° \cos 240°$
  33. $\cos 45° \sin 210° - \sin 30° \cos 135°$
  34. $\cos 180° \cos 45° - \sin 180° \sin 45°$
  35. $\tan 30° \cot 30° + \tan 60° \cot 60°$
  36. $\sec 60° \tan 135° - \cot 60° \sin 60°$
  37. $\cos^2 60° + \sin^2 60°$ 38. $\cos^2 150° + \sin^2 150°$
  39. $\cot^2 330° - \csc^2 330°$ 40. $\tan^2 240° - \sec^2 240°$
  41. $\cos^2 45° - \sin^2 135°$ 42. $\sin^2 150° + \cos^2 30°$

  43. $\dfrac{\sec 30°}{\cos 30°}$ 44. $\dfrac{\sin\ 120°}{\cos 120°}$

  45. $\sin^2 30° + \cos^2 30° + \tan^2 30° - \sec^2 30°$
  46. $\sin^2 30° + \cos^2 150° + \tan^2 60°$

47. Find all values of θ from $0°$ through $360°$ for which

    a. $\sin \theta = 0$ b. $\cos \theta = 0$ c. $\tan \theta = 0$
    d. $\cot \theta = 0$ e. $\sec \theta = 0$ f. $\csc \theta = 0$

48. Find all values of θ from $0°$ through $360°$ for which

    a. $\sin \theta = 1$ b. $\cos \theta = 1$ c. $\tan \theta = 1$
    d. $\cot \theta = 1$ e. $\sec \theta = 1$ f. $\csc \theta = 1$

49. From geometry you recall that complementary angles have a sum equal to $90°$. The following questions concern trigonometric functions of angles that are complements of each other.

    a. If $\theta = 60°$, what is the complement of θ?
    b. Find $\cos 60°$ and find the sine of the complement of $60°$.
    c. What relationship is there between the cosine of an angle and the sine of the complementary angle?
    d. What do you suppose the prefix "co–" stands for in the names cosine, cotangent, and cosecant?

50. There is an interesting pattern followed by the sequence of numbers $\sin 0°$, $\sin 30°$, $\sin 45°$, $\sin 60°$, $\sin 90°$, which shows up if all of the denominators are made equal to 2 and all the numerators are written as radicals. Write these five numbers in the form described, and thus demonstrate that you have discovered the pattern.

51. Use a calculator to find $\cos 30°$. Show that the decimal approximation it gives you is equal to the decimal approximation for the radical value you find by the techniques of this section.

52. Find the reference angle for $873°$, and draw $873°$ in standard position.

53. Suppose that 60% of the students in a trigonometry class are female. Draw a pie chart showing the fractions of males and females. What is the measure of the central angle corresponding to the number of females? What special name is given to this kind of angle?

54. Phoebe Small waves at someone out the window of her moving car. Sketch a graph showing the path her hand traces as she waves.

1–5   APPROXIMATE VALUES OF TRIGONOMETRIC FUNCTIONS

Exact values of trigonometric functions can be found for certain angles, such as $30°$ or $45°$, or for angles for which you know a point on the terminal side. Unfortunately, most values of the functions cannot be expressed exactly even with radicals. For these "transcendental" numbers, the best you can hope for are decimal approximations. These may be calculated to any number of decimal places by the technique of "infinite series," as you will see in Chapter 6. This technique is used internally by calculators and computers that give decimal approximations for trigonometric functions. In this section you will use a calculator to find these values. Table I at the end of the book may be used if you do not have a calculator available.

Objectives

1. Given the degree measure of an angle, find decimal approximations for the six trigonometric functions.
2. Given a value of a trigonometric function, find the approximate degree measure of the angle.

Example 1:   Find the six trigonometric functions of 58.6°. Round off the answers to four significant digits.

Most scientific calculators have sin, cos, and tan keys. These functions can thus be found directly.

$\sin 58.6° = 0.8535507 \ldots \approx \underline{0.8536}$ (The "0" is not a significant digit.)

$\cos 58.6° = 0.5210096 \ldots \approx \underline{0.5210}$ (The right "0" *is* a significant digit.)

$\tan 58.6° = 1.6382629 \ldots \approx \underline{1.638}$ (Don't confuse significant digits with decimal places!)

To find the values of the cotangent, secant, and cosecant functions, you must take advantage of the fact that they are *reciprocals* of the other three functions.

$$\cot \theta = u/v = 1/\tan \theta$$
$$\sec \theta = r/u = 1/\cos \theta$$
$$\csc \theta = r/v = 1/\sin \theta$$

You press the appropriate function, then without clearing the calculator, press the "reciprocal" key.

$\cot 58.6° = 1/\tan 58.6° \approx \underline{0.6104}$

$\sec 58.6° = 1/\cos 58.6° \approx \underline{1.919}$

$\csc 58.6° = 1/\sin 58.6° \approx \underline{1.172}$

Example 2:   Find cos 39° 47', correct to 4 significant digits.
   To find trigonometric functions on most calculators, you must first have the angle in decimal degrees. Some calculators have a key for this transformation. If not, press 47 ÷ 60, then add 39, getting 39.78333 . . .°.
Therefore,

   cos 39° 47' = cos 39.78333 . . .° ≈ <u>0.7685</u>

This value can also be found without a calculator by using Table I at the end of the book.
   Accomplishing the second objective, finding the angle measure from the function value, involves pressing the *inverse* function keys on the calculator. These are usually marked $\sin^{-1}$, $\cos^{-1}$, and $\tan^{-1}$, and are read, "sine inverse," "cosine inverse," and "tangent inverse," respectively. Their meanings are:

$\sin^{-1} x$ means, "An angle whose sine is x."
$\cos^{-1} x$ means, "An angle whose cosine is x."
$\tan^{-1} x$ means, "An angle whose tangent is x."
$\cot^{-1} x$ means, "An angle whose cotangent is x."
$\sec^{-1} x$ means, "An angle whose secant is x."
$\csc^{-1} x$ means, "An angle whose cosecant is x."

Note: Do not confuse the expression $\sin^{-1} x$ with the *reciprocal* of $\sin x$. The "−1" exponent here is used to mean the *function* inverse, not the multiplicative inverse.

Example 3:   Find the acute angle $\theta = \sin^{-1} 0.3684$ correct to 2 decimal places.
   Pressing 0.3684, and then $\sin^{-1}$ gives

   $\theta = \sin^{-1} 0.3684 = 21.61697 . . .° ≈ \underline{21.62°}$

   If desired, the 0.61697 . . . can be converted to minutes by multiplying it by 60, giving

   $\theta = 21°37.018 . . .' ≈ \underline{21°37'}$

Example 4:   Find the acute angle $\theta = \sec^{-1} 1.273$ correct to 2 decimal places.
   Since there is no $\cot^{-1}$, $\sec^{-1}$, or $\csc^{-1}$ key on most calculators, you must take advantage of the reciprocal properties listed above. If $\sec \theta = 1.273$,

then $\cos \theta = 1/1.273$. So you take the *reciprocal* of 1.273 first, then press the $\cos^{-1}$ key.

$$\theta = \sec^{-1} 1.273 = \cos^{-1} (1/1.273) = 38.2287 \ldots° \approx \underline{38.23°}$$

Again, if degrees and minutes are desired, multiply the 0.2287 . . . by 60, getting

$$\theta \approx \underline{38°14'}$$

The following exercise gives you practice finding function values from given angle measures, and vice versa.

Exercise 1–5

For Problems 1 through 12, find the indicated function value correct to four significant digits.

1. $\sin 27.4°$	2. $\sin 32.9°$	3. $\cos 77.9°$	4. $\cos 23.2°$
5. $\tan 48.6°$	6. $\tan 59.7°$	7. $\cot 85.2°$	8. $\cot 75.1°$
9. $\sec 12.3°$	10. $\sec 62.8°$	11. $\csc 4.9°$	12. $\csc 87.5°$

13. On a computer screen or a piece of graph paper using a large scale, plot a circle of radius 1 unit. Then plot an angle of measure $26°$ in standard position.

   a. Measure the u- and v-coordinates of the point where the terminal side of the angle crosses the circle. Confirm that these values are approximately the cosine and sine of $26°$.
   b. Divide the coordinates of the point in part (a), vertical over horizontal. Confirm that the answer is approximately $\tan 26°$.

14. Repeat Problem 13 for an angle of $107°$.

For Problems 15 through 26, find the measure of the acute angle θ

   a.   correct to 2 decimal places,
   b.   correct to the nearest minute.

15. $\theta = \sin^{-1} 0.4791$	16. $\theta = \sin^{-1} 0.9353$
17. $\theta = \cos^{-1} 0.9125$	18. $\theta = \cos^{-1} 0.5271$
19. $\theta = \tan^{-1} 1.074$	20. $\theta = \tan^{-1} 4.613$
21. $\theta = \cot^{-1} 0.5234$	22. $\theta = \cot^{-1} 1.452$
23. $\theta = \sec^{-1} 2.581$	24. $\theta = \sec^{-1} 3.000$
25. $\theta = \csc^{-1} 1.062$	26. $\theta = \csc^{-1} 1.234$

For Problems 27 through 32, find θ by calculator and then find the given function of θ. (Do *not* clear the calculator between steps!) Then confirm that your answer is right by sketching the angle and using the definitions of the trigonometric functions.

27. Find $\sin \theta$ if $\cos \theta = 3/5$.   28. Find $\cos \theta$ if $\tan \theta = 5/12$.
29. Find $\tan \theta$ if $\sec \theta = 7/3$.   30. Find $\cot \theta$ if $\sin \theta = 2/3$.
31. Find $\sec \theta$ if $\cos \theta = 3/8$.   32. Find $\csc \theta$ is $\sin \theta = 8/17$.

For Problems 33 through 38, find the measure of θ

a.   correct to 2 decimal places,   b.   correct to the nearest minute.

33. $\sin \theta = 0.6468$ and $90° < \theta < 180°$
34. $\cos \theta = -0.4142$ and $180° < \theta < 270°$
35. $\tan \theta = -0.1844$ and $270° < \theta < 360°$
36. $\cot \theta = 3.941$ and $180° < \theta < 270°$
37. $\sec \theta = -12.84$ and $90° < \theta < 180°$
38. $\csc \theta = 1.395$ and $360° < \theta < 450°$

39. Sketch the graph of a direct square variation function.

40. Sketch the graph of a periodic function.

41. Sketch a right triangle with an acute angle of $33°$. If the hypotenuse is 47 yards long, how long is the side opposite the $33°$ angle?

42. A right triangle has legs 29 inches and 51 inches. What is the measure of the larger acute angle, correct to the nearest minute?

43. Prove that $\sec \theta$ is the reciprocal of $\cos \theta$.

44. Prove that $\tan \theta$ is equal to $(\sin \theta)/(\cos \theta)$.

1-6 RIGHT TRIANGLE PROBLEMS

As stated earlier, trigonometry really means triangle measurement, and it was invented for this purpose. Before you move on to some more recent applications of trigonometry, it is worthwhile to work a few triangle problems. The practice will help cement the definitions of the six trigonometric functions in your mind.

Objective:

Given two sides or a side and an angle of a right triangle, find measures of the other sides and angles.

Example 1:   Suppose you have
been assigned the job of measuring the height of the local water
tower. Climbing makes you
dizzy, so you decide to do the
whole job at ground level. From
a point 47.3 meters from the
base of the tower, you find that
you must look up at an angle of
$53°$ to see the top of the tower
(Figure 1-6a). How high is the
tower?

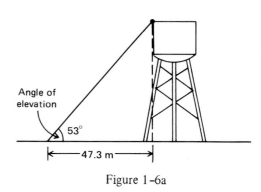

Figure 1-6a

From the picture, you can find the right triangle sketched in Figure 1-6b.
Placing the $53°$ angle in standard position, you can see that $u = 47.3$, and
you must find v. By the definition of tangent,

$$\frac{v}{47.3} = \tan 53°.$$

Multiplying by 47.3, then doing the indicated
operations, you get

$$v = 47.3 \tan 53°$$

By calculator,

$$v = 62.7692 \ldots .$$

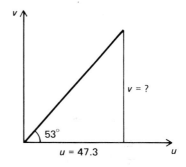

Figure 1-6b

So the tower is approximately 62.8 meters high.

Note that the 62.7692 . . . was rounded off to three significant digits because the 47.3 you started with is assumed to be known only to an accuracy
of three significant digits.

Example 2:   A ship is passing through the Strait of Gibraltar. At its
closest point of approach, Gibraltar radar determines that it is 2400 meters
away. Later, the radar determines that it is 2650 meters away (Figure 1-6c).

   a. By what angle θ did the ship's bearing from Gibraltar change?
   b. How far did the ship travel between the two observations?

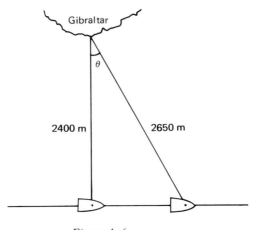

Figure 1–6c

If the triangle in Figure 1–6c is rotated, it can be placed in a *ur*-coordinate system with θ in standard position (Figure 1–6d). So $u = 2400$ and $r = 2650$. Since $\cos \theta = u/r$, you can write

$$\cos \theta = \frac{2400}{2650},$$

$$= 0.905660 \ldots$$

Taking the inverse cosine gives

$$\theta = 25.0876 \ldots .$$

So $\theta \approx 25.09° \approx 25°05'$

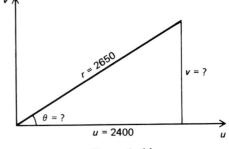

Figure 1–6d

This angle should be saved, without round-off, in the calculator's memory.

To find the distance the ship has traveled, you need to find v. You could use the relationship $v/r = \sin \theta$ or $v/u = \tan \theta$. Using the sine function,

$$\frac{v}{2650} = \sin \theta$$

$$v = 2650 \sin \theta$$

$$= 1123.61 \ldots$$

So the ship traveled about 1124 meters.

Notes:
   1.   You can leave the angle measure as θ while you do the algebra, then simply
        recall its value from the calculator's memory when it is needed for computation.
   2.   If it is assumed that the 2400 and 2650 are known correct to four significant
        digits, then it is meaningful to keep four significant digits in the answer. Any
        more digits would be meaningless in the real world.

Technique: From these two examples, you should be able to extract the
following procedure for solving right triangle problems:

   1.   Draw a picture and identify a right triangle.
   2.   Place the triangle with a *known* or *desired* acute angle in standard
        position.
   3.   If a distance is being sought, write a trigonometric ratio with the
        desired distance in the *numerator.* Then do the necessary algebra
        to calculate the distance.
   4.   If an angle is being sought, find one of its trigonometric functions by
        dividing the length of one known side by another. Then find the
        measure of the angle by calculator or tables.

Exercise 1-6

   1.   *Construction Problem Number 1:* Draw *accurately* a right triangle with
        one leg 8 cm long and one acute angle of measure 34° with the 8-cm leg
        as one of the angle's sides. Use a protractor for the 34° angle and a
        protractor or square for the right angle. Then do the following:

        a.   Measure the other leg and the hypotenuse correct to the nearest
             0.1 cm.
        b.   Calculate the lengths of the other leg and the hypotenuse using the
             appropriate trigonometric functions. Show that the measured and
             calculated lengths agree to within ±0.1 cm.

   2.   *Construction Problem Number 2:* Draw *accurately* a right triangle with
        legs 7.4 cm and 5.8 cm. Use a square or a protractor for the right angle.
        Then do the following:

        a.   Measure the larger acute angle correct to the nearest degree, and
             measure the hypotenuse correct to the nearest 0.1 cm.
        b.   Calculate the measure of the larger acute angle and the length of the
             hypotenuse using the appropriate trigonometric functions. Show
             that the measured and calculated angles agree to within ±1°, and
             that the measured and calculated hypotenuse agree to within
             ±0.1 cm.

3. *Ladder Problem:* You lean a ladder 6.7 meters long against the wall. It makes an angle of $63°$ with the level ground. How high up is the top of the ladder?

4. *Flagpole Problem:* You must order a new rope for the flagpole. To find out what length of rope is needed, you observe that the pole casts a shadow 11.6 meters long on the ground. The angle of elevation of the sun is $36°50'$ (Figure 1–6e). How tall is the pole?

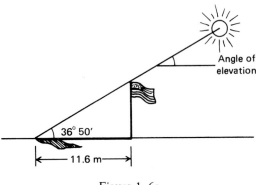

Figure 1–6e

5. *Cat Problem:* Your cat is trapped on a tree branch 6.5 meters above the ground. Your ladder is only 6.7 meters long. If you place the ladder's tip on the branch, what angle will the ladder make with the ground?

6. *Observation Tower Problem:* The tallest freestanding structure in the world is the 553-meter tall CN Tower in Toronto, Ontario. Suppose that at a certain time of day it casts a shadow 1100 meters long on the ground. What is the angle of elevation of the sun at that time of day?

7. *The Grapevine Problem:* Interstate 5 in California enters the San Joaquin Valley through a mountain pass called the Grapevine. The road descends from an altitude of 3000 feet to 500 feet above sea level in a distance of 6 miles. (A mile is 5280 feet.)

    a. Approximately what angle does the road make with the horizontal?
    b. What assumption must you make about how the road slopes?

8. *Grand Canyon Problem:* From a point on the North Rim of the Grand Canyon, a surveyor measures an angle of depression of $1°18'$ to a point on the South Rim (Figure 1–6f). From an aerial photograph, he determines that the horizontal distance between the two points is 10 miles. How many feet is the South Rim below the North Rim? (A mile is 5280 feet.)

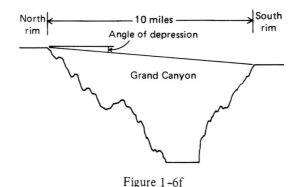

Figure 1-6f

9. *Moon Crater Problem:* Scientists estimate the heights of features on the moon by measuring the lengths of the shadows they cast on the moon's surface. From a photograph, you find that the shadow cast on the inside of a crater by its rim is 325 meters long (Figure 1-6g). At the time the photograph was taken, the sun's angle of elevation from this place on the moon's surface was 23°37′. How high does the rim rise above the inside of the crater?

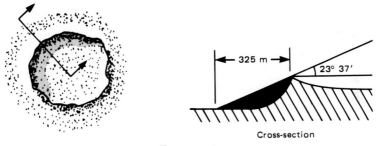

Cross-section

Figure 1-6g

10. *Lighthouse Problem:* An observer 80 feet above the surface of the water measures an angle of depression of 0°42′ to a distant ship (Figure 1-6h). How many miles is the ship from the base of the lighthouse? (A mile is 5280 feet.)

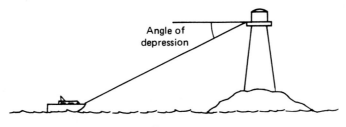

Figure 1-6h

11. *Airplane Landing Problem:* Commercial airliners fly at an altitude of about 10 kilometers. They start descending toward the airport when they are far away, so that they will not have to dive at a steep angle.

   a. If the pilot wants the plane's path to make an angle of 3° with the ground, at what horizontal distance from the airport must he start descending?
   b. If he starts descending a ground distance of 300 kilometers from the airport, what angle will the plane's path make with the horizontal?

12. *Radiotherapy Problem:* A beam of gamma rays is to be used to treat a tumor known to be 5.7 centimeters beneath the patient's skin. To avoid damaging a vital organ, the radiologist moves the source over 8.3 centimeters (Figure 1-6i).

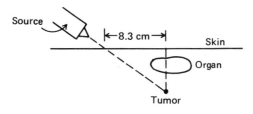

Figure 1-6i

   a. At what angle to the patient's skin must the radiologist aim the gamma ray source to hit the tumor?
   b. How far will the beam have to travel through the patient's body before reaching the tumor?

13. *Triangular Block Problem:* A block bordering Market Street is a right triangle (Figure 1-6j). You start walking around the block, taking 125 paces on Market Street and 102 paces on Pine Street.

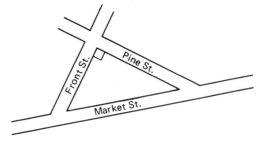

Figure 1-6j

   a. At what angle do Pine and Market Streets intersect?
   b. How many paces must you take on Front Street to complete the trip?

14. *Surveying Problem:* When surveyors measure land that slopes significantly, the distance which is measured will be *longer* than the *horizontal* distance which must be drawn on the map. Suppose that the distance

from the top edge of the Cibolo Creek bed to the edge of the water is 37.8 meters (Figure 1-6k). The land slopes downward at 27°36′ to the horizontal.

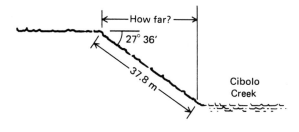

Figure 1-6k

a. What is the horizontal distance from the top of the bank to the edge of the creek?
b. How far is the surface of the creek below the level of the surrounding land?

15. *Guy Wire Problem:* A 2000 foot high television transmitting tower is to be supported by guy wires running from the ground to the top. The wires must make an angle of 63° with the ground (Figure 1-6ℓ).
   a. How long will each wire be?
   b. How far from the base of the tower must the wires be anchored in the ground?

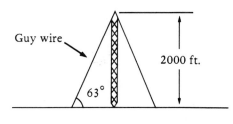

Figure 1-6ℓ

16. *Volcano Problem:* Haleakela (pronounced "hallay-ah-keh-la′′′") is a 10,000 foot high dormant volcano on Maui, Hawaii (Figure 1-6m). The peak is a horizontal distance of only about 30,000 feet from the ocean.
   a. At what angle would you have to look up to see the peak if you were standing on the beach?
   b. What is the straight-line distance from the beach to the peak?

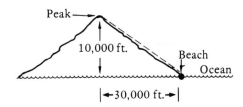

Figure 1-6m

17. *Highland Drive Problem:* One of the steeper streets in the USA is the
500 block of Highland Drive on Queen Anne Hill in Seattle. To measure
the slope of this hill, Calvin Butterball held a builder's level so that one
end touched the pavement. At the other end, the pavement was 14.4
cm below the level. The level itself was 71 cm long (Figure 1-6n).

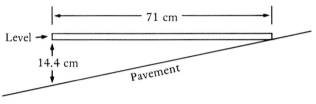

Figure 1-6n

a.   What angle does the road make with the level? Answer in degrees
and minutes.
b.   From a map of Seattle, the *horizontal* length of this block of Highland Drive is 365 feet. How much longer than 365 feet is the *slant*
distance up this hill?
c.   How far does the street rise up in this block?

18. *Cable Car Problem:* Wendy
Uptmore is waiting for the
cable car in the 600 block
of Powell Street in San
Francisco. Since the street
seems to be so steep, she
decides to find out what
angle it makes with the

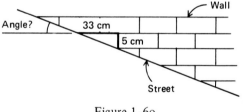

Figure 1-6o

horizontal. On the wall of a house, she measures horizontal and vertical distances of 33 centimeters and 5 centimeters, respectively (Figure
1-6o).

a. What angle does Powell Street make with the horizontal?
b. While she waited, Wendy went up to the top of the block, counting
101 paces. She is tall and figures each pace is 1 meter long. How
many meters did she go *vertically*?
c. If Powell Street had been level instead of slanted, how many paces
would Wendy have to go to walk the 600 block of Powell Street?
Surprising?!

19. *Submarine Problem:* A submarine at the surface of the ocean makes an emergency dive, its path making an angle of 21° with the surface.

    a. If it goes for 300 meters along its downward path, how deep will it be? What horizontal distance is it from its starting point?

    b. How many meters must it go along its downward path to reach a depth of 1000 meters?

20. *Missile Problem:* An observer 5.2 kilometers from the launch pad observes a missile ascending (Figure 1–6p).

    a. At a particular time, the angle of elevation is 31°27'. How high is the missile? How far is it from the observer?

    b. What will the angle of elevation be when the missile reaches 30 kilometers?

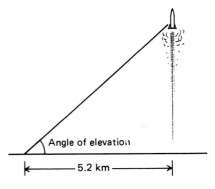

Figure 1–6p

21. *Window Problem:* The windows of a house are to be built so that the eaves completely shade them from the sun in the summer, and so that the sun completely fills them in the winter. The eaves have an overhang of 3 feet (Figure 1–6q).

    a. How far below the eaves should the top of the window be in order for the window to receive full sun in mid-winter, when its angle of elevation is 25°?

    b. How far below the eaves can the bottom of the window come and still receive no sun in mid-summer when its angle of elevation is 70°?

    c. How tall will the windows be if they meet both requirements in parts (a) and (b)?

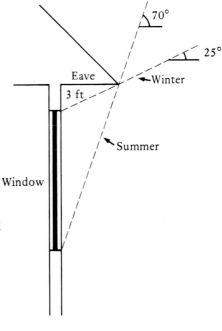

Figure 1–6q

22. *Planet Diameter Problem:* The approximate diameter of a planet can be found by measuring the angle between the lines of sight to the two sides of the planet (Figure 1–6r).

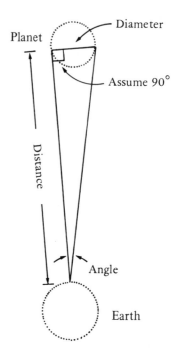

Figure 1–6r

a. When Venus is closest to Earth (25,000,000 miles), the angle is observed to be 0° 1′2.5″. Find the approximate diameter of Venus. (There are 60 minutes in a degree, and 60 seconds in a minute.) Round off to the nearest 10 miles.
b. When Jupiter is closest to Earth (390,000,000 miles), the angle is 0°0′46.9″. To the nearest 100 miles, what is the diameter of Jupiter?
c. Check an encyclopedia or almanac to see how close your answers are to the accepted diameters.

23. *Grand Piano Problem:* The lid on a grand piano is held open by a prop 28 inches long. The base of the prop is 55 inches from the lid's hinge (Figure 1–6s).

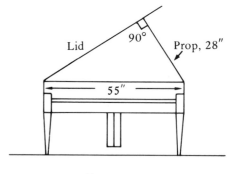

Figure 1–6s

a. To the nearest tenth of a degree, at what angle will the lid open when the prop is placed so that it makes a right angle with the lid?
b. To the nearest tenth of an inch, where on the lid should the prop be placed to make the angle in part (a)?
c. The piano also has a shorter prop 13 inches long. To the nearest tenth of an inch, where on the lid should this prop be placed to make a right angle with the lid?

24. *Pyramid Problem:* The
Great Pyramid of Cheops
in Egypt has a square base
230 meters on each side.
The faces of the pyramid
make an angle of 51°50′
with the horizontal
(Figure 1–6t).

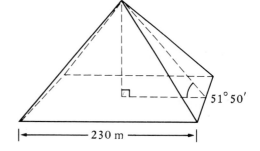

51°50′

|←——————— 230 m ———————→|

a.   How tall is the pyramid?

Figure 1–6t

b.   What is the shortest distance you would have to
climb up a face to reach the top?

c.   Suppose that you decide to make a model of the pyramid by cutting four triangles out of cardboard and gluing them together.
What must the angles of the triangle be?

d.   Show that the ratio of the answer from part b to half the length of
the base is very close to the Golden Ratio, $(\sqrt{5} + 1)/2$. (See Martin
Gardner's article in the June 1974 issue of *Scientific American* for
other startling relationships among the dimensions of this pyramid.)

1–7   CHAPTER REVIEW AND TEST

At the beginning of this chapter are listed six specific objectives. Briefly
stated, these objectives are:

1.   Name and graph a function from its equation.
2.   Sketch graphs of real-world phenomena.
3.   Find exact values for trigonometric functions of special angles.
4.   Find approximate values for trigonometric functions of an angle
from its degree measure.
5.   Find the degree measure of an angle from a trigonometric function
value.
6.   Solve right-triangle problems.

This section contains a review exercise and a chapter test. The review
exercise has six problems, one corresponding to each of the six objectives.
By working these problems, you will see how well you can do the necessary
things when you are *told* which objective is being tested.

However, it is more important for you to be able to select the correct
technique when you are *not* told which objective is being tested. From the
words of the problem, you should be able to draw together both new and
old techniques needed for the solution. It is this ability that will allow you
to apply your knowledge to a new problem, even if you have never seen one
quite like it before.

Therefore, the chapter test consists of a *single* problem. The various parts of this problem will test your ability to figure out *what* to do as well as how to do it. Some parts may require you to apply your knowledge in somewhat unfamiliar ways.

Review Problems

The problems below are numbered according to the objectives stated above.

1. For the function whose equation is $y = \frac{2}{3}x - 4$,

    a. Calculate y if $x = -3, 0, 3$, and 6.
    b. Plot the graph of the function.
    c. Name the kind of function.

2. Rock formations in the Earth's crust move slowly with respect to each other. Rather than sliding smoothly past one another, they stay fixed for years while the stress between them builds up. When the stress reaches a certain value, the formations move *suddenly* and the stress drops back to zero. This sudden movement is an earthquake. The whole process repeats itself until there is another earthquake, and so forth.

    a. Sketch a reasonable graph showing how stress between two particular formations depends on the number of years it has been since an earthquake.
    b. What special name is given to functions like this that repeat themselves at regular intervals?

3. Find the *exact* value of:

    a. the six trigonometric functions of $150°$
    b. $\sec \theta$, if $\theta_{\text{ref}} = 45°$, and θ terminates in Quadrant III.
    c. $\cos \theta$, if θ is in standard position and its terminal side contains the point $(-3, 5)$.
    d. $\tan \theta$, if $\sec \theta = 3$ and θ (in standard position) terminates in Quadrant IV.
    e. $\sec(-120°)$.
    f. $\tan 3060°$.
    g. $4 \sin 60° \cos 60°$.
    h. $\tan^2 30° - \csc^2 30°$.

4. Find decimal approximations.

    a. $\sec 15°42'$
    b. $\tan 85°54'$
    c. $\cos(-22°18')$
    d. $\csc 185°$
    e. $\sin(-3864°)$
    f. $\cot 325°17'$

5. Find the following inverse function values if θ terminates in the quadrant indicated, and $0° \leq \theta \leq 360°$. Answer in degrees and minutes.

   a. $\theta = \sin^{-1} 0.5948$,   Quadrant I
   b. $\theta = \cos^{-1} (-0.3145)$,   Quadrant II
   c. $\theta = \tan^{-1} 31.24$,   Quadrant III
   d. $\theta = \cot^{-1} (-2.605)$,   Quadrant IV
   e. $\theta = \sec^{-1} 1.307$,   Quadrant I
   f. $\theta = \csc^{-1} 1.238$,   Quadrant II

6. *Galleon Problem:*
   Suppose that you are on a salvage ship in the Gulf of Mexico. Your sonar system has located a sunken Spanish galleon at a slant distance of 683 meters from your ship, with an angle of depression of $27°52'$.

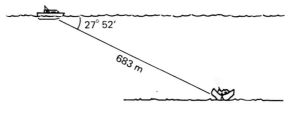

Figure 1-7a

   a. How deep is the water at the galleon's location?
   b. How far must you sail to be directly above the galleon?
   c. You sail directly toward the spot over the galleon. When you have gone 520 meters, what should the angle of depression be?

Chapter Test

The various parts of this problem are designed to see if you can draw together the techniques of this chapter and use them to analyze a single real-world situation. Work each part of the problem. Then tell by numbers 1 through 6 which objective(s) of this chapter you used in working that part.

   You climb into your private plane and start the engine. The propeller turns counterclockwise, starting from a horizontal position (Figure 1-7b).

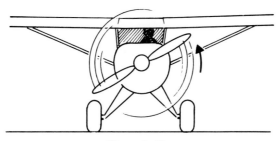

Figure 1-7b

1. As the propeller turns, the distance of its blade tip from the ground de-
    pends on the number of degrees through which the propeller has rotated.
    Sketch a reasonable graph showing how the angle and distance are related
    to each other.

2. You set up a *uv*-coordinate system with
    its origin at the axis of the propeller
    (Figure 1–7c). What are the *exact* values
    of the six trigonometric functions of θ
    when the propeller has rotated:

    a. 120°
    b. 270°
    c. 315°

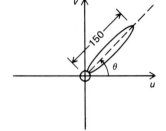

Figure 1–7c

3. The blade is 150 centimeters long. When the *u*-coordinate of its tip is
    100, and the *v*-coordinate is negative,

    a. find the exact values of the six trigonometric functions of θ,
    b. find the measure of the reference angle of θ, correct to the nearest
        minute,
    c. find an angle coterminal with θ, if it is between 0° and 360°, if the
        propeller has made 50 complete revolutions before reaching this
        position.
    d. find the measure of θ.

4. Correct to the nearest 0.1 centimeter, what are the *u*- and *v*-coordinates
    of the blade tip when $\theta = 152°37'$?

5. The center of the propeller is 260 centimeters above the ground. How
    close to the ground is the blade tip when $\theta = 152°37'$?

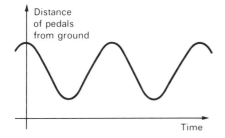

Because trigonometric functions repeat themselves at regular intervals, they make good mathematical models for things in the real world which involve periodic or rotary motion, such as the motion of a bicycle.

CHAPTER 2

So far in your study of trigonometric functions you have defined the six functions, learned how to find values of them, and used them to solve right triangle problems. The next question that logically arises in the study of a new type of function is, "What do their *graphs* look like?" In this chapter you will discover the answer to this question. You will find that their graphs look like some of the real-world graphs you sketched in Section 1-2. Therefore the trigonometric functions, or the closely related circular functions, can be used as mathematical models with which you can *calculate* values of variables in these real-world situations.

Specific objectives for this chapter are:

1. Given the equation of a trigonometric or circular function, be able to

   a. find the value of y for a given value of x,
   b. find the value of x for a given value of y,
   c. sketch the graph quickly.

2. Given the graph of a trigonometric or circular function, find an equation.

3. Given a real-world situation in which one variable repeats its values periodically as the other increases, use a circular function as a mathematical model.

2-1 INTRODUCTION TO SINE AND COSINE GRAPHS

Whenever you are called upon to draw the graph of an unfamiliar function, you must do it by pointwise plotting. That is, you calculate and plot enough points to detect a pattern. Then you connect the points with a line or smooth curve.

Objective:

Discover by pointwise plotting what the graphs of $y = \sin \theta$ and $y = \cos \theta$ look like.

The following exercise is designed to lead you stepwise to the accomplishment of this objective.

Exercise 2-1

1. Make a table of values of θ and $\sin \theta$ for each $10°$ from $0°$ through $90°$. Round off to two decimal places. Then add the values of $\sin 180°$, $\sin 270°$, and $\sin 360°$ to the table, which you should be able to do without using a calculator.

2. Plot the graph of $y = \sin \theta$ from $0°$ through $360°$ using the upper half of a sheet of graph paper. (The lower half will be used for Problem 3.) Draw a horizontal axis across the page and a vertical axis near the left side of the page. Choose scales that make the graph fill most of the upper half of the graph paper. Once you have made an accurate graph between $0°$ and $90°$, you should be able to extend the graph to $360°$ just by using $\sin 180°$, $\sin 270°$, and $\sin 360°$.

3. Make a table of values of θ and $\cos \theta$, as you did in Problem 1. Use these values to plot the graph of $y = \cos \theta$ from $0°$ through $360°$. Use the bottom half of the sheet of graph paper from Problem 2, and use the same scales on the axes as you used in Problem 2.

4. What similarities and differences do you notice between the graphs of the sine and cosine functions?

5. Find $\sin 45°$ and $\cos 65°$. Show that the corresponding points are on the graphs in Problems 2, and 3, respectively.

6. Find $\theta = \sin^{-1} 0.4$ and $\theta = \cos^{-1} 0.8$. Show that the corresponding points are on the graphs in Problems 2 and 3, respectively.

7. Every angle between $360°$ and $720°$ is coterminal with an angle between $0°$ and $360°$. So the sines and cosines of these larger angles are repeats of the values between $0°$ and $360°$. The same is true for angles from $-360°$ through $0°$. On notebook paper, or on another sheet of graph paper, sketch the graphs of $y = \sin \theta$ and $y = \cos \theta$ from $-360°$ through $720°$.

8. What are the domain and range of the sine and cosine functions?

9. What special name is given to functions whose graphs repeat themselves, as do the sine and cosine graphs?

10. Name at least two real-world situations in which two variables are related by a graph that looks like the sine or cosine function graph.

2-2   SINUSOIDS—AMPLITUDE AND PERIOD

In Exercise 2-1 you found that the graphs of $y = \sin \theta$ and $y = \cos \theta$ look like those shown in Figures 2-2a and 2-2b on page 44. The cosine graph is congruent to the sine graph. The only difference is that the cosine graph crosses the *y*-axis at a *high* point, whereas the sine graph crosses the *y*-axis at the origin. The cosine graph is just the sine graph shifted to the left by 90°.

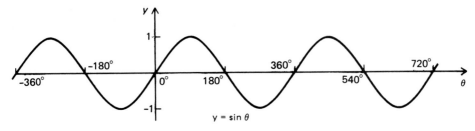

Figure 2–2a

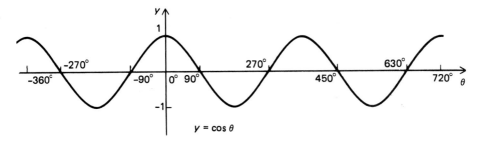

Figure 2–2b

These curves are called *sinusoids*, "sinus" coming from the same origin as "sine," and "–oid" being a suffix meaning "like." These functions are called *periodic* functions because they repeat themselves at regular intervals, or *periods*. Since the sine and cosine functions repeat themselves every 360°, their period is 360°. The portion of a sinusoid between one point and the point at which it first starts repeating itself is a *cycle.* These features are shown in Figure 2–2c.

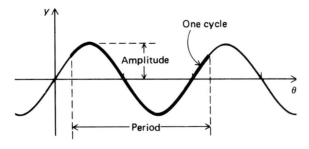

Figure 2–2c

DEFINITIONS

A *cycle* of a periodic function is a portion of the graph of the function from one point on the graph to the point at which the graph starts repeating itself.

The *period* of a trigonometric function is the number of degrees taken to complete one cycle.

A function f is *periodic* with period p if there exists some constant p for which $f(\theta + p) = f(\theta)$ for *all* values of θ.

The distances to which a sinusoid rises and falls above and below its axis is the *amplitude.* This distance is also shown in Figure 2–2c. The amplitude of $y = \sin \theta$ and of $y = \cos \theta$ is 1.

DEFINITION

The *amplitude* of a sinusoid is the distance from its axis to a high point or low point.

In this section you will discover how to draw sinusoids that have amplitudes other than 1 and periods other than 360°.

Objective:

From the equation of a sinusoid, find the amplitude and the period, and use these numbers to sketch the graph.

If you are asked to draw the graph of $y = 3 \sin \theta$, you could simply calculate and plot values as you did in Exercise 2–1. However, there is a quicker way. You already know what the graph of $y = \sin \theta$ looks like. Since each value of $\sin \theta$ is multiplied by 3, the graph will still be a sinusoid, but it will be "stretched out," making the amplitude 3 instead of 1. Such a stretching is called a *vertical magnification,* or a *vertical dilation.* By taking advantage of this fact you can sketch the graph quickly. Picking "critical" values of θ, where the graph reaches a maximum, a minimum, or crosses the θ-axis, you get the graph of Figure 2–2d.

Critical Points

θ	$y = 3 \sin \theta$
0°	0
90°	3
180°	0
270°	−3
360°	0
⋮	⋮

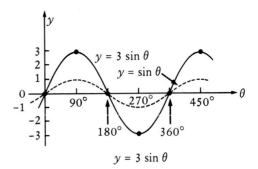

Figure 2-2d

For the graph of $y = \sin 2\theta$, note that θ is multiplied by 2 *before* the sine is taken. The result is quite different from multiplying by a constant after the sine is taken, as in $y = 3 \sin \theta$. The way to find critical points for this function is to pick values of θ which make the argument 2θ equal 0°, 90°, 180°, etc. So θ would equal 0°, 45°, 90°, etc. From these critical points you can sketch the graph in Figure 2-2e.

Critical Points

θ	$y = \sin 2\theta$
0°	0
45°	1
90°	0
135°	−1
180°	0
225°	1
⋮	⋮

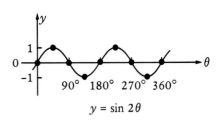

Figure 2-2e

The amplitude is 1, as it was for $y = \sin \theta$. However, the period has been shortened to 180°. The graph now makes *two* cycles every 360° instead of just one.

For the graph of $y = 3 \sin 2\theta$, both the argument and the sine are multiplied by constants. Finding critical points as above leads to the graph in Figure 2-2f.

Critical Points

θ	$y = 3 \sin 2\theta$
0°	0
45°	3
90°	0
135°	−3
180°	0
225°	3
⋮	⋮

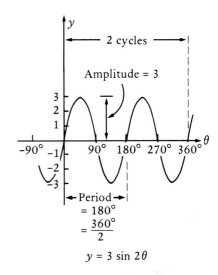

$y = 3 \sin 2\theta$

Figure 2-2f

From your work you can observe that the constant 3 is the *amplitude,* and the constant 2 is the *number of cycles* the graph makes in 360°. These observations lead to general conclusions about graphs of equations.

Conclusion:

For $y = A \sin B\theta$ or $y = A \cos B\theta$.

1. *A* is the *amplitude.*
2. *B* is the number of cycles the sinusoid completes in 360°.
3. The two constants *A* and *B* affect the graph *independently.*

From the second conclusion, there comes a quick way to find the period p:

$$p = \frac{360°}{B}$$

The exercise which follows has problems that will force you to distinguish clearly between the constants *A* and *B* in the equations $y = A \sin B\theta$ and $y = A \cos B\theta$.

Exercise 2-2

For Problems 1 through 12, sketch one complete cycle of each graph by finding high and low critical points and θ-intercepts.

1. $y = \cos \theta$ 2. $y = \sin \theta$
3. $y = 2 \cos \theta$ 4. $y = 4 \sin \theta$

5. $y = \cos 4\theta$ 6. $y = \sin 3\theta$
7. $y = 4 \cos 3\theta$ 8. $y = 5 \sin 2\theta$

9. $y = \cos \frac{1}{3}\theta$ 10. $y = \sin \frac{1}{2}\theta$

11. $y = 2 \cos \frac{1}{3}\theta$ 12. $y = 3 \sin \frac{1}{2}\theta$

13. a. Plot carefully the graph of $y = 3 \sin 2\theta$ by calculating points for each
        5° between $\theta = 0°$ and $\theta = 45°$. Use scales large enough to make the
        graph several inches high and several inches wide.
     b. Calculate y if $\theta = 23°$. Show that this point is on your graph.
     c. Let $y = 1.8$. By doing the appropriate algebra and taking the inverse
        sine, find the value of θ. Show that this point is on your graph.

14. Repeat Problem 13 for $y = 3 \cos 2\theta$.

The following problems are a review of Chapter 1 and other topics.

15. Find the length of the hypotenuse of a right triangle if one acute angle
     is 73° and the leg adjacent to this angle is 23.7 inches.

16. A right triangle has one leg 137 mm long and the hypotenuse is 183 mm
     long. Find the measure of the smaller acute angle, correct to the
     nearest minute.

17. If the measure of an acute angle is $\theta = \sec^{-1} 1.3724$, find the degree
     measure of θ and a decimal approximation for tan 0.

18. Find the largest negative value of θ for which the point $(-2, -7)$ is on
     the terminal side.

19. Find the exact value of tan 150°.

20. The measure of one acute angle of a triangle is 40% of the measure of
     the other acute angle. Find the measures of the two angles.

2–3 SINUSOIDS—PHASE SHIFT AND VERTICAL SHIFT

The constants A and B in $y = A \sin B\theta$ and $y = A \cos B\theta$ are *multiplied*
by the argument or function value. What happens if constants are *added*
rather than multiplied?

Objective:

Be able to draw graphs of functions such as $y = \cos (\theta + 60°)$ and
$y = 3 + \cos \theta$.

To plot $y = \cos(\theta + 60°)$, you seek critical values of θ which make the argument equal $0°, 90°, 180°$, and so forth. These values are $-60°, 30°, 120°, \ldots$. The corresponding function values and graph are shown in Figure 2-3a.

Critical Points

θ	$\theta + 60°$	$\cos(\theta + 60°)$
$-60°$	$0°$	1
$30°$	$90°$	0
$120°$	$180°$	-1
$210°$	$270°$	0
$300°$	$360°$	1

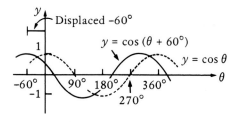

Figure 2-3a

As you can see, the graph of $y = \cos(\theta + 60°)$ is shifted *back*, to the *left*, by $60°$ from the graph of $y = \cos\theta$. The graph of $y = \cos(\theta - 30°)$ can be drawn the same way, using $\theta = 30°, 120°, 210°, \ldots$. The result is shown in Figure 2-3b.

Critical Points

θ	$\theta - 30°$	$\cos(\theta - 30°)$
$30°$	$0°$	1
$120°$	$90°$	0
$210°$	$180°$	-1
$300°$	$270°$	0
$390°$	$360°$	1

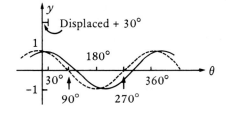

Figure 2-3b

The function $y = \cos(\theta - 30°)$ is said to be "displaced in phase" by $30°$ from the graph of $y = \cos\theta$. In an equation of the form $y = \cos(\theta - D)$, the constant D is called the *phase displacement,* or sometimes the *phase angle.* If this number is substituted for θ, it makes the argument of the cosine equal zero. This fact leads to a definition of phase displacement.

DEFINITION

The *phase displacement* of a sinusoid is the value of θ that makes the argument of the sine or cosine equal zero.

For the graph of $y = 3 + \cos \theta$, the constant 3 is added *after* the cosine is found. The effect is to increase each value of y by 3 units from the normal cosine graph. The entire graph is thus *raised up* by 3 units. Figure 2–3c shows the result.

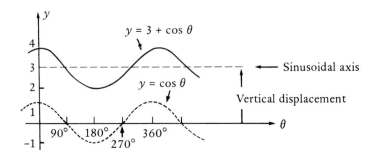

Figure 2–3c

The graph has a *vertical displacement* of 3 units. The axis running through the "middle" of the graph is called the *sinusoidal axis*. This axis moves up by 3 units from its original position on the θ-axis. The shape of the graph does not change.

If the function had been $y = 3 + \cos (\theta - 30°)$, the graph would have both a phase displacement of 30° and a vertical displacement of 3 units. The shape of the graph remains unchanged, as shown in Figure 2–3d.

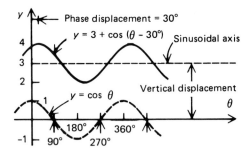

Figure 2–3d

These shifts are called vertical and horizontal *translations*. A translation is a movement of a graph to a new position without changing its shape or rotating it.

Conclusion:

For $y = C + \sin (\theta - D)$ or $y = C + \cos (\theta - D)$,

1. C is the *vertical displacement.*
2. D is the *phase displacement.*
3. The two constants affect the graph *independently.*

   In the following exercise you will sketch graphs that have phase displacements and vertical shifts. You will also sketch some graphs with different periods or amplitudes as you did in Exercise 2-2.

Exercise 2-3

For Problems 1 through 12, sketch one complete cycle of the graph by finding high and low critical points and points where the graph crosses the sinusoidal axis.

1. $y = \sin \theta$ 2. $y = \cos \theta$
3. $y = \sin (\theta - 30°)$ 4. $y = \cos (\theta - 60°)$
5. $y = 4 + \sin \theta$ 6. $y = 2 + \cos \theta$
7. $y = 4 + \sin (\theta - 30°)$ 8. $y = 2 + \cos (\theta - 60°)$
9. $y = 4 \sin \theta$ 10. $y = 2 \cos \theta$
11. $y = \sin 4\theta$ 12. $y = \cos 2\theta$

13. a. Plot accurately the graph of $y = 3 + \cos (\theta - 30°)$ by calculating points for each $10°$ from $\theta = 30°$ through $\theta = 120°$. Use graph paper, and choose scales large enough to make the graph several inches high and several inches wide.
   b. Calculate y when $\theta = 105°$. Show that this point is on your graph.
   c. Let $y = 3.7$. By doing the appropriate algebra and taking the inverse cosine, find the value of θ. Show that this point is on your graph.

14. Repeat Problem 13 for $y = 2 + \sin (\theta - 60°)$, taking each $10°$ from $\theta = 60°$ through $\theta = 150°$.

The following problems review old topics or pave the way for new ones.

15. Show that a triangle with sides 3, 4, and 5 inches long is a *right* triangle. Find the measure of the larger acute angle.

16. Write the exact value of $\sec \theta$ if the terminal side of 0 contains the point $(-7, 13)$.

17. Write the exact value of $\sin 240°$.

18. For $y = 3 + 7 \cos 5 (\theta - 28°)$, do the following.
   a. Find y when $\theta = 321°$.
   b. What is the maximum value y reaches?
   c. For what value of θ does y reach this maximum value?

19. The terminal side of an angle in standard position intersects a circle of radius 5 inches at a point where the curved length of the arc of the circle is also 5 inches (Figure 2–3e). Find the measure of the angle.

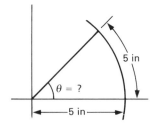

Figure 2–3e

2–4 GENERAL SINUSOIDAL GRAPHS

In Section 2–2 you learned that graphs of the form $y = A \cos B\theta$ have amplitude A and period $360°/B$. In Section 2–3 you learned that graphs of the form $y = C + \cos(\theta - D)$ have vertical displacement C and phase displacement D. In this section you will put together these ideas and graph functions whose equations have the form $y = C + A \cos B(\theta - D)$.

The graph of $y = 3 + \cos 2(\theta - 15°)$ can be drawn by finding critical values of θ, as you did in the last two sections. Substituting 15° for θ makes the argument $2(\theta - 15°)$ equal 0. So 15° is the phase displacement. Setting the argument $2(\theta - 15°)$ equal to 360° locates the end of the first cycle.

$$2(\theta - 15°) = 360°$$
$$\theta - 15° = 180° \qquad \text{Dividing by 2.}$$
$$\theta = 195° \qquad \text{Adding 15°.}$$

Since a cycle starts at 15° and ends at 195°, the period is 195° − 15°, or 180°. Other critical points are at $\theta = 60°$, 105°, and 150°, as shown in the table below.

θ	$2(\theta - 15°)$	$3 + \cos 2(\theta - 15°)$
15°	0°	4
60°	90°	3
105°	180°	2
150°	270°	3
195°	360°	4

The graph is shown in Figure 2–4a.

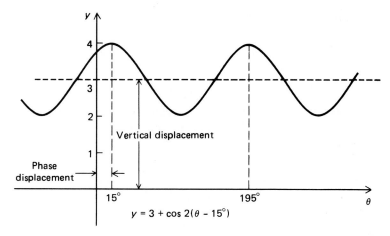

Figure 2–4a

Drawing together the multiplicative and additive constants that you have used in Sections 2–2 and 2–3 leads to a *general* sinusoidal equation of the form

$$y = C + A \cos B(\theta - D).$$

A graph of this equation is shown in Figure 2–4b.

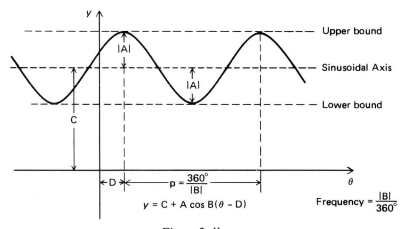

Figure 2–4b

The four constants A, B, C, and D have the following effects:

1. $|A|$ is the *amplitude* (the absolute value being needed since the constant A may be a negative number).

2. $|B|$ is the number of cycles the sinusoid makes in $360°$, so that the period $p = 360°/|B|$.
3. C is the *vertical displacement*.
4. D is the *phase displacement*.
5. The four constants affect the graph *independently*.

The period is the number of degrees per cycle. It is sometimes convenient to speak of the number of *cycles per degree*. This quantity is called the *frequency*.

DEFINITION

The *frequency* of a periodic function is the reciprocal of the period.

Objective:

Given any *one* of the following sets of information about a sinusoid, find the other two:

1. the equation
2. the graph
3. the amplitude, period or frequency, phase displacement, and vertical displacement

Example 1:   Suppose that the frequency of a sinusoid is $1/12$ cycle per degree, the amplitude is 7 units, the vertical shift is -5 units, and the phase displacement is $-4°$ for the cosine function. Write an equation and sketch the graph.

The four constants can be found as follows:

$A = 7$, because the amplitude is 7 units.

$$p = \text{period} = 1/\text{frequency} = \frac{1}{1/12} = 12° \text{ per cycle.}$$

Since $p = 360°/B$, it follows that $B = 360°/p$.

$$\therefore B = 360°/12° = 30.$$

$C = -5$, because the vertical shift is -5 units.

$D = -4$, because the phase displacement is $-4°$.

$\therefore$ Equation is $\underline{y = -5 + 7 \cos 30(\theta + 4°).}$

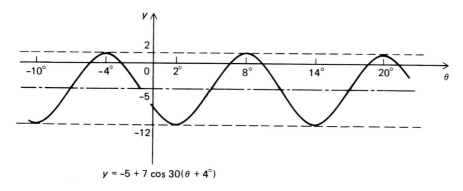

$$y = -5 + 7 \cos 30(\theta + 4°)$$

Figure 2-4c

The graph is shown in Figure 2-4c. An efficient stepwise procedure for drawing this sinusoid is:

1. Draw the sinusoidal axis at $y = -5$.
2. Draw upper and lower bounds by going 7 units above and 7 units below the sinusoidal axis.
3. Find the starting point of a cycle at $\theta = -4$, the phase displacement. Cosine starts a cycle at a high point. (Sine starts a cycle on the sinu-soidal axis, going *up*.)
4. This cycle will end one period later at $\theta = -4° + 12° = 8°$.
5. Halfway between the two high points will be a low point. Halfway between each high and low point, the graph crosses the sinusoidal axis.
6. Sketch the graph through these critical points.

Example 2:   For the sinusoid sketched in Figure 2-4d, tell the period, frequency, amplitude, vertical displacement, and phase displacement. Then write an equation.

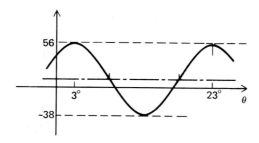

Figure 2-4d

Your reasoning should be as follows:

1. Use the cosine function, because cosine starts a cycle at a high point.
2. One cycle begins at $3°$ and ends at $23°$. So the period is $23° - 3° = 20°$.
3. The frequency is $1/20$ cycle per degree.
4. The sinusoidal axis is halfway between the upper bound, 56, and the lower bound, -38. So the vertical displacement is the *average* of 56 and -38.

$$\therefore C = \frac{1}{2}(56 + (-38)) = \frac{1}{2}(18) = \underline{9 \text{ units.}}$$

5. The amplitude is the distance between the sinusoidal axis and the upper bound.

$$\therefore A = 56 - 9 = \underline{47 \text{ units.}}$$

6. Using the cosine function, the phase displacement is $\underline{3°}$.

7. Since the period is $20°$, $B = \dfrac{360°}{20°} = 18$. Therefore, the equation is

$$\underline{y = 9 + 47 \cos 18(\theta - 3°).}$$

The exercise that follows is designed to give you practice accomplishing the objectives of getting the equation from the graph or drawing the graph from the equation.

Exercise 2-4

For Problems 1 through 8, find the period, amplitude, phase displacement, and vertical displacement. Then use this information to find critical points and sketch the graph.

1. $y = 7 + 4 \cos 3(\theta - 10°)$ 2. $y = 3 + 5 \cos 4(\theta - 15°)$

3. $y = -10 + 20 \sin 2(\theta + 30°)$ 4. $y = -8 + 10 \sin 5(\theta + 6°)$

5. $y = 3 + 5 \cos \frac{1}{2}(\theta + 90°)$ 6. $y = 1000 + 3000 \sin \frac{1}{3}(\theta + 60°)$

7. $y = 11 - 6 \sin (\theta - 17°)$ 8. $y = 15 - 2 \cos (\theta - 40°)$

For Problems 9 through 18, write an equation of the sinusoid. You may use either the sine or cosine, whichever you find more convenient. For each graph, write the period, frequency, amplitude, phase displacement, and vertical displacement.

(Instructions on page 56.)

9.
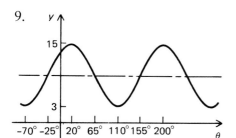

10.
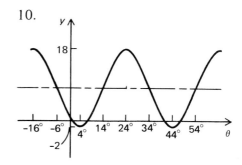

11.
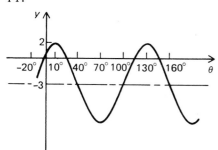

12.
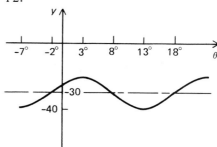

13.
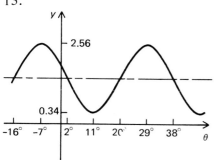

14.
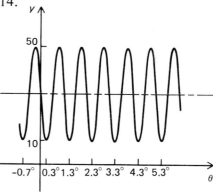

15.
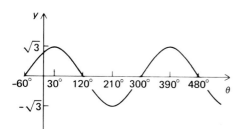

16.
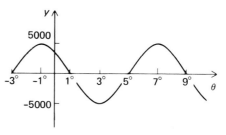

17.   18.

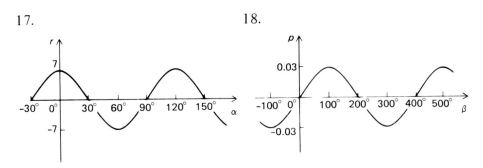

For Problems 19 and 20, draw a graph and find an equation of the sinusoid described.

19. period = 72°, amplitude = 3 units, phase displacement (for the cosine) equals 6°, vertical displacement = 4 units

20. frequency = 1/10 cycle per degree, amplitude = 2 units, phase displacement (for the cosine) equals −3°, vertical displacement = −5 units

21. a. Plot accurately the quarter-cycle of $y = 3 + 2 \cos 6(\theta - 5°)$ for values of θ from 5° through 20°. Use scales big enough to make the graph several inches wide and several inches high.
    b. Calculate y if $\theta = 13°$. Show that this point is on your graph.
    c. Let $y = 4.7$. By doing the appropriate algebra and taking the inverse cosine, find the value of θ. Show that this point is on your graph.

22. Repeat Problem 21 for $y = 3 + 2 \sin 6(\theta - 5°)$.

23. *Magnification and Translation Problem:* Do the necessary algebra to transform the equation

$$y = 3 + 7 \cos 0.2(\theta - 40°)$$

to the form

$$\frac{y - k}{m_y} = \cos \frac{\theta - h}{m_\theta}$$

where h, k, m_θ, and m_y stand for constants. Explain how the graph of the function can be obtained from the graph of $y = \cos \theta$ by magnifying it by m_θ in the θ-direction, magnifying it by m_y in the y-direction, then translating it by h units in the θ-direction and by k units in the y-direction.

24. Sketch graphs that show what would happen to the sinusoid
     $y = C + A \cos B(\theta - D)$ if:

     a. $A = 0$
     b. $B = 0$

The following problems review old concepts or pave the way to new ones.

25. Show that a triangle with sides 5 cm, 12 cm, and 13 cm is a *right*
     triangle. Find the measure of the smaller angle.

26. Write the exact value of cos (−45°).

27. Write the exact value of tan 90°.

28. Find the circumference of a circle with radius 13 inches. If a central
     angle of the circle has measure 57.29578°, how long an arc does it cut
     off on the circle? Surprising?

29. You recall that $f(x)$ is a name for the value of the dependent variable in
     function f if the independent variable is x. Suppose that for a particular
     function, $f(x) = x^2 - 7$.

     a.   Find $f(3)$ by substituting 3 for x.
     b.   Find $f(-5)$.
     c.   Find x if $f(x) = 57$.

30. If $f(\theta) = 3 + 2 \cos \theta$, find exact values for

     a. $f(30°)$ b. $f(180°)$ c. $f(-45°)$

2–5   RADIAN MEASURE OF ANGLES

The degree as a unit of angular measure came from ancient mathematicians,
probably Babylonians. They divided the circle into 360° parts, a convenient
number in the sexigesimal (base 60) number system which they used. A
mathematically more natural unit of angular measure is derived by wrapping
a number line around a unit circle (a circle of radius 1 unit), as shown in
Figure 2-5a.

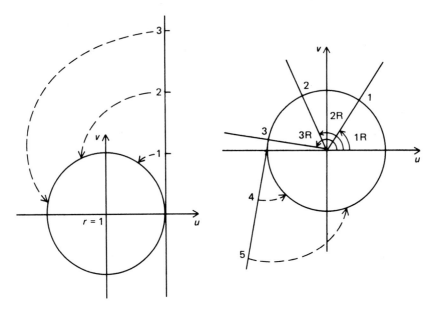

Figure 2–5a

Since the circumference of a circle is $2\pi r$, and r for a unit circle is 1, the wrapped number line divides the circle into 2π, or a bit more than 6, parts. A central angle that cuts off one unit of arc length has a measure of one *radian*. The radian measure of any angle is equal to the arc length cut off on a unit circle centered at the vertex of the angle.

Objectives:

1.   Given the measure of an angle in degrees, find its measure in radians, and vice versa.
2.   Find trigonometric function values for angles in radians.

Since it is now important to distinguish between the *angle* and its *measure*, the symbol θ will be used for the *name* of the angle. Measures of θ will be written:

$m^{\circ}(\theta)$ = degree measure of angle θ
$m^{R}(\theta)$ = radian measure of angle θ

If θ is a complete revolution, then $m^{\circ}(\theta) = 360$ and $m^{R}(\theta) = 2\pi$. Therefore,

$mR(\theta) = \dfrac{2\pi}{360}m°(\theta)$, or more simply:

$$mR(\theta) = \dfrac{\pi}{180}m°(\theta)$$

Multiplying both members by $180/\pi$ and using symmetry:

$$m°(\theta) = \dfrac{180}{\pi}mR(\theta)$$

These two equations lead to the following technique for accomplishing the objective:

Technique: To find the exact radian measure of θ, multiply its degree measure by $\pi/180$. To find the exact degree measure of θ, multiply its radian measure by $180/\pi$.

Example 1:   If $m°(\theta) = 135$, then

$$mR(\theta) = \dfrac{\pi}{180} \cdot 135$$

$$= \dfrac{3\pi}{4}.$$

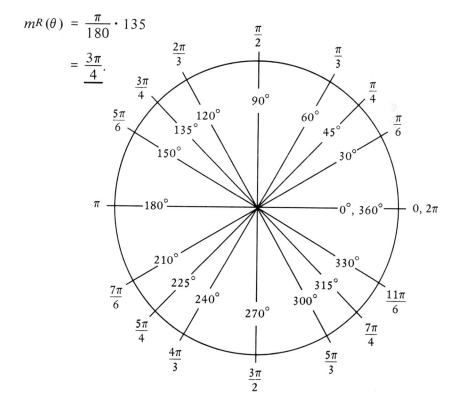

Figure 2–5b

It is worthwhile becoming familiar with the *exact* radian measures of angles that are multiples of 30° and 45°. As shown in Figure 2–5b on page 57, these measures are all multiples of π, and have denominators that are 2, 3, 4, or 6.

For these angles you can find exact values of trigonometric functions from memory.

Example 2:   Evaluate $4 \cos \frac{\pi}{6} + 10 \sin \frac{5\pi}{3}$.

Your thought process should be:

1. $\pi/6$ corresponds to 30° and $5\pi/3$ corresponds to 300°.
2. Therefore, $\cos \pi/6 = \sqrt{3}/2$ and $\sin 5\pi/3 = -\sqrt{3}/2$, the same as $\cos 30°$ and $\sin 300°$.
3. Substitute these numbers and evaluate the expression.

The actual work would look like this:

$$4 \cos \frac{\pi}{6} + 10 \sin \frac{5\pi}{3}$$

$$= 4 \left(\frac{\sqrt{3}}{2} \right) + 10 \left(-\frac{\sqrt{3}}{2} \right)$$

$$= \underline{-3\sqrt{3}}$$

The following exercise gives you practice transforming between degrees and radians, and evaluating functions with radian arguments.

Exercise 2–5

For Problems 1 through 8, find the *exact* number of radians in angles of measure:

1. 60°	2. 45°	3. 30°	4. 120°
5. 180°	6. 450°	7. −225°	8. 1080°

For Problems 9 through 14, find *decimal approximations* for the number of radians. Round off to 2 decimal places.

9. 37°	10. 54°	11. 123°	12. 258°
13. 41°27′	14. 57°18′		

For Problems 15 through 24, find the *exact* number of degrees in angles of radian measure:

15. $\dfrac{\pi}{3}$ 16. $\dfrac{\pi}{2}$ 17. $\dfrac{\pi}{6}$ 18. $\dfrac{\pi}{12}$ 19. $\dfrac{\pi}{4}$

20. $\dfrac{2\pi}{3}$ 21. $\dfrac{3\pi}{4}$ 22. π 23. $\dfrac{3\pi}{2}$ 24. $\dfrac{5\pi}{6}$

For Problems 25 through 30, find the *approximate* number of degrees and minutes in angles of radian measure:

25. 0.34   26. 0.62   27. 1.26   28. 1.57   29. 1   30. 3

For Problems 31 through 36, find the *exact* value of the function of the given number of radians.

31. $\sin \dfrac{\pi}{3}$ 32. $\cos \dfrac{3\pi}{4}$ 33. $\tan \pi$ 34. $\cot \dfrac{7\pi}{6}$

35. $\sec 2\pi$ 36. $\csc \dfrac{4\pi}{3}$

For Problems 37 through 46, evaluate the expression, leaving the answer in simple radical form.

37. $\sin \dfrac{\pi}{2} + 6 \cos \dfrac{\pi}{3}$ 38. $\csc \dfrac{\pi}{2} \sin \dfrac{\pi}{2}$

39. $4 \sin \dfrac{\pi}{3} \cos \dfrac{\pi}{3}$ 40. $\sin \dfrac{2\pi}{3} \cos \dfrac{5\pi}{6} - \cos \dfrac{2\pi}{3} \sin \dfrac{5\pi}{6}$

41. $\sec \dfrac{\pi}{4} \sin \dfrac{\pi}{4} - \tan \dfrac{3\pi}{4} \csc \dfrac{\pi}{3}$ 42. $\cos^2 \pi + \sin^2 \pi$

43. $\tan^2 \dfrac{\pi}{6} - \csc^2 \dfrac{\pi}{6}$ 44. $\cos^2 \dfrac{3\pi}{4} - \sin^2 \dfrac{\pi}{3}$

45. $\dfrac{\cos \dfrac{5\pi}{3}}{\sin \dfrac{5\pi}{3}}$ 46. $\tan \dfrac{\pi}{6} \cot \dfrac{\pi}{3} + \tan \dfrac{\pi}{4}$

Problems 47 through 52 review old concepts or pave the way to new ones.

47. Find the length of the hypotenuse of a right triangle if the larger acute angle is $67°$ and the longer side is 17 furlongs.

48.   Sketch a reasonable graph showing how a person's blood pressure varies as the heart pumps.

49.   Find the exact value of cot 120°.

50.   The word "periodic" occurs in chemistry with roughly the same meaning as it has in trigonometry. However, "periodic" also has a different pronunciation and a completely different meaning in chemistry. What is this other meaning?

51.   Press sin 41° on your calculator. Then, without clearing the calculator, find sin^{-1} of the answer. Surprising?

52.   Suppose that two functions, f and g, have particular equations

$$f(x) = \frac{3}{2}x + 12 \text{ and } g(x) = \frac{2}{3}x - 8.$$

a.   Show that $f(10) = 27$, and that $g(27) = 10$.
b.   Show that $f(37) = 67.5$, and that $g(67.5) = 37$.
c.   In parts (a) and (b) you showed that $g(f(x))$ was equal to x for two particular values of x. Show that $g(f(x)) = x$ for *all* values of x.
d.   There is a special name for two functions that have the property in part (c). What is this name?

2–6   CIRCULAR FUNCTIONS AND INVERSES

In Section 1–2 you encountered some real-world situations in which the graph repeated itself at regular intervals. Then you invented sine and cosine functions, which repeat themselves at regular intervals because the terminal side of the angle keeps coming back to the same position as it rotates around.

However, in many of the real-world situations there is no apparent angle. This was true of the tide problem, the breathing problem, and the sunrise problem. Consequently, it is desirable to invent a new function that behaves the same way as the trigonometric functions, but for which the independent variable is just a *number* rather than an angle.

Objective:

Define a set of functions that behaves like the trigonometric functions but whose independent variable is a number rather than an angle measure.

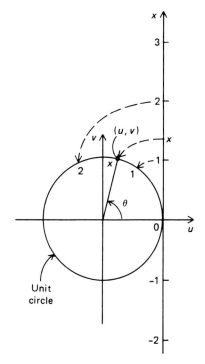

Numbers can be represented on a number line. As you saw in the previous section, a number line can be wrapped around a unit circle, as shown in Figure 2-6a. The point x on the number line is thus represented by an *arc* of the circle that starts at the point $(1, 0)$ and ends at the point x.

Suppose that you let (u, v) be the coordinate of point x on the circle. If you draw an angle θ whose terminal side passes through (u, v), you can write the trigonometric functions of θ. For example,

$$\sin \theta = v/r = v/1 = v.$$

Figure 2–6a

The point (u, v) is uniquely determined by both the angle θ and the number x. Therefore, it is natural to define the sine of the *number* x to be v also. That is,

$$\sin x = v.$$

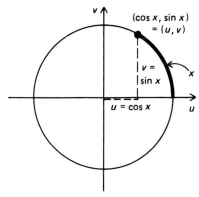

This new sine function is called a *circular function*, since its independent variable x equals the length of an arc on a unit circle (Figure 2–6b).

Definition of Circular Sine and Cosine

Figure 2–6b

DEFINITION

If (u, v) is the terminal point of an arc of length x on a unit circle that starts at the point $(1, 0)$, then the *circular sine and cosine* are:

$$\sin x = v \quad \text{and} \quad \cos x = u$$

The other circular functions are defined in terms of the sine and cosine. For example, the trigonometric function $\tan \theta$ equals v/u. Since $v = \sin x$ and $u = \cos x$, the circular tangent function is defined to be $\sin x / \cos x$.

DEFINITION

The remaining circular functions are defined as follows:

$$\tan x = \frac{\sin x}{\cos x} \qquad\qquad \cot x = \frac{\cos x}{\sin x}$$

$$\sec x = \frac{1}{\cos x} \qquad\qquad \csc x = \frac{1}{\sin x}$$

Since the circumference of a unit circle is 2π and there are 2π radians in a full circle, the variable x in Figure 2–6a is equal to the *radian* measure of θ. That is,

$$x = m^R (\theta).$$

It is this relationship that established the link between trigonometric and circular functions.

Example 1:   Find a decimal approximation for $\sin 0.5$.
    Since an arc length of 0.5 corresponds to an angle of 0.5 radian, you can put the calculator in the radians mode, then press 0.5 and the sin key. The answer, to 4 decimal places, is

$$\sin 0.5 \approx \underline{0.4794}$$

If you have no calculator, such values can be found in Table II at the back of the book.

Example 2:   Find the *exact* value of tan $\frac{2\pi}{3}$.

   Exact values of circular functions for special arc lengths are found in the same way as values of trigonometric functions for special angles in radians. An arc length of $2\pi/3$ has a central angle of $2\pi/3$ radians, or 120°. Therefore,

$$\tan\frac{2\pi}{3} = \underline{-\sqrt{3}}$$

Example 3:   Find a decimal approximation for the inverse circular function, $x = \cos^{-1} 0.7$.

   Make sure your calculator is in the radians mode. Then press 0.7 and the $\cos^{-1}$ keys. The answer, to 4 decimal places, is

$$x = \cos^{-1} 0.7 \approx \underline{0.7954}$$

If you got 45.57 . . . for the answer, your calculator was still in the degrees mode.

Example 4:   Find the *exact* value of $x = \sec^{-1} 2$.

   The secant of x is 2, so $\cos x = \frac{1}{2}$. Pressing 0.5 and $\cos^{-1}$ would give the decimal approximation 1.047. . . . Since the question asks for the *exact* answer, you must use another method. Recall that a 60° angle has a cosine of $\frac{1}{2}$. Since 60° corresponds to an arc length of $\pi/3$, the answer is

$$x = \sec^{-1} 2 = \cos^{-1} \tfrac{1}{2} = \pi/3$$

You can check this answer by dividing π by 3. The result is the same 1.047 . . . that you would get by pressing $\cos^{-1} 0.5$ on the calculator.

   The following exercise is designed to give you practice transforming among arc length, radians, and degrees, and finding values of circular and inverse circular functions.

Exercise 2-6

For Problems 1 through 8, tell the *exact* arc length of a unit circle corresponding to angles of the given number of degrees.

1. 30°	2. 90°	3. 60°	4. 45°
5. 180°	6. −270°	7. 120°	8. 315°

For Problems 9 through 16, tell the *exact* number of degrees in angles corresponding to the given arc lengths of a unit circle.

9. $\dfrac{\pi}{3}$ 10. $\dfrac{\pi}{2}$ 11. 2π 12. $\dfrac{7\pi}{3}$

13. $\dfrac{\pi}{6}$ 14. $\dfrac{\pi}{12}$ 15. $\dfrac{5\pi}{6}$ 16. $\dfrac{7\pi}{12}$

For Problems 17 through 20, tell the *exact* number of radians corresponding to the given arc lengths of a unit circle.

17. $\dfrac{\pi}{3}$ 18. π 19. 2   20. 1.467

For Problems 21 through 28, find the *exact* values of the function.

21. $\sin \dfrac{\pi}{3}$ 22. $\cos \dfrac{\pi}{4}$ 23. $\tan \dfrac{3\pi}{4}$ 24. $\cot \dfrac{4\pi}{3}$

25. $\sec \dfrac{5\pi}{6}$ 26. $\csc \dfrac{11\pi}{6}$ 27. $\cot \pi$ 28. $\tan 2\pi$

For Problems 29 through 38, evaluate the expression, leaving the answer in simple radical form.

29. $\sin \dfrac{\pi}{3} + 6 \cos \dfrac{\pi}{4}$ 30. $4 \sin \dfrac{4\pi}{3} \cos \dfrac{4\pi}{3}$

31. $\sin \dfrac{\pi}{6} \csc \dfrac{\pi}{6}$ 32. $\sin \dfrac{2\pi}{3} \cos \dfrac{\pi}{6} + \cos \dfrac{2\pi}{3} \sin \dfrac{\pi}{6}$

33. $\sec \dfrac{\pi}{3} \cos \dfrac{\pi}{3} + \tan \dfrac{\pi}{3} \cot \dfrac{\pi}{3}$ 34. $\cos^2 \dfrac{2\pi}{3} + \sin^2 \dfrac{2\pi}{3}$

35. $\csc^2 \pi - \tan^2 \pi$ 36. $\sin^2 \dfrac{7\pi}{6} + \cos^2 \dfrac{\pi}{4}$

37. $\dfrac{\cos \dfrac{\pi}{4}}{\sec \dfrac{\pi}{4}}$ 38. $\tan^2 \dfrac{2\pi}{3} \left(1 - \tan^2 \dfrac{7\pi}{6} \right)$

For Problems 39 through 46, find a decimal approximation for the circular function. Round off to 4 decimal places. (Be sure to put your calculator in the radians mode!)

39. $\sin 0.74$ 40. $\cos 1.17$ 41. $\tan 5.3$ 42. $\cot 7.8$
43. $\sec (-2.5)$ 44. $\csc 5$ 45. $\sin 1$ 46. $\cos 2$

For Problems 47 through 54, find a decimal approximation for the inverse circular function. Round off to 4 decimal places. (Be sure to put your calculator in the radians mode!)

47. $x = \sin^{-1} 0.6210$ 48. $x = \cos^{-1} 0.2092$
49. $x = \cot^{-1} 1.345$ 50. $x = \tan^{-1} 3.482$
51. $x = \sec^{-1} 3.7$ 52. $x = \csc^{-1} 10$
53. $x = \cos^{-1} 0.8458$ 54. $x = \sin^{-1} 0.3651$

Problems 55 through 59 review old concepts or introduce new ones.

55. One angle of a right triangle is $\sin^{-1} 0.78$, and the hypotenuse is 20 feet long. How long is the leg opposite the given angle? Be clever!

56. Show by calculator that $\cos^2 67° + \sin^2 67°$ is equal to 1. Find another prime-number value of θ, besides $67°$, for which $\cos^2 + \sin^2 \theta$ is equal to 1.

57. Sketch the graph of $f(\theta) = 3 + 5 \cos 4(\theta - 20°)$.

58. Find the exact value of $\tan 210°$.

59. *The Wrapping Function:*
     Figure 2–6c shows an x-axis wrapped around the unit circle $u^2 + v^2 = 1$ in the uv-coordinate system. For each number x on the number line, there is a unique point (u, v) on the circle. Thus, the point on the circle is a *function* of x. This function is called the *wrapping function, W,* defined by

Figure 2–6c

   $$W(x) = (u, v)$$

   As shown in Figure 2–6c,

   $$W(0) = (1, 0)$$
   $$W(\pi) = (-1, 0)$$

   and so forth. Answer the following questions.

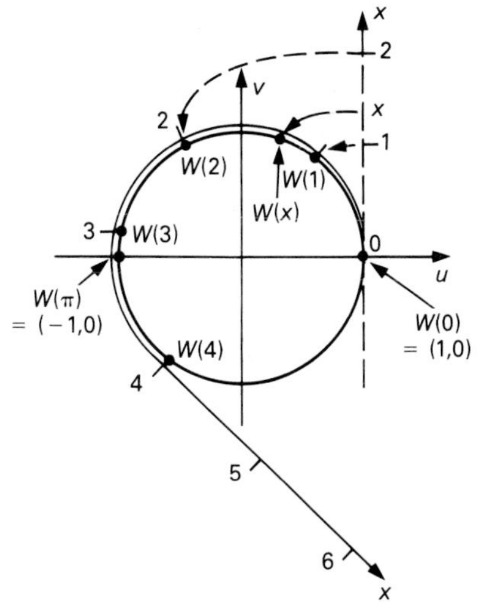

a.   Find $W(\pi/2)$, $W(3\pi/2)$, $W(-\pi/2)$, and $W(2\pi)$.
b.   True or false: For each point on the unit circle, there is a unique value of x. Explain.
c.   Explain why $W(x) = (\cos x, \sin x)$.
d.   Find exact values of $W(\pi/3)$, $W(5\pi/6)$, and $W(-3\pi/4)$.
e.   Find decimal approximations for $W(5)$ and $W(-2.37)$.
f.   Explain why $(0.6, 0.8)$ *can* be a value of $W(x)$, but $(0.3, 0.9)$ *cannot*.
g.   Find three possible values of x for which $W(x) = (0.6, 0.8)$.
h.   Given $W(x) = (0.28, 0.96)$, find $W(x + \pi)$, $W(-x)$, and $W(2\pi + x)$.

2–7 GRAPHS OF CIRCULAR FUNCTION SINUSOIDS

The general equation for a sinusoidal function, which you learned in Section 2–4, is $y = C + A \cos B(\theta - D)$. The independent and dependent variables are θ and y, respectively, and the constants A, B, C, and D determine the shape and placement of the graph. The general equation of a *circular* sinusoidal function has exactly the same form except that x is used for the independent variable rather than θ.

$$y = C + A \cos B(x - D).$$

Because x stands for a *number* rather than an angle, this function is more suitable than the trigonometric functions as a real-world model. For example, x could stand for a *time* or a *distance.*

The only difference in the graphs of circular functions and trigonometric functions is that the circular sine and cosine make a complete cycle for each 2π-unit change in the argument rather than 360°. So the period is given by

$$\text{period} = \frac{2\pi}{|B|},$$

instead of $360°/|B|$.

Objective:

Given the equation of a sinusoid involving circular functions, sketch the graph, and vice versa.

Example 1:   Sketch the graph of $y = -3 + 4 \cos \frac{\pi}{10}(x - 2)$.

If the coefficient B is a multiple of π, then the period will be a rational number. In this case the period is $2\pi/(\pi/10)$, which equals 20. The phase displacement is 2, because substituting 2 for x makes the argument $(\pi/10)(x - 2)$ equal zero. The sinusoidal axis has a vertical displacement of -3, and the amplitude is 4. The graph is shown in Figure 2–7a.

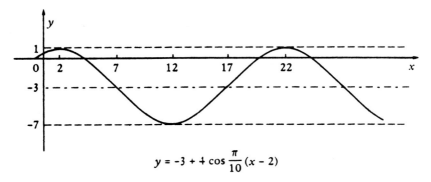

$$y = -3 + 4 \cos \frac{\pi}{10}(x - 2)$$

Figure 2–7a

If B is *not* a multiple of π, then the period will be a multiple of π. A clever way to draw the graph in this case is to mark the x-axis with a scale in multiples of π.

Example 2:   Sketch a graph of $y = 5 + 3 \cos \frac{1}{4}(x + \pi)$.

The period will be $2\pi/\frac{1}{4}$, which equals 8π. So you mark off the x-axis, "$\pi, 2\pi, 3\pi, \ldots$." The phase displacement is $-\pi$, so a cycle starts at $x = -\pi$. The sinusoidal axis is at $y = 5$, and the amplitude is 3. The graph is shown in Figure 2–7b.

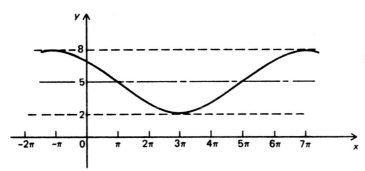

Figure 2–7b

Exercise 2-7

For Problems 1 through 4, sketch at least two cycles of the graph of the circular functions.

1. $y = 3 + 2 \cos \frac{1}{5}(x - \pi)$

2. $y = -4 + 5 \sin \frac{2}{3}(x + \frac{\pi}{2})$

3. $y = 2 + 6 \sin \frac{\pi}{4}(x - 1)$

4. $y = -5 + 4 \cos \frac{\pi}{3}(x + 2)$

For Problems 5 through 10, write an equation of the sinusoid sketched, using a *circular* function.

5.

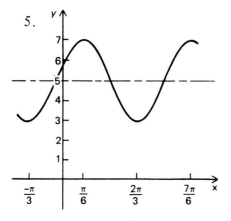

6.

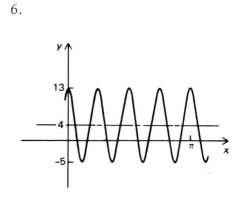

7.

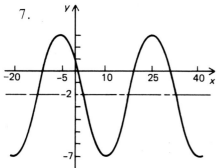

8.

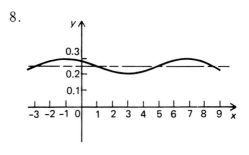

9.

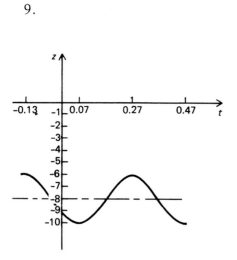

10.

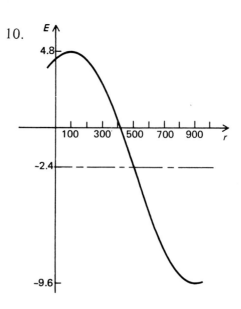

The following problems review old concepts or introduce new ones.

11. Find the approximate number of degrees in 3 radians.

12. Find the exact number of radians in 30°.

13. Find cos 3.

14. Find cos 3°.

15. A right triangle has an acute angle of 1 radian and a hypotenuse of 40 mm. How long is the leg that is adjacent to the 1 radian angle?

16. From Table II, what do you notice about the values of x, sin x, and tan x for very small values of x? How do you explain what you observe?

2-8 SINUSOIDS BY COMPUTER GRAPHICS

Now that you know how to sketch graphs of sinusoids with pencil and paper, you can turn over the routine plotting chores to the computer. Computer-generated graphs are more accurate than most people can draw by hand. They will be more or less coarse, however, because most computers plot only dots on the screen, not smooth curves.

Objective:

Use computer graphics to reinforce your understanding of the shape, amplitude, period, phase, and vertical shift of sinusoidal graphs.

The program PLOT SINUSOID on the disk that goes with this text is adequate to handle the problems in this section. You may choose to use more sophisticated plotting programs or to write your own program.

Example: Given the equation $y = 4 + 5 \cos \frac{\pi}{6}(x - 1)$, do the following.

a. Write down what you expect the period, amplitude, phase displacement, and vertical shift to be.

b. Plot the graph on the computer by running PLOT SINUSOID, or a similar plotting program.

c. Draw a horizontal line at the place you predicted for the sinusoidal axis. Is this line really the sinusoidal axis?

d. Plot a vertical line at the value of x you predicted for the phase displacement. Does the graph really have a high point at this value of x?

e. Add the number you predicted for the period to the number you predicted for the phase displacement. Plot a vertical line at this value of x. How do you tell that your predicted period is really correct?

a.   period = *12*, amplitude = *5*, phase displacement = *1*, vertical shift = *4*.

b.   Use the GRAPH option of
PLOT SINUSOID. The
graph is shown in
Figure 2–8a.

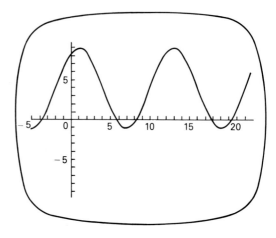

Figure 2–8a

c.   Use the LINE option of
PLOT SINUSOID to draw a
horizontal line at *y* = 4.
The prediction was correct,
as shown in Figure 2–8b.

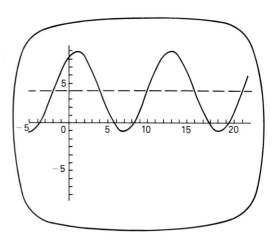

Figure 2–8b

d. Use the LINE option of PLOT SINUSOID to draw a vertical line at $x = 1$ (Figure 2-8c). The line does go through a high point.

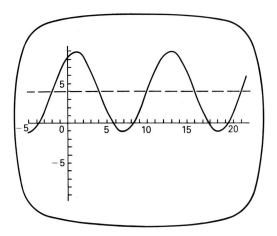

Figure 2-8c

e. Draw a vertical line at $x = 13$ (Figure 2-8d). The predicted period is correct because there is exactly 1 cycle of the graph between $x = 1$ and $x = 13$.

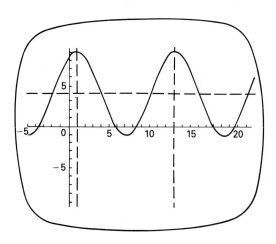

Figure 2-8d

In the following exercise you will plot more graphs by computer. Problem 20 asks you to write your own program.

Exercise 2-8

1. Plot the graph of $y = \sin x$ on the computer screen. If you use PLOT SINUSOID on the accompanying disk, which asks you to enter C, A, B, and D for the equation $y = C + A \cos B(x - D)$, you must enter 0, 1, 1, 0 for these coefficients. You may also want to change scales so that the graph appears larger on the screen.

    a. Measure the period of the graph. How does this value compare with what you expect it to be?
    b. What is the amplitude of the graph on the screen?
    c. What is approximately the first positive value of x at which the graph reaches a maximum? How does this value compare with what you expect it to be?

2. Plot the graph of $y = \cos x$ on the computer screen.

    a. Measure the period of the graph. How does this value compare with what you expect it to be?
    b. What is the amplitude of the graph on the screen?
    c. What is approximately the first positive value of x at which the graph reaches a minimum? How does this value compare with what you expect it to be?

3. a. Plot the graph of $f(x) = \cos x$ and $g(x) = 3 + \cos x$ on the same set of axes.
    b. Draw a horizontal line at $y = 3$. What relationship does this line have to the graph of function g?

4. a. Plot the graph of $f(x) = \sin x$ and $g(x) = -2 + \sin x$ on the same set of axes.
    b. What is the equation of the sinusoidal axis for function g? Plot this line on your graph from part (a), showing that your equation is correct.

5. Let $f(x) = \sin x$ and $g(x) = 3 \sin x$.

    a. How do you expect the graph of function g to differ from that of function f?
    b. Plot both graphs on the screen. Do the graphs look as you predicted in part (a)? You can use the GRID option of PLOT SINUSOID so that you can tell more accurately.

6. Let $f(x) = \cos x$ and $g(x) = -2 \cos x$.

    a. How do you expect the graph of function g to differ from that of function f?

      b. Plot both graphs on the screen. Do the graphs look as you predicted in part (a)?

7. Given: $f(x) = 3 + \cos x$ and $g(x) = 3 \cos x$.

      a. What do you expect the difference to be between *adding* 3 to $\cos x$ in function f and *multiplying* by 3 in function g?

      b. Plot both graphs. Do they confirm your prediction?

8. Given: $f(x) = -2 + \sin x$ and $g(x) = -2 \sin x$.

      a. What do you expect the difference to be between *adding* -2 to $\sin x$ in function f and *multiplying* by -2 in function g?

      b. Plot both graphs. Do they confirm your prediction?

9. a. Plot the graph of $f(x) = \sin x$.

      b. Let $g(x) = \cos (x - D)$. What value of D will make the graph of function g exactly coincide with the graph of function f? Plot the graph of g and show that it really does overlay the graph of f.

10. a. Plot the graph of $f(x) = \cos x$.

      b. Let $g(x) = \sin (x - D)$. What value of D will make the graph of function g exactly coincide with the graph of function f? Demonstrate that you are right by plotting g.

11. Let $f(x) = \cos x$ and $g(x) = \cos 2x$. In what way will the graph of g differ from the graph of f? Confirm that you are right by plotting both functions on the same set of axes. You may want to use a scale that makes one cycle of the graph of f use most of the screen.

12. Let $f(x) = \sin x$ and $g(x) = \sin 3x$. In what way will the graph of g differ from the graph of f? Confirm that you are right by plotting both functions on the same set of axes.

13. Let $y = \sin \dfrac{\pi}{3}x$.

      a. What do you expect the period to be?

      b. Find a decimal approximation for $\dfrac{\pi}{3}$. Plot the graph, using a decimal approximation for $\dfrac{\pi}{3}$ if necessary, confirming your prediction in part (a). Draw a vertical line on the screen at the place where $x =$ one period.

14.   Let $y = \cos \frac{\pi}{5}x$.

  a.   What do you expect the period to be?

  b.   Find a decimal approximation for $\frac{\pi}{5}$. Plot the graph and confirm your prediction in part (a). Draw a vertical line on the screen at the place where $x =$ one period.

15. a.   If $y = \cos Bx$, figure out what B must equal to make the period exactly 4 units.

  b.   Plot the graph using this value of B. Is the period really 4? If not, erase the graph and repeat the problem.

16. a.   If $y = \sin Bx$, figure out what B must equal to make the period exactly 6 units.

  b.   Plot the graph using this value of B. Is the period really 4? If not, erase the graph and repeat the problem.

For Problems 17 and 18, figure out an equation for the sinusoid sketched. Then plot your equation on the computer and confirm that it matches the given graph.

17.   18.

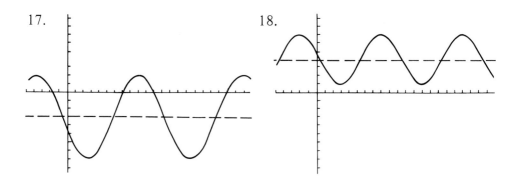

19.   Given the equation $y = 3 + 4 \sin \frac{\pi}{5}(x + 1)$,

  a.   write down what you expect the period, amplitude, phase displacement, and vertical shift to be.

  b.   plot the graph on the computer.

  c.   draw a horizontal line at the place you predicted for the sinusoidal axis. Is this line really the sinusoidal axis?

    d.   plot a vertical line at the value of x you predicted for the phase displacement. Does the graph really cross its axis, going up, at this value of x?

    e.   Add the number you predicted for the period to the number you predicted for the phase displacement. Plot a vertical line at this value of x. How do you tell that your predicted period is really correct?

20. *Sinusoid Plotting Program:*   Write a computer program to plot the graph of a sinusoid of the form $y = C + A \cos B(x - D)$. The input should be the values of C, A, B, and D. The computer should plot axes on the screen, then plot the graph of the given function. You should build in protection against going off the screen, either by having the computer ignore those points or by having it automatically adjust the scales so that the graph fits.

Problems 21 and 22 are intended to refresh your knowledge of other kinds of functions which you learned about in previous courses.

21. *Quadratic Function Problem:*   Let $y = x^2 - 2x - 3$.

    a.   What geometric figure will the graph be?
    b.   Without actually plotting the graph, figure out where the vertex will be.
    c.   Calculate the x- and y-intercepts.
    d.   Plot the graph on the computer using PLOT FUNCTION from the accompanying disk, or another similar plotting program. You might want to compress the vertical scale to make the graph have reasonable proportions. Were all of your predictions correct?

22. *Linear Function Problem:*   Given the system of linear equations

$$3x + 5y = 32$$
$$x - 2y = 6$$

    a.   calculate the coordinates of the point where the graphs will intersect.
    b.   plot both graphs using the program PLOT LINEAR from the accompanying disk or a similar plotting program.
    c.   draw vertical and horizontal lines at the values of x and y you calculated in part (a). Were your calculations correct? How do you tell?

2–9 GRAPHS OF TANGENT, COTANGENT, SECANT, AND COSECANT FUNCTIONS

The graphs of the tangent, cotangent, secant, and cosecant functions may be plotted pointwise as you did at first with sinusoids in Section 2–1. You should get graphs that look like those in Figures 2–9a and 2–9b.

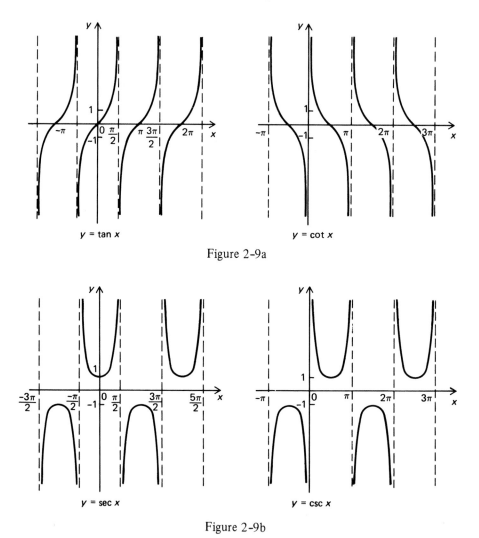

$y = \tan x$

$y = \cot x$

Figure 2-9a

$y = \sec x$

$y = \csc x$

Figure 2-9b

Once you learn the shapes of the graphs, you can plot them quickly by finding crictical features. This is how you plotted sinusoids rapidly in Section 2-4.

The most significant difference between these graphs and the sinusoidal graphs is that they are *unbounded* in the y-direction. They have vertical asymptotes at regular intervals. To see why, recall that these functions can be written as ratios involving sines and cosines.

$$\tan x = \frac{\sin x}{\cos x}, \cot x = \frac{\cos x}{\sin x}, \sec x = \frac{1}{\sin x}, \csc x = \frac{1}{\cos x}$$

Wherever the cosine function is zero, the tangent and cosecant functions will have asymptotes. Wherever the sine function is zero, the cotangent and secant functions will have asymptotes. Figure 2–9c shows two examples.

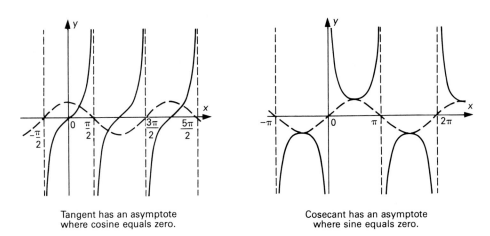

Tangent has an asymptote
where cosine equals zero.

Cosecant has an asymptote
where sine equals zero.

Figure 2–9c

Objective:

Given an equation of the form $y = C + A\, f(B(x - D))$, where f is tan, cot, sec, or csc, be able to sketch the graph quickly.

Example 1:   Sketch a graph of $y = 3 + 2 \tan (\frac{\pi}{6})(x - 1)$.

The process is similar to sketching sinusoids, as you did in Section 2–4. The constant 3 tells you that the axis of the graph is 3 units above the x-axis. The constant 1 tells you that the phase displacement is 1 unit (to the right). These features are marked on the first sketch of Figure 2–9d.

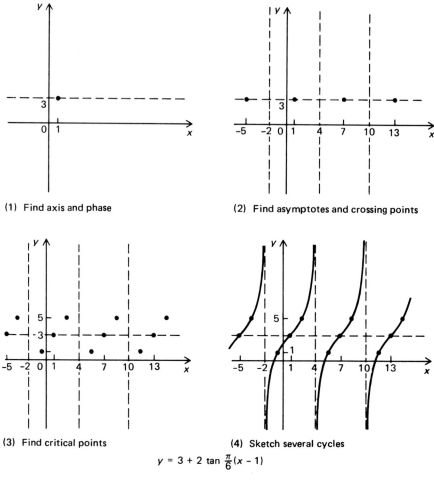

(1) Find axis and phase

(2) Find asymptotes and crossing points

(3) Find critical points

(4) Sketch several cycles

$$y = 3 + 2 \tan \tfrac{\pi}{6}(x - 1)$$

Figure 2-9d

The next thing to do is to locate the asymptotes. Since the period of $y = \tan x$ is π rather than 2π, the period of the given function is $\pi/(\pi/6) = 6$ units. Going 3 units in each direction from the axis-crossing point locates two asymptotes, as shown in the second sketch of Figure 2–9d. Other axis crossings and asymptotes are 6 units apart. The constant 2 is the vertical magnification. It tells you how "stretched out" the graph is vertically. Since $\tan \pi/4 = 1$, the constant 2 tells you that halfway between an asymptote and a crossing point the graph is 2 units above or below its axis. These critical points are shown in the third sketch of Figure 2–9d. All that remains is sketching several cycles of the graph, as shown in the last sketch of Figure 2–9d.

Example 2: Sketch a graph of $y = 3 + 2 \csc (\pi/6)(x - 1)$.

As you can observe, the constants in this equation are the same as those in Example 1. Only the *function* has been changed. The axis location and phase displacement will be the same as in Example 1. Since the cosecant has an *asymptote* where the argument equals zero, there will be an asymptote at $x = 1$. The period is $2\pi/B$, since the period of $y = \csc x$ is 2π. So the period of the given function is $2\pi/(\pi/6) = 12$ units. But the cosecant has an asymptote in the middle of the cycle, too. So the asymptotes will still be 6 units apart. Halfway between asymptotes there will be maximum or minimum points. The constant "2" tells you that these points are 2 units above or below the graph's axis (*not* the x-axis!). The completed graph is shown in Figure 2–9e.

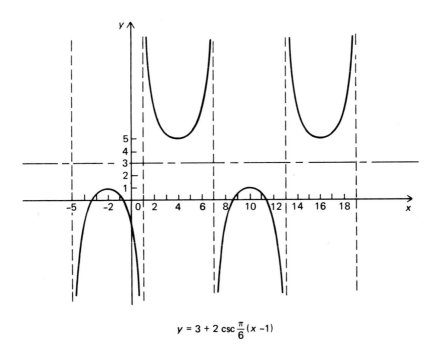

$$y = 3 + 2 \csc \frac{\pi}{6}(x - 1)$$

Figure 2-9e

In the exercise that follows, you will sketch graphs of tangent, cotangent, secant and cosecant functions. You will also use computer graphics to plot tangent and secant graphs on the screen.

Exercise 2-9

For Problems 1 through 4, plot an accurate graph of the function by finding
y for each $10°$ and plotting the points. The purpose of these problems is for
you to see by actual plotting what the exact shapes of the graphs are. Therefore, you should use scales that are fairly large, and plot and draw carefully.
The knowledge of these shapes will help you in sketching the graphs for the
rest of the problems in this section.

1. $y = \tan \theta$, $-90° < \theta < 90°$ 2. $y = \cot \theta$, $0° < \theta < 180°$

3. $y = \sec \theta$, $-90° < \theta < 90°$ 4. $y = \csc \theta$, $0° < \theta < 180°$

For Problems 5 through 8, sketch graphs of the given circular functions.

5. $y = \sec x$ 6. $y = \csc x$ 7. $y = \cot x$ 8. $y = \tan x$

For Problems 9 through 24, sketch at least one cycle of the given function's
graph. Assume that the function is circular if the independent variable is x
and trigonometric if the independent variable is θ.

9. $y = \tan 2\theta$

10. $y = \cot \frac{\pi}{3}x$

11. $y = \csc \frac{\pi}{2}x$

12. $y = \sec 3\theta$

13. $y = 2 \cot x$

14. $y = \frac{1}{2} \tan \theta$

15. $y = \frac{1}{3} \sec \theta$

16. $y = 2 \csc x$

17. $y = 4 + 3 \tan \pi x$

18. $y = -5 + 3 \cot 4\theta$

19. $y = -6 + 2 \csc 5\theta$

20. $y = 1 + 4 \sec \frac{\pi}{10}x$

21. $y = -1 + 3 \cot 2(\theta - 30°)$

22. $y = 2 + 5 \tan \frac{\pi}{8} (x - 3)$

23. $y = 4 + 6 \sec \frac{\pi}{2}(x + 1)$

24. $y = -3 + 2 \csc 4(\theta + 10°)$

25. *Tangent Graphs by Computer:*   Use the program PLOT TANGENT or a similar plotting program to plot the following graphs.

  a. $y = \tan \frac{\pi}{20} x$

  b. $y = \tan \frac{\pi}{8} (x - 3)$

  c. $y = 0.5 \tan \frac{\pi}{4} x$

  d. $y = 3 + \tan \frac{\pi}{10} (x + 2)$

  e. $y = -1 \tan \frac{\pi}{6} (x - 3)$ (What function is this the graph of?)

26. *Secant Graphs by Computer:*   Use the program PLOT SECANT or a similar plotting program to plot the following graphs.

  a. $y = \sec \frac{\pi}{12} x$

  b. $y = \sec \frac{\pi}{4} (x - 3)$

  c. $y = 2 \sec \frac{\pi}{5} x$

  d. $y = 3 + 2 \sec \frac{\pi}{5} (x - 1)$

  e. $y = \sec \frac{\pi}{6} (x - 3)$ (What function is this the graph of?)

27. *Asymptotic Behavior Problem:*   Figures 2–9f and 2–9g show computer-drawn graphs of tangent and secant functions. Based on your observations of the computer as it was drawing the graphs in Problems 25 and 26, describe the behavior of a function when its argument crosses an asymptote.

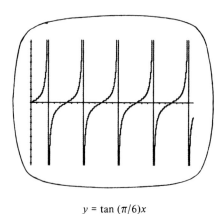

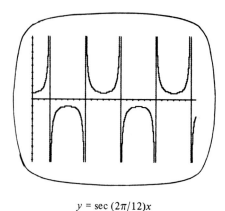

$$y = \tan (\pi/6)x \qquad\qquad\qquad\qquad y = \sec (2\pi/12)x$$

Figure 2-9f   Figure 2-9g

28. *Long Triangle Problem:*   Figure 2-9h shows triangle
     ABC with base $c = 10$, and variable altitude a and
     hypotenuse b.

     a. Find a and b when θ equals:
         i. 89°,
         ii. 89.9°,
         iii. 89.99°.

     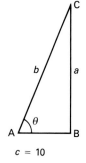

     b. Describe what happens to the values of a and b as
         θ nears 90°

     c. Show that in spite of the fact that a and b get
         closer to each other, the difference between
         their squares stays 100. Name the geometrical theorem which
         indicates that this fact is true.

     d. Explain how the behavior of sides b and c as θ nears 90° corre-
         sponds to the behavior of the tangent and secant graphs as they
         approach their asymptotes.

Figure 2-9h

2-10 GENERAL INVERSE SINE AND COSINE RELATIONS

The definition of $\theta = \sin^{-1} 0.8$ tells you that θ is "an angle whose sine is
0.8." As you can see from Figure 2-10a, there are *many* angles whose sine
is 0.8. Similarly, there is an infinite number of values of $\theta = \cos^{-1} 0.8$, as
shown in Figure 2-10b.

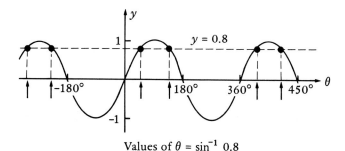

Values of $\theta = \sin^{-1} 0.8$

Figure 2-10a

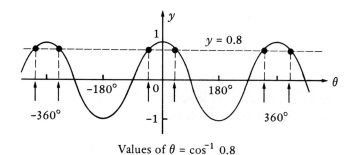

Values of $\theta = \cos^{-1} 0.8$

Figure 2-10b

In this section you will learn how to find any desired value of an inverse trigonometric or circular relation.

Objective:

Be able to find values of θ or x for $\sin^{-1} y$ and $\cos^{-1} y$.

If you press $\sin^{-1} 0.8$ and $\cos^{-1} 0.8$ on a calculator, the answers are first-quadrant angles.

$$\sin^{-1} 0.8 \approx 53°$$

$$\cos^{-1} 0.8 \approx 37°$$

If the argument is negative, a surprise shows up!

$$\sin^{-1} (-0.8) \approx -53°$$

$$\cos^{-1} (-0.8) \approx 143°$$

On the calculator, $\sin^{-1} (-0.8)$ is a *fourth*-quadrant angle, $-53°$. But $\cos^{-1} (-0.8)$ is a *second*-quadrant angle, $143°$. Figure 2-10c shows why this is true.

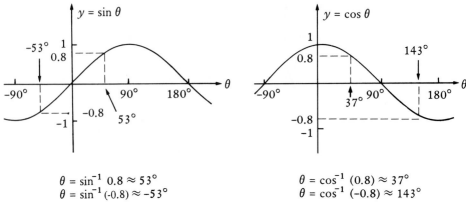

$$\theta = \sin^{-1} 0.8 \approx 53°$$
$$\theta = \sin^{-1} (\text{-}0.8) \approx \text{-}53°$$

$$\theta = \cos^{-1} (0.8) \approx 37°$$
$$\theta = \cos^{-1} (\text{-}0.8) \approx 143°$$

Figure 2–10c

On the calculator, $\sin^{-1} y$ is always an angle from $-90°$ to $90°$ (or an arc from $-\pi/2$ to $\pi/2$). However, $\cos^{-1} y$ is an angle from $0°$ to $180°$ (or an arc from 0 to π). Values of $\sin^{-1} y$ and $\cos^{-1} y$ in these ranges are called the *principal values* of the inverse sine and inverse cosine relations. As you will see in Chapter 4, these are also called values of the inverse sine and inverse cosine *functions*.

To distinguish between the principal values and any other values of $\sin^{-1} y$ and $\cos^{-1} y$, a *capital* letter is used for the name, $\text{Sin}^{-1} y$ and $\text{Cos}^{-1} y$.

DEFINITION

Principal values of inverse trigonometric relations:

$$\theta = \text{Sin}^{-1} y \quad \text{means} \quad y = \sin \theta, \text{ and } -90° \leqslant \theta \leqslant 90°.$$

$$\theta = \text{Cos}^{-1} y \quad \text{means} \quad y = \cos \theta, \text{ and } 0° \leqslant \theta \leqslant 180°.$$

Principal values of inverse circular relations:

$$x = \text{Sin}^{-1} y \quad \text{means} \quad y = \sin x, \text{ and } -\pi/2 \leqslant x \leqslant \pi/2.$$

$$x = \text{Cos}^{-1} y \quad \text{means} \quad y = \cos x, \text{ and } 0 \leqslant x \leqslant \pi.$$

Example 1: Find all values of $\theta = \cos^{-1} (-0.3)$.

By calculator, $\text{Cos}^{-1}(-0.3)$ $\approx 107.46°$. As shown in Figure 2-10d, $\cos(-107.46°)$ is also equal to -0.3. So you could write

$$\cos^{-1}(-0.3) \approx \pm 107.46°$$

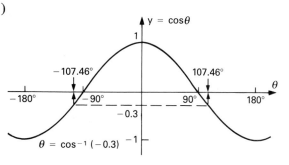

All other angles will be *coterminal* with $107.46°$ or with $-107.46°$. A compact way of writing this fact is

Figure 2-10d

$$\theta = \cos^{-1}(-0.3) \approx \underline{\pm 107.46° + 360n°} \ ,$$

where n stands for an *integer* (positive, negative, or 0). This set of values of θ is called the *general* solution of $\theta = \cos^{-1}(-0.3)$.

Example 2:   Find the first three positive values of $\theta = \cos^{-1}(-0.3)$.
    From Example 1, setting $n = 0, 1, 2, \ldots$, and adding the multiples of $360°$ produces the following particular values of θ:

$$\theta \approx 107.46°, \ 467.46°, \ 827.46°, \ldots, \ \text{or}$$
$$\theta \approx -107.46°, \ 252.54°, \ 612.54°, \ldots \ .$$

From these, you simply pick the first three that are positive.

$$\theta \approx \underline{107.46°, \ 252.54°, \ 467.46°}$$

Example 3:   Find the first three positive values of $x = \cos^{-1} 0.427$, correct to 4 decimal places.
    The procedure is the same as for Examples 1 and 2, except that the calculator must be in the radians mode. Finding the general solution,

$$x = \cos^{-1} 0.427 = \pm 1.12962 \ldots + 2\pi n$$

The "$2\pi n$" is added to find coterminal arcs because the period of the circular cosine or sine is 2π, rather than $360°$ for the trigonometric functions. The $1.12962 \ldots$ should be stored in the calculator's memory without round-off.

Adding multiples of 2π to 1.12962 ... and then to -1.12962 ... and rounding off gives

$$x \approx 1.1296, \quad 7.4128, \quad 13.6960, \ldots, \quad \text{or}$$

$$x \approx -1.1296, \quad 5.1536, \quad 11.4367, \ldots .$$

From these, the first three positive values of x are

$$x = \cos^{-1} 0.427 \approx \underline{1.1296, \quad 5.1536, \quad 7.4128}$$

Example 4:   Find all values of $x = \sin^{-1} 0.67$, to 4 decimal places.

The calculator, in radians mode, gives $\text{Sin}^{-1} 0.67 =$ 0.734208 ... . Between 0 and 2π there are *two* arcs, 0.734208 ..., and $\pi - 0.734208$ ... (which equals 2.40738 ...) whose sines are 0.67 (Figure 2–10e). So the general solution for x is

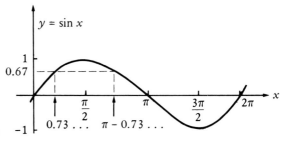

$$x = \sin^{-1} 0.67$$

$$\approx \underline{0.7342 + 2\pi n \text{ or } 2.4074 + 2\pi n}$$

$$x = \sin^{-1} 0.67$$

Figure 2-10e

Since $\sin(-x)$ does *not* equal $\sin x$, $\sin^{-1} y$ cannot be written with a $\pm$ sign, as can $\cos^{-1} y$.

The following exercise gives you practice finding values of inverse trigonometric and circular sines and cosines.

Exercise 2-10

For Problems 1 through 8, find the indicated *principal* value to 2 decimal places for θ, or 4 decimal places for x.

1. $\theta = \text{Sin}^{-1} 0.195$
2. $\theta = \text{Cos}^{-1} 0.605$
3. $\theta = \text{Cos}^{-1} (-0.2843)$
4. $\theta = \text{Sin}^{-1} (-0.9541)$
5. $x = \text{Cos}^{-1} 0.845$
6. $x = \text{Sin}^{-1} 0.227$
7. $x = \text{Sin}^{-1} (-0.97)$
8. $x = \text{Cos}^{-1} (-0.007)$

For Problems 9 through 24, find θ to 2 decimal places or x to 4 decimal places, getting:

a.   the general solution,
b.   the first three positive values of θ or x.

9. $\theta = \cos^{-1} 0.91$
10. $\theta = \cos^{-1} 0.36$
11. $\theta = \sin^{-1} 0.53$
12. $\theta = \sin^{-1} 0.28$
13. $\theta = \cos^{-1} (-0.15)$
14. $\theta = \cos^{-1} (-0.84)$
15. $\theta = \sin^{-1} (-0.76)$
16. $\theta = \sin^{-1} (-0.62)$
17. $x = \cos^{-1} 0.26$
18. $x = \cos^{-1} 0.73$
19. $x = \sin^{-1} 0.98$
20. $x = \sin^{-1} 0.52$
21. $x = \cos^{-1} (-0.1)$
22. $x = \cos^{-1} (-0.2)$
23. $x = \sin^{-1} (-0.63)$
24. $x = \sin^{-1} (-0.04)$

For Problems 25 through 40, find the *exact* principal value of θ or x, using a multiple of π, if necessary.

25. $\theta = \mathrm{Cos}^{-1} \dfrac{\sqrt{3}}{2}$
26. $\theta = \mathrm{Sin}^{-1} \dfrac{\sqrt{3}}{2}$

27. $\theta = \mathrm{Sin}^{-1} \left(-\dfrac{1}{2}\right)$
28. $\theta = \mathrm{Cos}^{-1} \left(-\dfrac{\sqrt{2}}{2}\right)$

29. $\theta = \mathrm{Sin}^{-1} 1$
30. $\theta = \mathrm{Cos}^{-1} 1$

31. $x = \mathrm{Cos}^{-1} 0$
32. $x = \mathrm{Sin}^{-1} 1$

33. $x = \mathrm{Sin}^{-1} \dfrac{\sqrt{2}}{2}$
34. $x = \mathrm{Cos}^{-1} \dfrac{1}{2}$

35. $x = \mathrm{Cos}^{-1} (-1)$
36. $x = \mathrm{Sin}^{-1} (-1)$

37. $x = \mathrm{Sin}^{-1} 0$
38. $x = \mathrm{Cos}^{-1} \left(-\dfrac{\sqrt{3}}{2}\right)$

39. $x = \mathrm{Cos}^{-1} 3$ (Surprise?!)
40. $x = \mathrm{Sin}^{-1} 2$ (Surprise!!?)

41. If $y = 7 + 4 \cos 2(\theta - 50°)$,

    a. find y when $\theta = 173°$.
    b. find the first three positive values of θ for which $y = 10$. Be careful!

42. *Computer Graphics Verification of Inverse Values:*

    a. Plot two cycles of $y = \cos x$ on the screen using PLOT SINUSOID or a similar program. Draw a horizontal line across the screen at $y = 0.26$. Then draw vertical lines at each of the three values of $x = \cos^{-1} 0.26$ calculated in Problem 17. How does the computer graphing tell you that these answers are correct?
    b. Repeat part (a) with $y = \sin x$, to confirm the values of $\sin^{-1} 0.52$ from Problem 20 above.

2-11 EVALUATION OF SINUSOIDAL FUNCTIONS

You have learned that the general equation for a sinusoidal function is

$$y = f(x) = C + A \cos B(x - D), \quad \text{or}$$
$$y = f(x) = C + A \sin B(x - D).$$

For application of these functions to problems in the real world, you must be able to find values of $f(x)$ if x is given, and find values of x if $f(x)$ is given. In this section you will put together the techniques you have been learning and do these things.

Objectives:

Given the equation of a sinusoidal function,

    1. find values of $f(x)$ for given values of x,

    2. find values of x for given values of $f(x)$.

Example 1:   If $f(x) = 2 + 3 \cos \frac{\pi}{9}(x - 6)$, find $f(8)$ correct to three decimal places.

    All you need to do is substitute 8 for x and do the arithmetic. The calculator should be in the radians mode since these are *circular* functions.

$$f(8) = 2 + 3 \cos \frac{\pi}{9}(8 - 6) \qquad \text{Substituting 8 for } x.$$

$$= 2 + 3 \cos \frac{2\pi}{9} \qquad\qquad \text{Arithmetic.}$$

$$= 2 + 3 \cos (0.698131 \ldots) \quad \text{Evaluating the argument.}$$

$$= 4.29813 \ldots \qquad\qquad \text{By calculator.}$$

$$\approx \underline{4.298} \qquad\qquad\qquad \text{Rounding off.}$$

The entire computation can be done on the calculator without writing down any intermediate steps. The minimum you should write is

$$f(8) = 2 + 3 \cos \frac{\pi}{9}(8 - 6)$$

$$\approx \underline{4.298}$$

    If there are very many values of y to be calculated, it may be worthwhile to use a computer or a programmable calculator. Problem 12 in the following exercise asks you to write a computer program.

Example 2:   If $f(x) = 2 + 3 \cos \frac{\pi}{9}(x - 6)$, find the first three positive values of x for which $f(x) = 1.3$. Round off to two decimal places.

You should recognize that this problem is similar to the inverse cosine problems of Exercise 2–8. The only difference is that more algebra must be done.

$$2 + 3 \cos \frac{\pi}{9}(x - 6) = 1.3 \qquad \text{Setting } f(x) = 1.3.$$

$$\cos \frac{\pi}{9}(x - 6) = -\frac{0.7}{3} \qquad \text{Isolating the cosine term.}$$

$$\frac{\pi}{9}(x - 6) = \cos^{-1}\left(-\frac{0.7}{3}\right) \qquad \text{Taking } \cos^{-1} \text{ of each member.}$$

$$x = 6 + \frac{9}{\pi} \cos^{-1}\left(-\frac{0.7}{3}\right) \qquad \text{Multiplying by } 9/\pi \text{ and adding 6.}$$

Once x has been isolated on the left, it is time to start using the calculator. You should avoid trying to use the calculator while doing the algebra, since mistakes are more easily made that way.

$$x = 6 + \frac{9}{\pi}(\pm 1.8063 \ldots + 2\pi n) \qquad \text{By calculator.}$$

$$x = 6 \pm 5.1746 \ldots + 18n \qquad \text{Distributing } 9/\pi.$$

$$x = 11.1746 \ldots + 18n \text{ or}$$
$$0.8253 \ldots + 18n \qquad \text{Arithmetic.}$$

$$x = 11.1746 \ldots, 29.1746 \ldots, \ldots$$
$$\text{or } 0.8253 \ldots, 18.8253 \ldots, \ldots \qquad \text{More arithmetic.}$$

$$\underline{x \approx 0.83, \quad 11.17, \quad 18.83} \qquad \text{Selecting values and rounding off.}$$

Figure 2–11a shows the function in Examples 1 and 2 as drawn by PLOT SINUSOID. The vertical line at $x = 8$ and horizontal line at $y = 4.3$ really do cross each other at a point on the graph.

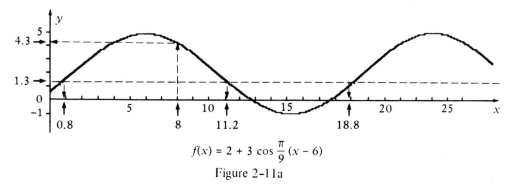

$$f(x) = 2 + 3 \cos \frac{\pi}{9}(x - 6)$$

Figure 2–11a

Exercise 2-11

For each of the following functions,

a.   Find $f(x)$ for the given value of x.
b.   Find the first three positive values of x for the given value of $f(x)$.
c.   Confirm that your answers are right by drawing the graph. You may use the computer graphics program PLOT SINUSOID for this purpose.

1. $f(x) = 2 + 5 \cos \frac{\pi}{10}(x - 3)$

    a.   Find $f(7.8)$.
    b. $f(x) = 6$
    c.   Check by graphing.

2. $f(x) = 4 + 3 \cos \frac{\pi}{6}(x - 2)$

    a.   Find $f(10.2)$.
    b. $f(x) = 6$
    c.   Check by graphing.

3. $f(x) = -2 + 4 \cos \frac{\pi}{2}(x - 0.3)$

    a.   Find $f(3)$.
    b. $f(x) = 1$
    c.   Check by graphing.

4. $f(x) = -1 + 3 \cos \frac{\pi}{3}(x - 0.7)$

    a.   Find $f(5)$.
    b. $f(x) = 1$
    c.   Check by graphing.

5. $f(x) = 1 + 3 \cos \frac{\pi}{8}(x + 7)$

    a.   Find $f(14)$.
    b. $f(x) = 1.5$
    c.   Check by graphing.

6. $f(x) = -2 + 5 \cos \frac{\pi}{11}(x + 13)$

    a.   Find $f(8)$.
    b. $f(x) = -4$
    c.   Check by graphing.

7. $f(x) = 5 + 2 \cos \frac{\pi}{4}(x - 10)$

    a.   Find $f(17.3)$.
    b. $f(x) = 6.7$
    c.   Check by graphing.

8. $f(x) = 1 + 6 \cos \frac{\pi}{13}(x - 20)$

    a.   Find $f(3.4)$.
    b. $f(x) = -4.9$
    c.   Check by graphing.

9. $f(x) = 3 + 5 \sin \frac{\pi}{9}(x - 11)$

    a.   Find $f(8)$.
    b. $f(x) = 2$
    c.   Check by graphing.

10. $f(x) = 5 + 4 \sin \frac{\pi}{12}(x + 10)$

    a.   Find $f(1)$.
    b. $f(x) = 2$
    c.   Check by graphing.

11. *Tangent Function Evaluation Problem:*   Given $f(x) = 2 + 0.5 \tan \frac{\pi}{8}(x - 3)$,

    a.   find $f(2)$.
    b.   find the first three positive values of x for which $f(x) = 7$.
    c.   check by computer graphing. You may use PLOT TANGENT from the accompanying disk.

12. *Secant Function Evaluation Problem:* Given $f(x) = 3 + 2 \sec \dfrac{\pi}{10}(x - 1)$,

    a. find $f(4)$.
    b. find the first three positive values of x for which $f(x) = 8$.
    c. check by computer graphing. You may use PLOT SECANT from the accompanying disk.

13. *Computer Evaluation of Sinusoidal Functions:* Write a computer program to evaluate sinusoidal functions of the form $y = C + A \cos B(x - D)$. The values of A, B, C, and D should be input as the computer begins to run the program. The starting and stopping values of x, and the increment between values of x should also be input. The output should be a table of values of x and y.

    Test your program by using it to evaluate

$$y = 2 + 3 \cos \frac{\pi}{9}(x - 6)$$

for $x = 0, 0.5, 1, 1.5, 2, \ldots, 9.5, 10$. This function appears in Examples 1 and 2 of this section. When the program is debugged and working, save it on a disk for future use.

2-12 SINUSOIDAL FUNCTIONS AS MATHEMATICAL MODELS

In Section 1-2 you found several real-world situations in which a dependent variable repeated its values at regular intervals as the independent variable changed. For example, the volume of air in your lungs varies periodically with time as you breathe. A reasonable sketch of the graph of this function is shown in Figure 2-12a.

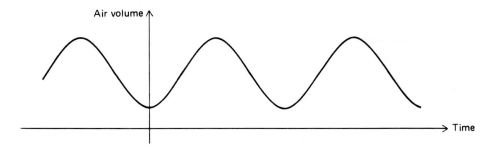

Figure 2-12a

Since the graph looks like a sinusoid, a sine or cosine function would be a reasonable mathematical model. You now know how to write an equation for a sinusoidal function with any given period, amplitude, phase, and axis location. This is the technique you will use for mathematical modeling.

Objective:

Given a situation from the real world in which something varies sinusoidally, derive an equation and use it as a mathematical model to make predictions and reach conclusions about the real world.

Example: Suppose that the waterwheel in Figure 2–12b rotates at 6 revolutions per minute (rpm). You start your stopwatch. Two seconds later, point P on the rim of the wheel is at its greatest height. Assume that P's distance, d feet, above the water is a sinusoidal function of the number of seconds, t, the stopwatch reads.

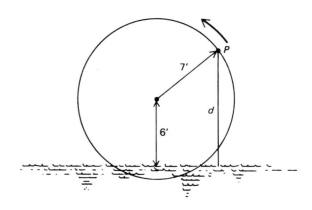

Figure 2-12b

a. Sketch the graph of d versus t.
b. Write the particular equation expressing d in terms of t.
c. When t = 7.7, is P underwater or above water? How far?
d. Find the first positive time at which P emerges from the water.

a. Your thought process should be as follows:

1. Draw the sinusoidal axis that is 6 units above the t axis because the center of the wheel is 6 feet above the water surface.
2. The amplitude is 7 units, since P goes 7 feet above and 7 feet below the center of the wheel. Draw upper and lower bounds at d = 13 and d = −1, respectively.
3. The phase displacement is 2, since P was at its highest 2 seconds after the watch was started.
4. The period is 10, since the wheel makes 6 revolutions every minute.
5. Draw critical points on the upper bound, lower bound, and sinusoidal axis, and sketch the graph. The result is shown in Figure 2–12c.

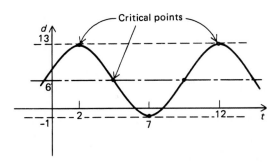

Figure 2-12c

b. Once the graph has been sketched, you have made the transition from the real world to the mathematical world. From here on, this is an "old" problem. From the graph,

$$A = 7, \ B = 2\frac{\pi}{\text{period}} = 2\frac{\pi}{10} = \frac{\pi}{5}, \ C = 6, \ \text{and } D = 2.$$

So the equation is

$$d = 6 + 7 \cos\frac{\pi}{5}(t - 2).$$

c. If $t = 7.7$, then

$$d = 6 + 7 \cos\frac{\pi}{5}(7.7 - 2)$$

$$d = -0.3337 \ldots$$

P is about 0.3 feet below the water surface.

d. P is emerging from the water when $d = 0$ and is going up. Setting $d = 0$ gives

$$6 + 7 \cos\frac{\pi}{5}(t - 2) = 0 \qquad\qquad \text{Set } d = 0.$$

$$\cos\frac{\pi}{5}(t - 2) = -\frac{6}{7} \qquad\qquad \text{Isolate the cosine.}$$

$$\frac{\pi}{5}(t - 2) = \cos^{-1}\left(-\frac{6}{7}\right) \qquad\qquad \text{Take cosine inverse.}$$

$$t = 2 + \left(\frac{5}{\pi}\right)\cos^{-1}\left(-\frac{6}{7}\right) \qquad\qquad \text{Isolate } t.$$

$t = 2 \pm 4.1388 \ldots + 10n$ Use a calculator.

$t \approx -2.14, 6.14, 7.86, 16.14, \ldots$ Select integers, n.

From the graph in Figure 2–12c, P is going into the water when $t = 6.14$ and coming out when $t = 7.86$. So the desired time is about 7.9 seconds.

The exercise that follows is designed to give you experience using sinusoidal functions as mathematical models. In doing this, you will use all of the trigonometric techniques you have learned in this chapter as well as a lot of algebraic techniques you have learned in the past.

Exercise 2–12

1. *Ferris Wheel Problem:* As you ride the Ferris wheel, your distance from the ground varies sinusoidally with time. When the last seat is filled and the Ferris wheel starts, your seat is at the position shown in Figure 2–12d. Let t be the number of seconds that have elapsed since the Ferris wheel started. You find that it takes you 3 seconds to reach the top, 43 feet above the ground, and that the wheel makes a revo-lution once every 8 seconds. The diameter of the wheel is 40 feet.

    a. Sketch a graph of this sinusoid.
    b. What is the lowest you go as the Ferris wheel turns, and why is this number greater than zero?
    c. Write an equation of this sinu-soid.
    d. Predict your height above the ground when

    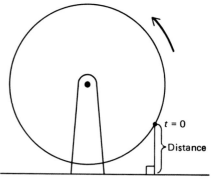

    Figure 2–12d

    (i) $t = 6$,
    (ii) $t = 4\,1/3$,
    (iii) $t = 9$,
    (iv) $t = 0$.

    e. What is the value of t the *second* time you are 18 feet above the ground?

2. *Steamboat Problem:*   Mark Twain sat on the deck of a river steamboat.
    As the paddlewheel turned, a point on the paddle blade moved in such
    a way that its distance, *d* from the water's surface was a sinusoidal
    function of time. When his stopwatch read 4 seconds, the point was at
    its highest, 16 feet above the water's surface. The wheel's diameter was
    18 feet, and it completed a revolution every 10 seconds.

    a. Sketch a graph of the sinusoid.
    b. Write the equation of the sinusoid.
    c. How far above the surface was the point when Mark's stopwatch
        read
        i.   5 seconds?
        ii. 17 seconds?
    d. What is the first positive value of time at which the point was at the
        water's surface? At that time, was it going into, or coming out of
        the water? Explain.

3. *Extraterrestial Being Problem:*   Researchers find a creature from an
    alien planet. Its body temperature is varying sinusoidally with time.
    35 minutes after they start timing, it reaches a high of $120°$F. 20 min-
    utes after that it reaches its next low, $104°$F.

    a. Sketch a graph of this sinusoid.
    b. Write an equation expressing temperature in terms of minutes since
        they started timing.
    c. What was its temperature when they first started timing?
    d. Find the first three times after they started timing at which the
        temperature was $114°$F.

4. *Fox Population Problem:*   Naturalists find that the populations of some
    kinds of predatory animals vary periodically. Assume that the popula-
    tion of foxes in a certain forest varies sinusoidally with time. Records
    started being kept when time $t = 0$ years. A minimum number, 200
    foxes, occurred when $t = 2.9$ years. The next maximum, 800 foxes,
    occurred at $t = 5.1$ years.

    a. Sketch a graph of this sinusoid.
    b. Write an equation expressing the number of foxes as a function of
        time, *t.*
    c. Predict the population when $t = 7$.
    d. Foxes are declared to be an endangered species when their popula-
        tion drops below 300. Between what two non-negative values of *t*
        were foxes first endangered?
    e. Show on your graph that your answers to part (d) are correct.

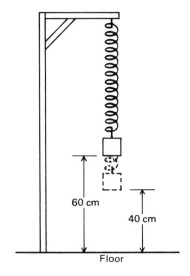

5. *Bouncing Spring Problem:* A weight attached to the end of a long spring is bouncing up and down (Figure 2–12e). As it bounces, its distance from the floor varies sinusoidally with time. You start a stopwatch. When the stopwatch reads 0.3 second, the weight first reaches a high point 60 centimeters above the floor. The next low point, 40 centimeters above the floor, occurs at 1.8 seconds.

60 cm

40 cm

Floor

Figure 2–12e

a. Sketch a graph of this sinusoidal function.

b. Write an equation expressing distance from the floor in terms of the number of seconds the stopwatch reads.

c. Predict the distance from the floor when the stopwatch reads 17.2 seconds.

d. What was the distance from the floor when you started the stopwatch?

e. Predict the first positive value of time at which the weight is 59 centimeters above the floor.

6. *Tarzan Problem:* Tarzan is swinging back and forth on his grapevine. As he swings, he goes back and forth across the river bank, going alternately over land and water (Figure 2–12f). Jane decides to model mathematically his motion and starts her stopwatch. Let t be the number of seconds the stopwatch reads and let y be the number of meters Tarzan is from the river bank. Assume that y varies sinusoidally with t, and that y is positive when Tarzan is over water and negative when he is over land.

Jane finds that when $t = 2$, Tarzan is at one end of his swing, where $y = -23$. She finds that when $t = 5$ he reaches the other end of his swing and $y = 17$.

a. Sketch a graph of this sinusoidal function.

b. Write an equation expressing Tarzan's distance from the river bank in terms of t.

c. Predict y when

(i) $t = 2.8$,
(ii) $t = 6.3$,
(iii) $t = 15$.

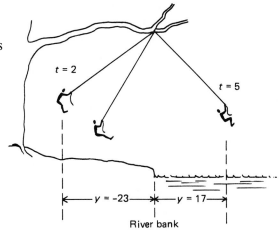

Figure 2-12f

d. Where was Tarzan when Jane started the stopwatch?
e. Find the least positive value of t for which Tarzan is directly over the river bank (i.e., $y = 0$).

7. *Roller Coaster Problem:* A portion of a roller coaster track is to be built in the shape of a sinusoid (Figure 2–12g). You have been hired to calculate the lengths of the horizontal and vertical timber supports to be used.

a. The high and low points on the track are separated by 50 meters horizontally and by 30 meters vertically. The low point is 3 meters below the ground. Letting y be the number of meters the track is

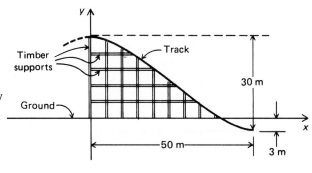

Figure 2-12g

above the ground and x the number of meters horizontally from the high point, write an equation expressing y in terms of x.

    b. How long is the vertical timber at the high point? At $x = 4$ meters? At $x = 32$ meters?

    c. How long is the horizontal timber that is 25 meters above the ground? 5 meters above the ground?

    d. Where does the track first go below ground?

    e. The vertical timbers are spaced every 2 m, starting at $x = 0$ and ending where the track goes below the ground. Find the length of each vertical timber. Also, find the total length of all timbers so that you will know how much to purchase. You may modify the computer program EVALUATE FUNCTION on the accompanying disk or write your own program.

8. *Buried Treasure Problem:*
You seek a treasure that is buried in the side of a mountain. The mountain range has a sinusoidal cross-section (Figure 2–12h). The valley to the left is filled with water to a depth of 50 meters, and the top of the range is 150 meters above the water level. You set up an x-axis at water level and a y-axis 200 meters to the right of the deepest part of the water. The top of the mountain is at $x = 400$ meters.

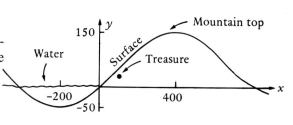

Figure 2–12h

    a. Write an equation expressing y in terms of x for points on the *surface* of the mountain.

    b. Show by calculation that this sinusoid contains the origin, $(0, 0)$.

    c. The treasure is located within the mountain at the point $(x, y) = (130, 40)$. (This point is *not* on the graph!) Which would be a shorter way to dig to the treasure, a horizontal tunnel or a vertical tunnel? Justify your answer.

9. *Sunspot Problem:* For several hundred years, astronomers have kept track of the number of solar flares, or "sunspots," which occur on the surface of the Sun. The number of sunspots counted in a given year varies periodically from a minimum of about 10 per year to a maximum of about 110 per year. Between the maximums that occurred in the years 1750 and 1948, there were 18 complete cycles.

    a. What is the period of the sunspot cycle?

    b. Assume that the number of sunspots counted in a year varies sinusoidally with the year. Sketch a graph of two sunspot cycles, starting in 1948.

   c. Write an equation expressing the number of sunspots per year in terms of the year. Use an appropriate value for the phase displacement.

   d. How many sunspots would you expect in the year 2000? In *this* year?

   e. What is the first year after 2000 in which the number of sunspots will be about 35? A maximum?

   f. Look in the September 1975 issue of *Scientific American,* page 166, to see how closely the sunspot cycle resembles a sinusoid.

10. *Tide Problem:* Suppose that you are on the beach at Port Aransas, Texas. At 2:00 p.m. on March 19, the tide is in (i.e., the water is at its deepest). At that time you find that the depth of the water at the end of the pier is 1.5 meters. At 8:00 p.m. the same day when the tide is out, you find that the depth of the water is 1.1 meters. Assume that the depth of the water varies sinusoidally with time.

   a. Derive an equation expressing depth of the water in terms of the number of hours that have elapsed since 12:00 noon on March 19.

   b. Use your mathematical model to predict the depth of the water at

     (i) 4:00 p.m. on March 19,
     (ii) 7:00 a.m. on March 20,
     (iii) 5:00 p.m. on March 20.

   c. At what time will the first low tide occur on March 20?

   d. What is the earliest time on March 20 that the water will be 1.27 meters deep?

11. *Tidal Wave Problem:* A tsunami (commonly called a "tidal wave" because its effect is like a rapid change in tide) is a fast-moving ocean wave caused by an underwater earthquake. The water first goes down from its normal level, then rises an equal distance above its normal level, and finally returns to its normal level. The period is about 15 minutes.

     Suppose that a tsunami with an amplitude of 10 meters approaches the pier at Honolulu, where the normal depth of the water is 9 meters.

   a. Assuming that the depth of the water varies sinusoidally with time as the tsunami passes, predict the depth of the water at the following times after the tsunami first reaches the pier:

     (i)   2 minutes
     (ii)   4 minutes
     (iii) 12 minutes

  b. According to your model, what will the *minimum* depth of the water be? How do you interpret this answer in terms of what will happen in the real world?
  c. Between what two times is there *no* water at the pier?
  d. The "wavelength" of a wave is the distance a crest of the wave travels in one period. It is also equal to the distance between two adjacent crests. If a tsunami travels at 1200 kilometers per hour, what is its wavelength?
  e. If you were far from land on a ship at sea and a tsunami was approaching your ship, what would you *see*? Explain.

12. *Shock-Felt-Round-the-World Problem:* Suppose that one day all 200 million people in the United States climb up on tables. At time $t = 0$, we all jump off. The resulting shock as we hit the Earth's surface will start the entire Earth vibrating in such a way that its surface first moves *down* from its normal position and then moves up an equal distance *above* its normal position (Figure 2–12i). The displacement y of the surface is a sinusoidal function of time with a period of about 54 minutes. Assuming that the amplitude is 50 meters, answer the following questions:

  a. At what time will the first *maximum* (i.e., the greatest distance *above* the normal position) occur?
  b. Write an equation expressing displacement in terms of time lapsed since the people jumped.
  c. Predict the displacement when $t = 21$.
  d. What are the first *three* times at which the displacement is −37 meters?

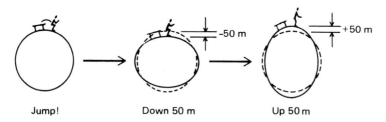

Jump!   Down 50 m   Up 50 m

Figure 2–12i

13. *Spaceship Problem:* When a spaceship is fired into orbit from a site such as Cape Canaveral, which is not on the equator, it goes into an orbit that takes it alternately north and south of the equator. Its distance from the equator is approximately a sinusoidal function of time.

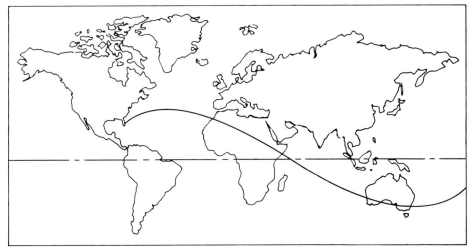

Figure 2-12j

Suppose that a spaceship is fired into orbit from Cape Canaveral. Ten minutes after it leaves the Cape, it reaches its farthest distance *north* of the equator, 4000 kilometers. Half a cycle later it reaches its farthest distance *south* of the equator (on the other side of the Earth, of course!), also 4000 kilometers. The spaceship completes an orbit once every 90 minutes.

Let y be the number of kilometers the spaceship is *north* of the equator (you may consider distances south of the equator to be negative). Let t be the number of minutes that have elapsed since liftoff.

a. Sketch a complete cycle of the graph of y versus t.
b. Write an equation expressing y in terms of t.
c. Use your equation to predict the distance of the spaceship from the equator when

      (i) $t = 25$,   (ii) $t = 41$,   (iii) $t = 163$.

d. What is the smallest positive value of t at which the spaceship is 1600 kilometers *south* of the equator?
e. Calculate the distance of Cape Canaveral from the equator by calculating y when $t = 0$.
f. See if you can find how far Cape Canaveral *really* is from the equator to see if the model gives reasonably accurate answers.

14. *Rock Formation Problem:* An old rock formation is warped into the shape of a sinusoid. Over the centuries, the top has eroded away, leaving the ground with a flat surface from which various layers of rock are cropping out (Figure 2–12k).

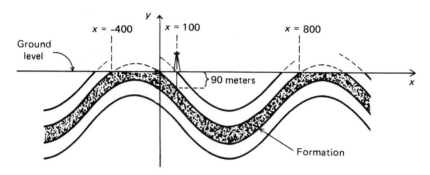

Figure 2-12k

Since you have studied sinusoids, the geologists call upon you to predict the depth of a particular formation at various points. You construct an x-axis along the ground and a y-axis at the edge of an outcropping, as shown. A hole drilled at $x = 100$ meters shows that the
top of the formation is 90 meters deep at that point.

a. Write an equation expressing the y-coordinate of the formation in
   terms of x.
b. If a hole were drilled to the top of the formation at $x = 510$, how
   deep would it be?
c. What is the maximum depth of the top of the formation, and what
   is the value of x where it reaches this depth?
d. How high above the present ground level did the formation go before it eroded away?
e. For what values of x between 0 and 800 meters is the top of the
   formation within 120 meters of the surface?
f. The geologists decide to drill holes to the top of the formation
   every 50 m from $x = 50$ through $x = 750$. The drilling costs $75 per
   meter of depth. Find the cost of drilling each hole and the total
   cost of the drilling. You may modify the computer program
   EVALUATE FUNCTION on the accompanying disk or write your
   own program.

15. *Biorhythm Problem:* According to biorhythm theory, your body is
    governed by three independent sinusoidal functions, each with a
    different period, as follows:

    Physical function: Period = 23 days
    Emotional function: Period = 28 days
    Intellectual function: Period = 33 days.

    a. Phoebe Small is at a high point on all three cycles today! This means that she is at her very highest ability in all three areas today. Assume that the amplitude of each sinusoid is 100 units, and that the vertical displacement of each is zero. Write equations for these three functions, in terms of the number of days after today.

    b. 33 days from now, Phoebe will again be at an intellectual high point. What will be the values of her physical and her emotional functions on that day?

    c. Biorhythm theory says that the most dangerous time for a particular function is when it crosses the axis. What is the first time this happens for Phoebe's

       i. physical function?

      ii. emotional function?

     iii. intellectual function?

16. *Pebble-in-the-Tire Problem:* As you stop your car at a traffic light, a pebble becomes wedged between the tire treads. When you start off, the distance of the pebble from the pavement varies sinusoidally with the distance you have traveled. The period is, of course, the circumference of the wheel. Assume that the diameter of the wheel is 24 inches.

    a. Sketch the graph of this function.

    b. Write an equation of this function. It is possible to get a form of the equation that has *zero* phase displacement.

    c. Predict the distance from the pavement when you have gone 15 inches.

    d. What are the first two distances when the pebble is 11 inches from the pavement?

17. *Electrical Current and Voltage Problem:* The electricity supplied to your house is called alternating current (AC) because the current varies sinusoidally with time. The voltage which causes this current to flow also varies sinusoidally with time. Both current and voltage have a frequency of 60 cycles per second, but have different phase displacements (Figure 2–12ℓ).

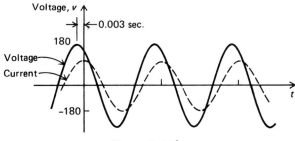

Figure 2–12ℓ

   a. Suppose that the current is at its maximum, $i = 5$ amperes, when $t = 0$ seconds. Write an equation for this sinusoid.

   b. As shown in Figure 2–12ℓ, the voltage leads the current by 0.003 second, meaning that it reaches a maximum 0.003 second *before* the current does. ("Leading" corresponds to a *negative* phase displacement, and "lagging" corresponds to a *positive* phase displacement.) If the peak voltage is $v = 180$ volts, write an equation for this sinusoid. (Note that the 115 volts supplied to your house is an *average* value, whereas the 180 volts is an instantaneous peak voltage.)

   c. Predict the voltage at the time the current is a maximum.

   d. Predict the current at the time the voltage is a maximum.

   e. Predict the first positive time at which the voltage reaches 170 volts.

18. *Sound Wave Problem:* The hum you hear on a radio when it is not tuned to a station is a sound wave of 60 cycles per second.

   a. Is the 60 cycles per second the period or the frequency?

   b. If it is the period, find the frequency. If it is the frequency, find the period.

   c. The wavelength of a sound wave is defined to be the distance the wave travels in one period. If sound travels at 1100 feet per second, find the wavelength of a 60-cycle-per-second sound wave.

   d. The lowest musical note the human ear can hear is about 16 cycles per second. In order for the pipe on a church organ to generate this note, the pipe must be exactly half as long as the wavelength. How long an organ pipe would be required to generate a 16-cycle-per-second note?

   e. See the article "The Physics of Organ Pipes," by Neville Fletcher and Suzanne Thwaites in the January, 1983, issue of *Scientific American* magazine.

19. *Sun Elevation Problem:* The "angle of elevation" of an object above you is the angle between a horizontal line and the line of sight between you and the object, as shown in Figure 2–12m. After the Sun rises, its angle of elevation increases rapidly at first, then more slowly, reaching a maximum near noontime. Then the

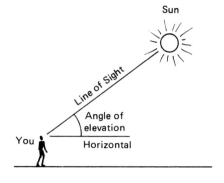

Figure 2–12m

angle decreases until sunset. The next day the phenomenon repeats itself.

Assume that when the Sun is up, its angle of elevation E varies sinusoidally with the time of day. Let t be the number of hours that has elapsed since midnight last night. Assume that the amplitude of this sinusoid is $60°$, and the maximum angle of elevation occurs at 12:45 p.m. Assume that at this time of year the sinusoidal axis is at $E = -5°$. The period is, of course, 24 hours.

a. Sketch a graph of this function.
b. What is the real-world significance of the t-intercepts?
c. What is the real-world significance of the portion of the sinusoid which is *below* the t-axis?
d. Predict the angle of elevation at 9:27 a.m., at 2:30 p.m.
e. Predict the time of sunrise.
f. As you know, the maximum angle of elevation increases and decreases with the changes of season. Also, the times of sunrise and sunset change with the seasons. What *one* change could you make in your mathematical model that would allow you to use it for predicting the angle of elevation of the Sun at *any* time on *any* day of the year?

20. *Sunrise Problem:* In Problem 19 you assumed that the time of sunrise was given by the t-intercepts of the Sun's angle of elevation graph. In this problem assume that the time of sunrise varies sinusoidally with the day of the year, and use the model to make predictions about sunrise times.

Let t be the time of day that the Sun rises, and let d be the number of the day of the year, starting with $d = 1$ on January 1. To calculate the constants in the equation, recall that the period is 365 days. The amplitude and axis location can be calculated from the times of sunrise on the longest and shortest days of the year (i.e., June 21 and December 21). You may find these times for various cities in an almanac (they are 5:34 a.m. and 7:24 a.m. CST for San Antonio). The phase displacement will, of course, be related to the day number on which the sinusoid reaches its maximum, if you use cosine.

a. Sketch a graph of this sinusoid. You may neglect daylight-saving time.
b. Write an equation for this function.
c. Calculate the time of sunrise for your city *today*. Check your answer with today's newspaper to see how close your model is to the actual sunrise time.

d. Predict the time of sunrise on your birthday, taking daylight-saving time into account if necessary.

e. Predict the first day of the year on which the sun rises at 6:07 a.m. standard time in your city.

f. Use the program EVALUATE FUNCTION or a similar program, to search for the answer to part (e). What are the advantages of using the computer for this calculation? What are the disadvantages?

g. If you plot a graph of predicted and actual sunrise times versus d, you will find something like Figure 2–12n, where the maximum occurs *after* the predicted maximu, but the minimum occurs *before* the predicted minimum. From what you have learned about how the Earth orbits the Sun, think of a reason why the actual sunrise times differ from the predicted ones in this manner.

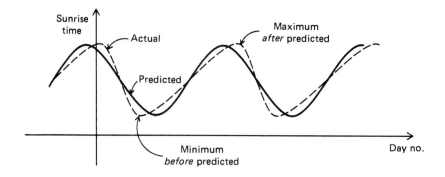

Figure 2–12n

21. *Variable-Amplitude Pendulum Problem:* A pendulum may be made by tying a weight on the end of a string and swinging the weight back and forth, as in Figure 2–12o. As the pendulum swings, the distance of the weight from the wall varies sinusoidally with time. You will observe that in the real world the amplitude gradually decreases with time while the period remains the same. In this problem you will make a mathematical model of a pendulum that accounts for the decrease in amplitude.

Suppose that the weight in Figure 2–12o is released from its closest point to the wall at time $t = 0$, where its distance from the wall is 10 centimeters. On its first swing, it goes 50 centimeters from the wall, making its initial amplitude equal 20 centimeters. After 30 seconds the amplitude has decreased to 4 centimeters. Assume that the amplitude decreases exponentially with time (i.e., $A = a \cdot b^t$, where a and b are constants).

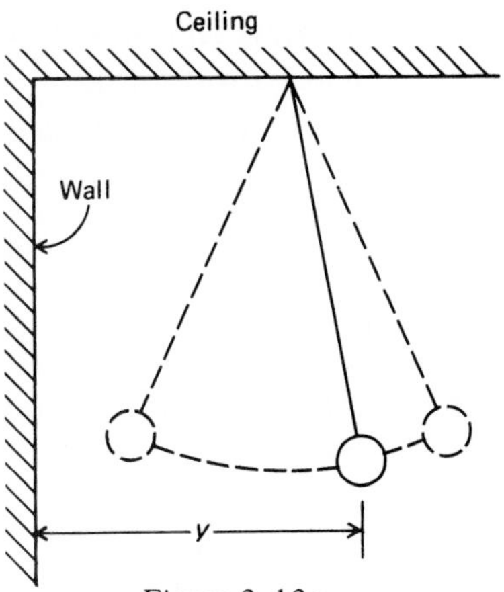

Figure 2–12o

a. Find an equation expressing the amplitude A in terms of time t.

b. If the period of the pendulum is 2.2 seconds, find the constants B, C, and D in the sinusoidal part of the equation.

c. By appropriate combination of the results of parts a and b, write an equation expressing y in terms of t.

d. Draw several cycles of the graph of this function. You may use the program PLOT FUNCTION.

e. Predict the value of y when $t = 5.4$ seconds.

2–13 CHAPTER REVIEW AND TEST

At the beginning of this chapter you encountered three specific objectives. These objectives are summarized below to refresh your memory.

1. Given the equation of a trigonometric or circular function, find values of y or x, and sketch the graph.

2. Get the equation of a trigonometric or circular function from its graph.

3. Use circular functions as mathematical models.

Once you know how to accomplish each specific objective, it is your *general* objective to be able to use any *combination* of them to analyze problems from the real world or the mathematical world. For example, the mathematical model problems you have worked require you to use almost all of the skills you have learned.

In the review section you will work examples of each specific objective. The chapter test will consist of a single problem in which *all* of the techniques must be used. After working each step in the problem, you will identify which ones of the specific objectives you used.

Review Problems

The following problems are numbered according to the three objectives listed above.

1. a. If $y = 5 + 7 \cos 4(\theta - 7°)$,

    (i) find y when $\theta = 42°$,
    (ii) find the smallest positive value of θ for which $y = 1.5$,
    (iii) sketch one complete cycle of the graph.

    b. If $y = -2 + 8 \cos \frac{\pi}{6}(x + 1)$,

    (i) find the *exact* value of y when $x = 3$,
    (ii) find the approximate value of y when $x = 0.3$,
    (iii) find the two smallest positive values of x for which $y = 0$,
    (iv) sketch one complete cycle of the graph.

    c. If $y = \tan \theta$, sketch two cycles of the graph.

    d. If $y = \sec x$, sketch one cycle of the graph.

    e. Find *exact* values for:

    (i) $\cos \frac{\pi}{3}$.   (ii) $\tan \frac{3\pi}{4}$ (iii) $\sec \pi$ (iv) $\sin \frac{7\pi}{6}$

    (v) $10 \cos \frac{\pi}{6} \sin \frac{\pi}{6}$ (vi) $\tan^2 \frac{5\pi}{3} - \sec^2 \frac{5\pi}{3}$

    f. Find *exact* values for:

    (i) $x = \mathrm{Sin}^{-1} \, 0.5$ (ii) $x = \sin^{-1} \, 0.5$ (iii) $x = \mathrm{Tan}^{-1} \, 1$

    (iv) $x = \mathrm{Cos}^{-1} (-1)$ (v) $x = \cos^{-1} (-1)$ (vi) $x = \mathrm{Sec}^{-1} \, 2$

    g. Find *exact* values for:

    (i)   the number of radians in 270°.
    (ii) the number of degrees in $5\pi/6$ radians.
    (iii) the number of degrees for an arc of π on a unit circle.
    (iv) the number of radians for an arc of $4\pi/3$ on a unit circle.

2. Write an equation of the sinusoid sketched (Figure 2–13a).

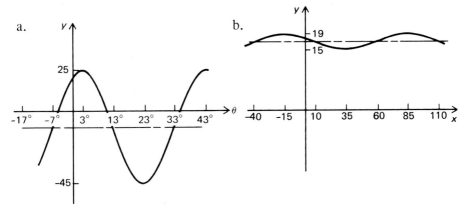

Figure 2-13a

3. *Porpoising Problem:* Assume that you are aboard a submarine, sub-merged in the Pacific Ocean. At time $t = 0$ you make contact with an enemy destroyer. Immediately, you start porpoising (going deeper and shallower). At time $t = 4$ minutes, you are at your deepest, $y = -1000$ meters. At time $t = 9$ minutes, you next reach your shallowest, $y = -200$ meters. Assume that y varies sinusoidally with t for $t \geq 0$.

   a. Sketch the graph of y versus t.
   b. Write an equation expressing y in terms of t.
   c. Your submarine is safe when it is below $y = -300$ meters. At time $t = 0$, was your submarine safe? Justify your answer.
   d. Between what two non-negative times is your submarine first safe?

Chapter Test

The following questions concern the oil well pump jack shown in Figure 2-13b. The test is designed to insure that you can draw together all the skills you have learned in this chapter to apply to a single problem. Work each problem. Then tell by numbers, 1, 2, or 3, which objectives of this chapter you used in working that problem.

Pump Jack Problem: As the motor on the jack turns, the walking beam rocks back and forth, pulling the pump rod in and out of the well. The distance of point P from the ground, d, varies sinusoidally with time as the pump runs.

   1. Suppose that the pump is started at time $t = 0$ seconds. One second later, P is at its highest, $d = 14$ feet above the ground. 2.5 seconds after that, P is at its next low point, $d = 10$ feet. Sketch the graph of this sinusoid.

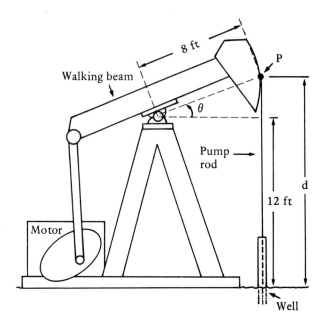

Figure 2-13b

2. Write an equation expressing d in terms of t.

3. Predict d when $t = 9$.

4. For how long a time does P stay above 11 feet each cycle?

5. The angle of elevation, θ, which the walking beam makes with the ground varies with time. Recalling what you learned about right triangles in Chapter 1, find the maximum positive degree measure which θ attains.

6. Correct to 4 decimal places, how many radians is the angle in Problem 5?

7. When θ is exactly $\dfrac{\pi}{20}$ radian,

   a. What is its degree measure?
   b. What is the value of d?
   c. What is the first positive value of t for this value of d?

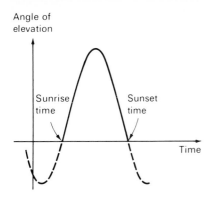

The angle of elevation of the sun varies sinusoidally with the time of day. Predicting the time of sunrise or sunset involves solving a trigonometric equation. Properties of trigonometric functions allow you to do this.

When you use circular functions as mathematical models of the real world, you must sometimes find values of x for given values of y. Substituting some number for y into an equation such as $y = C + A \cos B(x - D)$ leaves a trigonometric equation with only one variable, x. In this chapter you will learn how to solve more complicated trigonometric equations with one variable. Some of these will involve several of the trigonometric or circular functions. Others will involve functions of more than one argument. Solving equations such as

$$\cos 4x - \sin 2x = 0$$

or

$$4 \sin (x + 75°) \cos (x - 75°) = 1$$

requires you to learn some *properties* relating the trigonometric functions to one another. With the aid of these properties, you will be able to *transform* such things as sines to cosines, functions of $4x$ to functions of x, and functions of $(x + 75°)$ to functions of x and of $75°$. These simplifying transformations are what you need to solve this type of equation. Solutions of these equations are inverse trigonometric or circular functions, which you studied in the first two chapters.

Since the properties of trigonometric and circular functions are virtually the same, the distinction between these two is of relatively minor importance here. Consequently, the word "trigonometric" function will be used to include circular functions unless it is necessary to distinguish between them.

Specific objectives are:

1. Given one trigonometric function, express it as another function with the *same* argument.
2. Given a trigonometric function with a negative argument, such as $\sin (-x)$, transform it to a function with a positive argument.
3. Given a trigonometric function whose argument is a *sum* of two numbers, such as $\cos (x + y)$, transform it to functions of these two numbers.
4. Given a trigonometric function, transform it to a function of *half* the argument or *twice* the argument.
5. Given a *sum* of two sines or cosines, transform it to a *product* of sines and cosines.
6. Given a linear combination of sine and cosine, transform it to a cosine with a phase displacement.
7. Verify the properties by computer graphics.

8. Use any of the preceding transformations to *simplify* a given trig-
    onometric expression.
9. Use any of the preceding transformations to *solve* a given trigono-
    metric equation.

3–1   THREE PROPERTIES OF TRIGONOMETRIC FUNCTIONS

There are three types of properties of the trigonometric functions, which
come directly from their definitions.

1. *Reciprocal Properties:* By the defi-
    nitions of the trigonometric functions,

    $$\tan x = \frac{v}{u} \quad \text{and} \quad \cot x = \frac{u}{v},$$

    where u and v are the abscissa and
    ordinate, respectively, of a point on
    the terminal side of the angle or arc
    x (see Figure 3–1a). Therefore,
    $\tan x$ and $\cot x$ are *reciprocals* of
    each other. Similarly, $\sin x$ and
    $\csc x$ are reciprocals of each other,
    and $\cos x$ and $\sec x$ are reciprocals
    of each other. In summary:

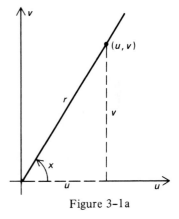

Figure 3–1a

$$\cot x = \frac{1}{\tan x} \qquad \csc x = \frac{1}{\sin x} \qquad \sec x = \frac{1}{\cos x}$$

These are known as the *reciprocal* properties. Since the product of
a number and its reciprocal equals 1, these properties may also be
written:

$$\tan x \cot x = 1 \qquad \sin x \csc x = 1 \qquad \cos x \sec x = 1$$

2. *Quotient Properties:* The expression $\sin x / \cos x$ can be written us-
    ing the definitions of the trigonometric functions as:

$$\frac{\sin x}{\cos x} = \frac{\dfrac{v}{r}}{\dfrac{u}{r}} \qquad \text{Definition of } \sin x \text{ and } \cos x$$

$$= \frac{v}{r} \cdot \frac{r}{u} \qquad \text{Definition of division}$$

$$= \frac{v}{u} \qquad \text{Multiplication property of fractions and canceling}$$

But v/u is defined to be $\tan x$ (Figure 3-1a). So by transitivity:

$$\boxed{\tan x = \frac{\sin x}{\cos x}}$$

This is called a *quotient* property because $\tan x$ is expressed as a quotient. Since $\cot x$ is the reciprocal of $\tan x$, the quotient can be inverted to give a second quotient property:

$$\boxed{\cot x = \frac{\cos x}{\sin x}}$$

There is another form of these two quotient properties that is sometimes useful. The $\sin x$ and $\cos x$ can be replaced by using the reciprocal properties to give:

$$\tan x$$

$$= \frac{\sin x}{\cos x} \qquad \text{Quotient property}$$

$$= \frac{\dfrac{1}{\csc x}}{\dfrac{1}{\sec x}} \qquad \text{Reciprocal properties}$$

$$= \frac{1}{\csc x} \cdot \frac{\sec x}{1} \qquad \text{Definition of division}$$

$$= \frac{\sec x}{\csc x} \qquad \text{Multiplication property of fractions}$$

$$\therefore \boxed{\tan x = \frac{\sec x}{\csc x}} \qquad \text{Transitivity}$$

Again using the reciprocal property, $\cot x = 1/\tan x$:

$$\boxed{\cot x = \frac{\csc x}{\sec x}}$$

These two are usually not considered to be new properties, but rather to be alternate forms of the two quotient properties.

3. *Pythagorean Properties:* The numbers u, v, and r in Figure 3–1b are the legs and hypotenuse of a right triangle. By the Pythagorean theorem,

$$u^2 + v^2 = r^2.$$

Dividing both members by r^2 gives

$$\frac{u^2}{r^2} + \frac{v^2}{r^2} = 1.$$

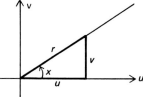

Figure 3–1b

Since $u/r = \cos x$ and $v/r = \sin x$, it follows that

$$(\cos x)^2 + (\sin x)^2 = 1.$$

It is customary to drop the parentheses and to write "$(\cos x)^2$" as "$\cos^2 x$." The exponent is placed in a position where it cannot possibly be mistaken for x^2. So this property is usually written:

$$\boxed{\cos^2 x + \sin^2 x = 1}$$

By dividing both members of $u^2 + v^2 = r^2$ by u^2, you get

$$\boxed{1 + \tan^2 x = \sec^2 x}\ ,$$

and by dividing both members by v^2, you get

$$\boxed{\cot^2 x + 1 = \csc^2 x}\ .$$

These three properties are called the *Pythagorean* properties, since they come from the Pythagorean theorem.

Objective:

Use the reciprocal, quotient, and Pythagorean properties to transform given expressions to equivalent, simpler forms.

Example 1: Suppose you are asked to transform $\sin x \cot x$ to $\cos x$. The thought process you would go through is as follows:

1. Neither factor in $\sin x \cot x$ has $\cos x$ in it.
2. Therefore, either $\sin x$ or $\cot x$ should be *replaced* by something that *does* have $\cos x$ in it.
3. Sin x has no convenient forms that have $\cos x$ in them.
4. But by the quotient properties, $\cot x = \cos x/\sin x$.

The actual work would be done as follows:

$\sin x \cot x$	Given expression
$= \sin x \cdot \dfrac{\cos x}{\sin x}$	Quotient properties
$= \cos x$	Multiplication property of fractions and canceling $\sin x$
$\therefore \quad \sin x \cot x = \cos x$	Transitivity

Example 2: Suppose that you are asked to transform the expression $\sin x \sec x \cot x$ into 1. The thought process is:

1. Since the answer is 1, there must be some canceling that can be done.
2. Canceling requires *fractions*, which can be obtained either from *reciprocal* properties or from *quotient* properties.
3. By the reciprocal properties, $\sec x = 1\dfrac{1}{\cos} x$. By the quotient properties, $\cot x = \dfrac{\cos x}{\sin x}$.

$\sin x \sec x \cot x$	Given expression
$= \sin x \cdot \dfrac{1}{\cos x} \cdot \dfrac{\cos x}{\sin x}$	Reciprocal and quotient properties
$= \dfrac{\sin x \cos x}{\cos x \sin x}$	Multiplication property of fractions
$= 1$	Canceling, or $\dfrac{n}{n} = 1$
$\therefore \quad \sin x \sec x \cot x = 1$	Transitivity

There are often several ways the transformation can be done. In the preceding example, you could have written

$\sin x \sec x \cot x$	Given expression
$= \sin x \cdot \dfrac{1}{\cos x} \cdot \cot x$	Reciprocal properties
$= \dfrac{\sin x}{\cos x} \cdot \cot x$	Multiplication property of fractions

$$= \tan x \cot x \qquad \text{Quotient properties}$$
$$= 1 \qquad \text{Reciprocal properties}$$
$$\therefore \quad \sin x \sec x \cot x = 1 \quad \text{Transitivity}$$

Example 3:   Suppose you are asked to transform the expression $\cos^2 x - \sin^2 x$ into the equivalent expression $1 - 2 \sin^2 x$. Your thought process would be:

1. The answer has no cosines in it. So you must get *rid* of the $\cos^2 x$.
2. Since the expression involves *squares* of functions, the Pythagorean properties should be helpful.
3. The Pythagorean property that has cosines in it is $\cos^2 x + \sin^2 x = 1$, from which $\cos^2 x = 1 - \sin^2 x$.

The actual steps in the transformation would be

$$\cos^2 x - \sin^2 x \qquad \text{Given expression}$$
$$= (1 - \sin^2 x) - \sin^2 x \qquad \text{Pythagorean properties}$$
$$= 1 - \sin^2 x - \sin^2 x \qquad \text{Associativity}$$
$$= 1 - 2 \sin^2 x \qquad \text{Combining like terms}$$
$$\therefore \quad \cos^2 x - \sin^2 x = 1 - 2 \sin^2 x \qquad \text{Transitivity}$$

In the exercise that follows, you will get practice using the reciprocal, quotient, and Pythagorean properties to transform expressions.

Exercise 3–1

For Problems 1 through 26, transform the expression on the left to the one on the right.

1. $\cos x \tan x$ to $\sin x$
2. $\csc x \tan x$ to $\sec x$
3. $\sec x \cot x \sin x$ to 1
4. $\csc x \tan x \cos x$ to 1
5. $\sin^2 \theta \sec \theta \csc \theta$ to $\tan \theta$
6. $\cos^2 A \csc A \sec A$ to $\cot A$
7. $\tan A + \cot A$ to $\csc A \sec A$
8. $\sin \theta + \cot \theta \cos \theta$ to $\csc \theta$
9. $\csc x - \sin x$ to $\cot x \cos x$
10. $\sec \theta - \cos \theta$ to $\sin \theta \tan \theta$
11. $\tan x (\sin x + \cot x \cos x)$ to $\sec x$
12. $\cos x (\sec x + \cos x \csc^2 x)$ to $\csc^2 x$
13. $(1 + \sin B)(1 - \sin B)$ to $\cos^2 B$

14. $(\sec x - 1)(\sec x + 1)$ to $\tan^2 x$
15. $(\cos \phi - \sin \phi)^2$ to $1 - 2 \cos \phi \sin \phi$
16. $(1 - \tan \phi)^2$ to $\sec^2 \phi - 2 \tan \phi$
17. $(\tan n + \cot n)^2$ to $\sec^2 n + \csc^2 n$
18. $(\cos k - \sec k)^2$ to $\tan^2 k - \sin^2 k$

19. $\dfrac{\csc^2 x - 1}{\cos x}$ to $\cot x \csc x$ 20. $\dfrac{1 - \cos^2 x}{\tan x}$ to $\sin x \cos x$

21. $\dfrac{\sec^2 \theta - 1}{\sin \theta}$ to $\tan \theta \sec \theta$ 22. $\dfrac{1 + \cot^2 \theta}{\sec^2 \theta}$ to $\cot^2 \theta$

23. $\dfrac{\sec A}{\sin A} - \dfrac{\sin A}{\cos A}$ to $\cot A$ 24. $\dfrac{\csc B}{\cos B} - \dfrac{\cos B}{\sin B}$ to $\tan B$

25. $\dfrac{1}{1 - \cos C} + \dfrac{1}{1 + \cos C}$ to $2 \csc^2 C$

26. $\dfrac{1}{\sec D - \tan D} + \dfrac{1}{\sec D + \tan D}$ to $2 \sec D$

27. There are quite a few properties in which the number 1 occurs. By appropriate algebra, if necessary, write *six* trigonometric expressions, each of which equals 1.

28. Use the Pythagorean properties to write expressions equivalent to:

    a. $\sin^2 x$ b. $\cos^2 x$ c. $\tan^2 x$
    d. $\cot^2 x$ e. $\sec^2 x$ f. $\csc^2 x$

29. Write equations expressing each of the six trigonometric functions in terms of $\sin x$.

30. Write equations expressing each of the six trigonometric functions in terms of $\cos x$.

31. Write the exact value of $\cos 30°$.

32. Write the exact value of $\sin \dfrac{5\pi}{4}$.

33. Write the exact value of $0 = \mathrm{Cot}^{-1} - \sqrt{3}$.

34. Write the exact values of $x = \sec^{-1} \sqrt{2}$.

35. *Triangle Problem:* A right triangle has a hypotenuse 30 meters long and one leg 23 meters long. How long is the other leg? What size is the smaller acute angle?

36. *Sinusoid Problem:* Sketch the graph of $y = 3 - 4 \cos \dfrac{\pi}{5}(x - 1)$.

3–2   TRIGONOMETRIC IDENTITIES AND EQUATIONS

A *trigonometric* open sentence is (obviously!) an open sentence that contains trigonometric functions. For example,

$$\sin \theta = 1/2$$

is a trigonometric equation. The solution set of such an open sentence is the set of all values of the angle θ that makes the sentence true. By taking the inverse sine of each member, as in Chapter 2, you find that the solutions for θ are 30°, 150°, or any angle coterminal with these. Such an equation is called a *conditional* equation, because it is true only under certain conditions.

Some open sentences are true under *all* conditions. For example,

$$\cos^2 \theta = 1 - \sin^2 \theta$$

is true for *every* value of θ. Such an equation is called an *identity*, because the two members are "identical" to each other. (Actually, the two members are *equivalent* expressions.)

Objective:

Given a trigonometric equation, prove that it is an *identity*.

There are two purposes for learning how to prove identities.

1. To learn the relationships among the functions.
2. To learn to transform one trigonometric expression to another equivalent form, usually simplifying it.

To accomplish the objective without defeating these purposes, the following agreement will be made:

Agreement: To prove that an equation is an identity, start with one member and transform it into the other.

Note that this is exactly what you were doing in the previous section! The only thing that is new is that you are free to pick *either* member to start with.

Example 1:   Prove that $(1 + \cos x)(1 - \cos x) = \sin^2 x$.
Proof:

$(1 + \cos x)(1 - \cos x)$	Start with the more complicated member.
$= 1 - \cos^2 x$	Do the obvious algebra.

$= \sin^2 x$ — Look for familiar expressions.

$\therefore (1 + \cos x)(1 - \cos x) = \sin^2 x$, Q.E.D. — Transitivity.

Notes:

1. It is tempting to *start* with the given equation and then work on *both* members until you have reduced the equation to an obviously true statement, such as "$\cos x = \cos x$." What this actually does is prove the *converse* of what you were asked to prove. That is, "*If* the identity is true, *then* the reflexive property is true." This is circular reasoning. It is dangerous because you might actually "prove" a *false* identity by taking an irreversible step, such as squaring both members.

2. The letters "Q.E.D." at the end stand for the Latin words *quod erat demonstrandum*, that mean, "which was to be demonstrated."

Example 2:   Prove that $\cot x + \tan x = \csc x \sec x$.
Proof:

$\cot x + \tan x$ — Pick a member to work on.

$= \dfrac{\cos x}{\sin x} + \dfrac{\sin x}{\cos x}$ — Answer has only *one* term, so try adding fractions. The fractions must be *created* first.

$= \dfrac{\cos^2 x + \sin^2 x}{\sin x \cos x}$ — Find common denominator and add the fractions.

$= \dfrac{1}{\sin x \cos x}$ — Familiar Pythagorean property.

$= \dfrac{1}{\sin x} \cdot \dfrac{1}{\cos x}$ — Answer has *two* factors, so *make* two factors.

$= \csc x \sec x$ — Familiar reciprocal properties.

$\therefore \cot x + \tan x = \csc x \sec x$, Q.E.D. — Transitivity.

Example 3:   Prove that $\dfrac{\sin x}{1 + \cos x} = \dfrac{1 - \cos x}{\sin x}$.
Proof:

$\dfrac{\sin x}{1 + \cos x}$ — Pick a member to work on.

$= \dfrac{\sin x}{1 + \cos x} \cdot \dfrac{1 - \cos x}{1 - \cos x}$ — Multiply by a clever form of 1.

$$= \frac{\sin x (1 - \cos x)}{1 - \cos^2 x}$$

Do the obvious algebra, but *don't* destroy the "$1 - \cos x$," because you want it in the answer.

$$= \frac{\sin x (1 - \cos x)}{\sin^2 x}$$

Familiar Pythagorean property.

$$= \frac{1 - \cos x}{\sin x}$$

Do the obvious canceling.

$$\therefore \quad \frac{\sin x}{1 + \cos x} = \frac{1 - \cos x}{\sin x}, \text{ Q.E.D.}$$

Transitivity.

Note that there could be *two* reasons for picking the form of "1" used in the first step. It has the *conjugate* of $1 + \cos x$ in its denominator. Or it has $1 - \cos x$ in its numerator, an expression you *want* in the answer.

Example 4:   Prove that $\csc \theta \cos^2 \theta + \sin \theta = \csc \theta$.
Proof:

$$\csc \theta \cos^2 \theta + \sin \theta$$

Pick the more complicated member.

$$= \csc \theta \left(\cos^2 \theta + \frac{\sin \theta}{\csc \theta} \right)$$

If you want $\csc \theta$ as a factor of the answer, then *factor it out!*

$$= \csc \theta (\cos^2 \theta + \sin \theta \cdot \sin \theta)$$

Familiar reciprocal property.

$$= \csc \theta (\cos^2 \theta + \sin^2 \theta)$$

Obvious algebra.

$$= \csc \theta$$

Familiar Pythagorean property.

$$\therefore \quad \csc \theta \cos^2 \theta + \sin \theta = \csc \theta, \text{ Q.E.D.}$$

Transitivity.

Factoring out the $\csc \theta$ in the second line of the proof is sometimes called "factoring out a rabbit," because you are reaching in and pulling out a common factor that wasn't there!

Note that the reasons written for the steps in the above examples are reasons you *chose to do* the particular step, rather than mathematical reasons why the steps are true. From these examples, certain useful techniques emerge that help guide your thought process as you attempt to prove identities. These steps are summarized below for your convenience.

The exercise that follows is designed to give you practice proving identities, so that you may become more familiar with the properties of the trigonometric functions and may gain practice transforming one expression into another simpler form.

Exercise 3–2

In Problems 1 through 34, prove that each equation is an identity.

1. $\sec x (\sec x - \cos x) = \tan^2 x$
2. $\tan x (\cot x + \tan x) = \sec^2 x$
3. $\sin x (\csc x - \sin x) = \cos^2 x$
4. $\cos x (\sec x - \cos x) = \sin^2 x$
5. $\csc^2 \theta - \cos^2 \theta \csc^2 \theta = 1$
6. $\cos^2 \theta + \tan^2 \theta \cos^2 \theta = 1$
7. $(\sec \theta + 1)(\sec \theta - 1) = \tan^2 \theta$
8. $(1 + \sin \theta)(1 - \sin \theta) = \cos^2 \theta$
9. $\sec^2 A + \tan^2 A \sec^2 A = \sec^4 A$
10. $\cot^2 A \csc^2 A - \cot^2 A = \cot^4 A$
11. $\cos^4 t - \sin^4 t = 1 - 2 \sin^2 t$
12. $\sec^4 t - \tan^4 t = 1 + 2 \tan^2 t$
13. $\dfrac{1}{\sin x \cos x} - \dfrac{\cos x}{\sin x} = \tan x$
14. $\dfrac{\sec x}{\sin x} - \dfrac{\sin x}{\cos x} = \cot x$
15. $\dfrac{\sin x}{\csc x} + \dfrac{\cos x}{\sec x} = 1$
16. $\dfrac{1}{\sec^2 x} + \dfrac{1}{\csc^2 x} = 1$
17. $\dfrac{1}{1 + \cos s} = \csc^2 s - \csc s \cot s$
18. $\dfrac{1}{1 - \sin r} = \sec^2 r + \sec r \tan r$
19. $\dfrac{\cos x}{\sec x - 1} - \dfrac{\cos x}{\tan^2 x} = \cot^2 x$
20. $\dfrac{\sin x}{1 - \cos x} + \dfrac{1 - \cos x}{\sin x} = 2 \csc x$
21. $\dfrac{\sec x}{\sec x - \tan x} = \sec^2 x + \sec x \tan x$
22. $\dfrac{1 + \sin x}{1 - \sin x} = 2 \sec^2 x + 2 \sec x \tan x - 1$
23. $\sin^3 z \cos^2 z = \sin^3 z - \sin^5 z$

24. $\sin^3 z \cos^2 z = \cos^2 z \sin z - \cos^4 z \sin z$

25. $\sec^2 \theta + \csc^2 \theta = \sec^2 \theta \csc^2 \theta$

26. $\sec \theta + \tan \theta = \dfrac{1}{\sec \theta - \tan \theta}$

27. $\dfrac{1 - 3 \cos x - 4 \cos^2 x}{\sin^2 x} = \dfrac{1 - 4 \cos x}{1 - \cos x}$

28. $\dfrac{\sec^2 x - 6 \tan x + 7}{\sec^2 x - 5} = \dfrac{\tan x - 4}{\tan x + 2}$

29. $\dfrac{\sin^3 A + \cos^3 A}{\sin A + \cos A} = 1 - \sin A \cos A$

30. $\dfrac{\sec^3 B - \cos^3 B}{\sec B - \cos B} = \sec^2 B + 1 + \cos^2 B$

31. $\csc^6 x - \cot^6 x = 1 + 3 \csc^2 x \cot^2 x$

32. $(2 \sin x + 3 \cos x)^2 + (3 \sin x - 2 \cos x)^2 = 13$

33. $\dfrac{1 + \sin x + \cos x}{1 + \sin x - \cos x} = \dfrac{1 + \cos x}{\sin x}$

34. $\dfrac{1 + \sin x + \cos x}{1 - \sin x + \cos x} = \dfrac{1 + \sin x}{\cos x}$

35. *Graphs of* $\tan^2 \theta$ *and* $\sec^2 \theta$:

   a. Plot an accurate graph of $y = \tan^2 \theta$ in the domain $-90° < \theta < 90°$. Calculate plotting data by finding values of $\tan \theta$ on the calculator, then squaring them, for each 10° from $-80°$ through 80°.
   b. Plot an accurate graph of $y = \sec^2 \theta$ the same way as in part (a), using the *same* set of axes.
   c. What relationship do you notice between the two sets of plotting data? Explain how the two graphs confirm the Pythagorean property relating secants and tangents.

36. *Introduction to Odd and Even Functions:* In this problem you will learn a property possessed by some algebraic functions and all six trigonometric functions, namely, "oddness" and "evenness." Suppose that functions f_a, f_b, f_c, and f_d are defined as follows:

   $$f_a(x) = x, \qquad f_b(x) = x^2, \qquad f_c(x) = x^3, \qquad f_d(x) = x^4.$$

   a. For each function, find $f(-3)$, $f(-2)$, $f(2)$, and $f(3)$.
   b. A function is called an *even* function if $f(-x) = f(x)$ for all values of x. From your answers in part a, tell which of the above functions are even functions.
   c. A function is called an *odd* function if $f(-x) = -f(x)$ for all values of x. From your answers to part a, tell which of the above functions are odd functions.

d. Why do you suppose the names "odd" and "even" were picked to describe the properties in parts b and c?

e. Write down the values of the six trigonometric functions of –30°. Then decide which of the trigonometric functions satisfy the requirements of an *odd* function and which ones satisfy the requirements of an *even* function. Write your answers in a form such as

$$\sin(-\theta) = \sin\theta \qquad \text{or} \qquad \sin(-\theta) = -\sin\theta,$$

whichever is correct.

STEPS IN PROVING IDENTITIES

1. Pick the member you wish to work with and write it down. Usually it is easier to start with the more complicated member.

2. Look for *algebraic* things to do.

   a. If there are two terms and you want only one,

      (i) add fractions,

      (ii) factor something out.

   b. Multiply by a clever form of 1

      (i) to multiply a numerator or denominator by its conjugate,

      (ii) to get a desired expression in numerator or denominator.

   c. Do any obvious algebra such as distributing, squaring, or multiplying polynomials.

3. Look for *trigonometric* things to do.

   a. Look for familiar trigonometric expressions like

      $$1 - \cos^2 x, \quad \cos x \sec x, \quad \text{or} \quad \sin x / \cos x.$$

   b. If there are *squares* of functions, think of Pythagorean properties.

   c. Reduce the number of different functions, transforming them to the ones you want in the answer.

4. Keep looking at the answer to make sure you are headed in the right direction.

---

37. Write the exact value of $\csc \dfrac{3\pi}{2}$.

38. Write the exact value of $\tan 210°$.

39. Write the exact value of $x = \text{Cos}^{-1}(-1)$.
40. Write the exact values of $\theta = \sin^{-1} 0.5$.
41. Sketch two cycles of the graph of $y = \tan 3\theta$.
42. *Triangle Problem:*   Find the length of the shorter leg in a right triangle with the hypotenuse 3 furlongs long and one acute angle 73° 44′.

3–3 PROPERTIES INVOLVING FUNCTIONS OF MORE THAN ONE ARGUMENT

The Pythagorean, quotient, and reciprocal properties of Section 3-1 involve *one* argument only. In this section you will learn properties in which more than one argument appears. For example, the argument may be composed of a *sum* of two numbers, such as $\cos(\theta - D)$, which you encountered when you worked with sinusoids.
   The operation cos does *not* distribute over addition or subtraction. That is, $\cos(\theta - D)$ does *not* equal $\cos\theta - \cos D$. You can prove this by substituting angles such as $\theta = 60°$ and $D = 90°$ and showing that the two expressions are not equal. In this section you will learn how to express functions of sums or differences of two angles in terms of functions of the angles themselves.

Objectives:
   1. Be able to express functions of $-x$ in terms of functions of x.
   2. Be able to express $\cos(A - B)$, $\cos(A + B)$, $\sin(A - B)$, and $\sin(A + B)$ in terms of $\sin A$, $\cos A$, $\sin B$, and $\cos B$.
   3. Be able to express $\tan(A - B)$ and $\tan(A + B)$ in terms of $\tan A$ and $\tan B$.
   4. Be able to solve equations and prove identities using these properties.
   5. Verify the identities by computer graphics.

1. *Functions of $-x$:* Suppose that $f(x) = x^5$. Then:

$f(-x) = (-x)^5$	Definition of f
$f(-x) = -x^5$	Negative number raised to odd power
$f(-x) = -f(x)$	Substitution

   But if $f(x) = x^4$, then

$f(-x) = (-x)^4$	Definition of f
$f(-x) = x^4$	Negative number raised to even power
$f(-x) = f(x)$	Definition of f

So when the exponent is odd, $f(-x) = -f(x)$; when the exponent is even, $f(-x) = f(x)$. This property of odd and even exponents leads to a general definition of odd and even functions.

DEFINITION

If $f(-x) = f(x)$, then f is called an *even function*. If $f(-x) = -f(x)$, then f is called an *odd function*.

The names "odd" and "even" carry over to functions that do not involve exponents. If you worked Problem 36 in the previous section, you discovered that the trigonometric functions possess these properties also.

Figure 3–3a shows two arcs on a unit circle, one with measure x, the other with measure $-x$. From the picture, you can see that if (u, v) is the endpoint of the arc x, then $(u, -v)$ is the endpoint of the arc $-x$. By the definition of circular functions, $\cos x = u$, and $\cos (-x) = u$ also. Therefore,

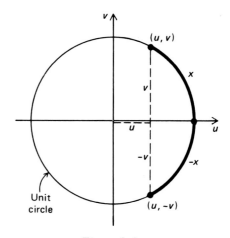

Figure 3–3a

$$\cos (-x) = \cos x,$$

which means that cosine is an *even* function. Similarly, $\sin x = v$ and $\sin (-x) = -v$, which implies that

$$\sin (-x) = -\sin x,$$

and sin is an *odd* function. Each function whose definition involves v will be an odd function, since the ordinate of $-x$ is $-v$. For example,

$$\tan (-x) = \frac{-v}{u} = -\frac{v}{u} = -\tan x.$$

The cosine and its reciprocal, the secant, which involve only u, are the only even functions. The properties are summarized below.

ODD AND EVEN FUNCTION PROPERTIES

$\cos(-x) = \cos x$	even function
$\sin(-x) = -\sin x$	odd function
$\tan(-x) = -\tan x$	odd function
$\cot(-x) = -\cot x$	odd function
$\sec(-x) = \sec x$	even function
$\csc(-x) = -\csc x$	odd function

Note that these properties also hold for the trigonometric functions. For example, $\sin(-\theta) = -\sin\theta$ and $\cos(-\theta) = \cos\theta$.

2. *Functions of Complementary Arcs:* You recall from Exercise 1–4 that the *co*sine of an angle equals the *sine* of its *complement.* For example, the complement of 76° is 90°–76°, or 14°. So cos 76° = sin 14°.

   Using the definitions of the circular functions, it is easy to see why this property is true. Figure 3–3b shows an arc x with endpoint (u, v). The *complement* of x is $\dfrac{\pi}{2} - x$. If this arc is moved into standard position, as in the right-hand sketch, its endpoint will be (v, u).

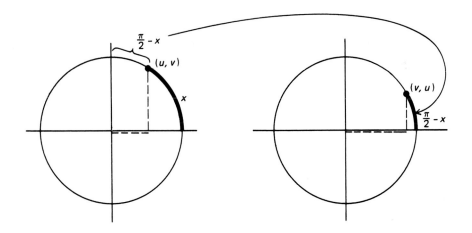

Figure 3–3b

Consequently,

$$\cos\left(\frac{\pi}{2} - x\right) = v,$$

the abscissa of the endpoint of $(\pi/2 - x)$. But $v = \sin x$, as shown in the left-hand sketch of Figure 3–3b. Therefore,

$$\cos\left(\frac{\pi}{2} - x\right) = \sin x.$$

By similar reasoning,

$$\sin\left(\frac{\pi}{2} - x\right) = \cos x.$$

The cofunction properties for tangent and secant are similarly derived. These are summarized below.

COFUNCTION PROPERTIES FOR CIRCULAR FUNCTIONS		
$\cos\left(\frac{\pi}{2} - x\right) = \sin x$	and	$\sin\left(\frac{\pi}{2} - x\right) = \cos x$
$\cot\left(\frac{\pi}{2} - x\right) = \tan x$	and	$\tan\left(\frac{\pi}{2} - x\right) = \cot x$
$\csc\left(\frac{\pi}{2} - x\right) = \sec x$	and	$\sec\left(\frac{\pi}{2} - x\right) = \csc x$

The cofunction properties for the trigonometric functions are virtually the same. Since an arc of $\frac{\pi}{2}$ corresponds to an angle of $90°$, the complement of θ is $(90° - \theta)$. The properties are summarized below.

COFUNCTION PROPERTIES FOR TRIGONOMETRIC FUNCTIONS		
$\cos(90° - \theta) = \sin\theta$	and	$\sin(90° - \theta) = \cos\theta$
$\cot(90° - \theta) = \tan\theta$	and	$\tan(90° - \theta) = \cot\theta$
$\csc(90° - \theta) = \sec\theta$	and	$\sec(90° - \theta) = \csc\theta$

3. *Cos (A − B):* You perhaps recall the distance formula for finding the distance between two points in a Cartesian coordinate system. It is really just a special case of the Pythagorean theorem. The distance between points (x_1, y_1) and (x_2, y_2) in Figure 3–3c is given by

$$d^2 = (\Delta x)^2 + (\Delta y)^2,$$

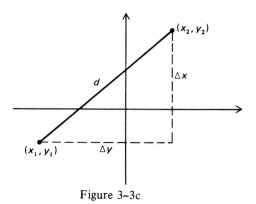

Figure 3–3c

from which

$$d^2 = (x_2 - x_1)^2 + (y_2 - y_1)^2.$$

With this piece of background information, you are now ready to derive a formula for cos $(A - B)$ in terms of sines and cosines of A and B. Figure 3–3d shows two arcs of measures A and B in standard position on a unit circle. Their terminal points have coordinates (cos A, sin A) and (cos B, sin B), respectively. The arc between these two terminal points has measure $(A - B)$.

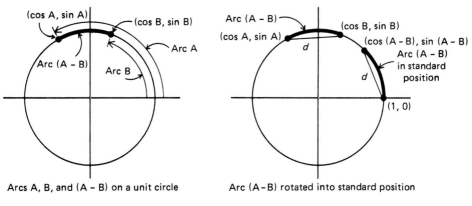

Arcs A, B, and (A – B) on a unit circle   Arc (A–B) rotated into standard position

Figure 3–3d   Figure 3–3e

The length d of the chord for this arc is simply the distance between two points in a Cartesian coordinate system. The distance formula can be used to calculate d in two different ways. When the arc $(A - B)$ is in its original position,

$$d^2 = (\cos A - \cos B)^2 + (\sin A - \sin B)^2.$$

Doing the indicated squaring gives

$$d^2 = \cos^2 A - 2 \cos A \cos B + \cos^2 B$$
$$+ \sin^2 A - 2 \sin A \sin B + \sin^2 B.$$

You have learned to think of Pythagorean properties whenever you see squares of functions. Commuting and associating $\cos^2 A + \sin^2 A$ and $\cos^2 B + \sin^2 B$ allows you to use the Pythagorean properties to replace each expression with the number 1. Therefore,

$$d^2 = 2 - 2 \cos A \cos B - 2 \sin A \sin B.$$

Figure 3–3e shows the arc of measure $(A - B)$ moved around the circle into standard position. In this position, the coordinates of its initial and terminal points are $(1, 0)$ and $(\cos (A - B), \sin (A - B))$. The distance formula can be applied again, giving

$$d^2 = (\cos (A - B) - 1)^2 + (\sin (A - B) - 0)^2.$$

Upon carrying out the indicated squaring, this becomes

$$d^2 = \cos^2 (A - B) - 2 \cos (A - B) + 1 + \sin^2 (A - B).$$

Associating the $\cos^2 (A - B) + \sin^2 (A - B)$ and using the Pythagorean properties gives

$$d^2 = 2 - 2 \cos (A - B).$$

Note that this form of d^2 contains the desired $\cos (A - B)$. The other form of d^2 above contains sines and cosines of A and B. Using the transitive property to equate these expressions gives

$$2 - 2 \cos (A - B) = 2 - 2 \cos A \cos B - 2 \sin A \sin B.$$

Subtracting 2 and then dividing by -2 gives

$$\boxed{\cos (A - B) = \cos A \cos B + \sin A \sin B}$$

This property is called a "composite argument" property, because the argument is composed of measures of two arcs or angles.

4. *Composite Argument Properties for cos (A+B), sin (A−B), sin (A+B):*
    The way to solve a new problem is to turn it into an old problem. To derive a formula for $\cos (A + B)$, you can first transform the argument into a *difference*, getting

    $$\cos (A + B) = \cos (A - (-B)).$$

    Using the composite argument property you have just derived, this becomes

    $$\cos A \cos (-B) + \sin A \sin (-B).$$

    Using the odd-even properties on this, you get

    $$\cos A \cos B - \sin A \sin B.$$

    $$\therefore \quad \boxed{\cos (A + B) = \cos A \cos B - \sin A \sin B}$$

The expression $\sin (A - B)$ can be transformed to a cosine using the cofunction properties. Considering A and B to be angles,

$$\sin (A - B) = \cos (90° - (A - B)) \qquad \text{Cofunction property}$$
$$= \cos ((90° - A) + B) \qquad \text{Associativity}$$

The last expression is now a *cosine* of a *sum*. Using the above composite-argument property gives

$$\sin (A - B) = \cos (90° - A) \cos B - \sin (90° - A) \sin B.$$

Applying the cofunction properties again gives:

$$\boxed{\sin (A - B) = \sin A \cos B - \cos A \sin B}$$

Similar reasoning gives:

$$\boxed{\sin (A + B) = \sin A \cos B + \cos A \sin B}$$

5. *Composite Argument Properties for* tan *(A + B) and* tan *(A – B):* The expression $\tan (A + B)$ can be written in terms of functions of A and B with the aid of the quotient properties:

$$\tan (A + B)$$

$$= \frac{\sin (A + B)}{\cos (A + B)} \qquad \text{Quotient property}$$

$$= \frac{\sin A \cos B + \cos A \sin B}{\cos A \cos B - \sin A \sin B} \qquad \begin{array}{l} \text{Composite argument} \\ \text{properties} \end{array}$$

It is possible to transform this into terms of tan A and tan B *alone.* Since tangents have cosines for denominators, you seek a way to get cos A and cos B as denominators. A clever way to do this is simply to *factor out* cos A cos B (i.e., "factor out a rabbit!").

$$\tan (A + B)$$

$$= \frac{\cos A \cos B \left(\dfrac{\sin A \cos B}{\cos A \cos B} + \dfrac{\cos A \sin B}{\cos A \cos B} \right)}{\cos A \cos B \left(\dfrac{\cos A \cos B}{\cos A \cos B} - \dfrac{\sin A \sin B}{\cos A \cos B} \right)} \qquad \text{Factoring}$$

$$= \frac{\dfrac{\sin A}{\cos A} + \dfrac{\sin B}{\cos B}}{1 - \dfrac{\sin A \sin B}{\cos A \cos B}} \qquad \text{Canceling}$$

$$= \frac{\tan A + \tan B}{1 - \tan A \tan B} \qquad \text{Quotient properties}$$

$$\therefore \quad \boxed{\tan (A + B) = \frac{\tan A + \tan B}{1 - \tan A \tan B}} \qquad \text{Transitivity}$$

Writing $\tan (A - B)$ as $\tan (A + (-B))$ and using the odd-even properties gives:

$$\boxed{\tan (A - B) = \frac{\tan A - \tan B}{1 + \tan A \tan B}}$$

The following exercise is designed to help you learn the odd-even, cofunction, and composite argument properties by using them.

Exercise 3–3

For Problems 1 through 6, show that the operations sin, cos, tan, cot, sec, and cos do *not* distribute over addition or subtraction by substituting $60°$ for A and $90°$ for B.

1. $\cos (A + B) \neq \cos A + \cos B$
2. $\sin (A + B) \neq \sin A + \sin B$
3. $\tan (A - B) \neq \tan A - \tan B$
4. $\cot (A - B) \neq \cot A - \cot B$
5. $\sec (A + B) \neq \sec A + \sec B$
6. $\csc (A - B) \neq \csc A - \csc B$

For Problems 7 through 12, demonstrate that the given property really works by substituting:

    a. $A = 60°,\ B = 30°$

    b. $A = \dfrac{2\pi}{3},\ B = \dfrac{\pi}{6}$

7. $\cos (A - B) = \cos A \cos B + \sin A \sin B$
8. $\cos (A + B) = \cos A \cos B - \sin A \sin B$
9. $\sin (A - B) = \sin A \cos B - \cos A \sin B$
10. $\sin (A + B) = \sin A \cos B + \cos A \sin B$

11. $\tan (A - B) = \dfrac{\tan A - \tan B}{1 + \tan A \,\tan B}$

12. $\tan (A + B) = \dfrac{\tan A + \tan B}{1 - \tan A \,\tan B}$

For Problems 13 through 16, prove that the given equation is an identity.

13. $\cos (\theta - 90°) = \sin \theta$

14. $\sin \left(x - \dfrac{\pi}{2}\right) = -\cos x$

15. $\tan \left(x - \dfrac{\pi}{2}\right) = -\cot x$

16. $\sec (\theta - 90°) = \csc \theta$

17.   *Computer Verification of Cofunction Properties:*   Use the program PLOT SINUSOID or a similar plotting program to plot on the same set of axes the graphs of

$$y = \sin x \quad \text{and} \quad y = \cos \left(\dfrac{\pi}{2} - x\right).$$

You must be clever to figure out what numbers to use for the coefficients B and D in the equation. Tell how the result demonstrates that the cofunction property is true.

18.   Repeat Problem 17 for $y = \cos x$ and $y = \sin \left(\dfrac{\pi}{2} - x\right)$.

19.   *Half-Cycle Displacement Problem #1:*   Prove that giving a sinusoid a phase displacement of half a cycle is equivalent to "turning it over." That is, prove that

$$\cos (x - \pi) = -\cos x.$$

Use the program PLOT SINUSOID or a similar plotting program to draw the graphs of

$$y = \cos (x - \pi) \quad \text{and} \quad y = -\cos x$$

on the same set of axes. Tell how the result verifies the identity you have proved.

20.   *Half-Cycle Displacement Problem #2:*   Use the technique of Problem 19 to prove that giving a sinusoid a phase displacement of half a cycle to the left is equivalent to giving it a half-cycle displacement to the

right. That is, prove that

$$\cos (x + \pi) = \cos (x - \pi).$$

Verify the result by computer graphics.

For Problems 21 through 26, assume that A and B are in standard position and that $\sin A = \frac{1}{2}$, $\cos A > 0$, $\tan B = \frac{3}{4}$, and $\sin B < 0$. Draw A and B in standard position, then find the following:

21. $\cos (A - B)$
22. $\sin (A - B)$
23. $\sin (A + B)$
24. $\cos (A + B)$
25. $\tan (A - B)$
26. $\tan (A + B)$

The composite argument properties may be used to find *exact* values of functions of 15°. Use clever choices of A and B (such as 45°, 30°, 60°, 90°, etc.), and any of the properties you need to find exact values of the following. Express the answers in simple radical form.

27. $\cos 15°$
28. $\sin 15°$
29. $\tan 15°$
30. $\cot 15°$
31. $\sec 15°$
32. $\csc 15°$

Use the cofunction properties and the answers to Problems 27 through 32 to find *exact* values of the following, leaving the answers in simple radical form.

33. $\sin 75°$
34. $\cos 75°$
35. $\cot 75°$
36. $\tan 75°$
37. $\csc 75°$
38. $\sec 75°$

Find decimal approximations for the following in two ways:

a. by evaluating the answers to Problems 27 through 38,
b. directly by calculator.
Show that the two answers are equal.

39. $\cos 15°$
40. $\sin 15°$
41. $\tan 15°$
42. $\tan 75°$
43. $\csc 75°$
44. $\sec 75°$

For Problems 45 through 50, solve the equation to find the values of x or θ. You must first transform the left member of the equation to a *single* function by using the Composite Argument Properties backwards. From there, on, the procedure is to take the inverse sine, cosine, or tangent of each member as you did in Section 2–11. For each equation, find

a.   the *general* solution for x or θ in terms of $2\pi n$ or $360n°$.
b.   the particular values of x or θ in the domain $0 \le x < 2\pi$, or $0° \le \theta < 360°$. Leave all answers in *exact* form, involving π if necessary.

45. $\cos x \cos \dfrac{\pi}{5} - \sin x \sin \dfrac{\pi}{5} = \dfrac{\sqrt{3}}{2}$

46. $\sin \theta \cos 35° + \cos \theta \sin 35° = \dfrac{1}{2}$

47. $\sin 2\theta \cos \theta - \cos 2\theta \sin \theta = \dfrac{\sqrt{2}}{2}$

48. $\cos 2x \cos x + \sin 2x \sin x = -1$

49. $\dfrac{\tan 2x - \tan x}{1 + \tan 2x \tan x} = \sqrt{3}$

50. $\dfrac{\tan \theta + \tan 27°}{1 - \tan \theta \tan 27°} = 1$

For Problems 51 through 56, prove that the given equation is an identity.

51. $\sin (\theta + 60°) - \cos (\theta + 30°) = \sin \theta$

52. $\sin (\theta + 30°) + \cos (\theta + 60°) = \cos \theta$

53. $\tan \left(x + \dfrac{\pi}{4}\right) + 1 = \sqrt{2} \cos x \sec \left(x + \dfrac{\pi}{4}\right)$

54. $\sqrt{2} \cos \left(x - \dfrac{\pi}{4}\right) = \cos x + \sin x$

55. $(\cos A \cos B - \sin A \sin B)^2 + (\sin A \cos B + \cos A \sin B)^2 = 1$

56. $\sin \dfrac{3x}{7} \cos \dfrac{4x}{7} + \cos \dfrac{3x}{7} \sin \dfrac{4x}{7} = \sin x$

The composite argument properties have sums of *two* angles or arcs. Similar properties for sums of *three* angles can be derived by first associating two of the angles. For Problems 57 and 58, write the given expression in terms of $\sin A$, $\sin B$, $\sin C$, $\cos A$, $\cos B$, and $\cos C$.

57. $\cos (A + B + C)$ 58. $\sin (A + B + C)$

Problems 59 through 62 let you discover for yourself some of the properties you will learn in the next section.

The composite argument properties can be used to express functions of *twice* an angle or arc in terms of functions of that angle or arc. For example, $\sin 2A = \sin (A + A)$, which is a function of a composite argument. Use this fact to derive "double argument" properties, expressing Problems 59 through 62 in terms of functions of A.

59. $\sin 2A$ 60. $\cos 2A$
61. $\tan 2A$ 62. $\cot 2A$

Problem 63 is intended as a challenge to the most ambitious students!

63. *Circular Reasoning Problem:* You derived the composite argument property for $\cos (A - B)$ directly from the Pythagorean theorem. Then you used the odd-even properties and cofunction properties to derive the other composite argument properties from this one.

      It is possible to "prove" that sine is an odd function by setting $A = 0$ in the property for $\sin (A - B)$ and getting $\sin (-B) = - \sin B$. Unfortunately, this is circular reasoning, since you used the odd-even properties to derive this composite argument property.

      Fortunately, there *is* a sequence of steps you can use to prove all four composite argument properties for sine and cosine as well as the odd-even and cofunction properties without circular reasoning. The sequence of proofs starts, of course, with $\cos (A - B)$.

      Without circular reasoning, prove the following properties:

      a. $\cos (A - B) = \cos A \cos B + \sin A \sin B$
      b. $\cos (A + B) = \cos A \cos B - \sin A \sin B$
      c. $\sin (A - B) = \sin A \cos B - \cos A \sin B$
      d. $\sin (A + B) = \sin A \cos B + \cos A \sin B$
      e. $\sin (-x) = - \sin x$
      f. $\cos (-x) = \cos x$
      g. $\sin (90° - x) = \cos x$
      h. $\cos (90° - x) = \sin x$

Note that you almost certainly will *not* be able to prove these in the order listed. But you should be able to find *some* sequence in which to prove them.

64. *Exact Value Review Problem:* Find exact values of the following. Verify your answers by calculator.

      a. $\cos 120°$ b. $\sin \dfrac{\pi}{6}$

      c. $\tan 240°$ d. $\cos \pi$

e. $\cot 2\pi$

f. $0 = \mathrm{Sin}^{-1}\ 0.5$

g. $x = \mathrm{Cos}^{-1}\ 0$

h. $x = \mathrm{Tan}^{-1}\ 1$

i. $\theta = \mathrm{Sec}^{-1}\ 2$

j. $\theta = \sin^{-1}\ (-1)$

3–4   MULTIPLE ARGUMENT PROPERTIES

In algebra you learn that you can commute factors in a product. For example,

$$z \cdot 2 \cdot x = 2zx.$$

The same is *not* true for trigonometric operations. For instance, in sin $2x$, the 2 affects the period. In $2 \sin x$, the 2 equals the amplitude. You can verify that the two expressions are not equivalent by graphing. Figure 3–4a shows computer graphs of $y = \sin 2x$ and $y = 2 \sin x$ as drawn by the program PLOT SINUSOID on the accompanying disk.

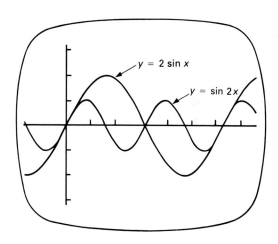

Figure 3–4a

There *are* properties that relate trigonometric functions of twice an argument to functions of that argument alone. The composite argument properties can be used to derive these properties.

Objective:

Be able to express sin $2A$, cos $2A$, and tan $2A$ in terms of sin A, cos A, and tan A.

1.   *Double Argument Property for sin $2A$:* Recognizing that sin $2A$ = sin $(A + A)$, you can write:

$$\sin 2A = \sin (A + A)$$

$$= \sin A \cos A + \cos A \sin A \qquad \text{Composite argument properties}$$

$$= 2 \sin A \cos A \qquad \text{Combining like terms}$$

$\therefore$ $\boxed{\sin 2A = 2 \sin A \cos A}$ \qquad Transitivity

2. *Double Argument Property for cos 2A:* Using the above reasoning:

$\cos 2A = \cos(A + A)$

$\qquad = \cos A \cos A - \sin A \sin A$ Composite argument properties

$\qquad = \cos^2 A - \sin^2 A$ Definition of exponentiation

$\therefore$ $\boxed{\cos 2A = \cos^2 A - \sin^2 A}$ Transitivity

Note that this property looks a lot like the Pythagorean property $\cos^2 A + \sin^2 A = 1$. In fact, the Pythagorean property can be used to transform the double argument property to two other forms.

$\cos 2A = \cos^2 A - \sin^2 A$ Double argument property

$\qquad = (1 - \sin^2 A) - \sin^2 A$ Pythagorean property

$\qquad = 1 - 2 \sin^2 A$ Associativity

$\therefore$ $\boxed{\cos 2A = 1 - 2 \sin^2 A}$ Transitivity

In this form, cos 2A is expressed in terms of sin A *alone.* Cos 2A can also be expressed in terms of cos A alone.

$\cos 2A = \cos^2 A - \sin^2 A$ Double argument property

$\qquad = \cos^2 A - (1 - \cos^2 A)$ Pythagorean property

$\qquad = 2 \cos^2 A - 1$ Distributivity, commutativity, and associativity

$\therefore$ $\boxed{\cos 2A = 2 \cos^2 A - 1}$ Transitivity

3. *Double Argument Property for tan 2A:* A double argument property for tan 2A may be derived the same way as for sin 2A and cos 2A.

$\tan 2A = \tan(A + A)$

$\qquad = \dfrac{\tan A + \tan A}{1 - \tan A \tan A}$ Composite argument properties

$\qquad = \dfrac{2 \tan A}{1 - \tan^2 A}$ Associativity and definition of exponentiation

$\therefore$ $\boxed{\tan 2A = \dfrac{2 \tan A}{1 - \tan^2 A}}$ Transitivity

Example: If $\sin A = 7/9$ and A terminates in Quadrant II,

a.   Find *exact* values for $\sin 2A$, $\cos 2A$, and $\tan 2A$.
b.   Find a decimal approximation for A using the $\sin^{-1}$ key on a calculator. Double this value to find $2A$, and store it, without round-off, in the calculator's memory. Then recall it to find $\sin 2A$, $\cos 2A$, and $\tan 2A$.
c.   Find decimal approximations for the answers in part (a), and show that these agree with your answers in part (b).

a.   From Figure 3–4b, you can find exact values of $\cos A$ and $\tan A$.

$$\cos A \; = \; -\frac{\sqrt{32}}{9}$$

$$\tan A \; = \; -\frac{7}{\sqrt{32}}$$

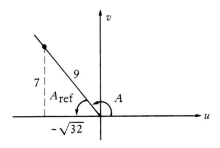

Figure 3–4b

Therefore,

$\sin 2A$

$= 2 \sin A \cos A$ Double argument property

$= 2 \cdot \dfrac{7}{9} \cdot \left(-\dfrac{\sqrt{32}}{9}\right)$ Substitution

$= -\dfrac{56\sqrt{2}}{81}$ Arithmetic, and simple radical form

$\cos 2A$

$= \cos^2 A - \sin^2 A$ Double argument property

$= \dfrac{32}{81} - \dfrac{49}{81}$ Substitution

$= -\dfrac{17}{81}$ Arithmetic

$\tan 2A$

$= \dfrac{\sin 2A}{\cos 2A}$ Quotient property

$= -\dfrac{56\sqrt{2}}{81} \cdot \left(-\dfrac{81}{17}\right)$ Substitution, and definition of division

$= \dfrac{56\sqrt{2}}{17}$ Arithmetic

b. $A_{\text{ref}} = \sin^{-1} \dfrac{7}{9}$

$\qquad\qquad = 51.05 \ldots^{\circ}$ $\qquad\qquad\qquad$ By calculator

$\therefore A \;\; = 180^{\circ} - 51.05 \ldots^{\circ}$ $\qquad\quad$ A terminates in Quadrant II

$\qquad\qquad = 128.94 \ldots^{\circ}$ $\qquad\qquad\quad$ Arithmetic

$\therefore 2A \; = 257.88 \ldots^{\circ}$ $\qquad\qquad\quad$ Doubling A

$\therefore \sin 2A \;\; = -0.97772 \ldots$

$\cos 2A \;= -0.20987 \ldots$

$\tan 2A \;= 4.65858 \ldots$ $\qquad\qquad\quad$ By calculator

c. $\quad -\dfrac{56\sqrt{2}}{81} = 0.97772 \ldots$

$\quad -\dfrac{17}{81} \qquad = -0.20987 \ldots$

$\quad \dfrac{56\sqrt{2}}{17} = 4.65858 \ldots$ $\qquad\qquad$ The answers agree.

The exercise that follows is intended to give you enough practice using these properties so that you will *learn* them. You will also use them to derive properties for *higher* multiples of angles.

Exercise 3–4

1. *Computer Verification of Double-Argument Properties:* Use the program PLOT TWO or a similar plotting program to draw on the same set of axes the graphs of

$$y = \cos 2x \quad \text{and} \quad y = \cos^2 x - \sin^2 x.$$

Explain how the result verifies the double-argument property for cosine. Repeat the procedure to verify the property

$$\sin 2x = 2 \sin x \cos x.$$

Explain why the title of this problem is computer *verification*, not computer proof.

2. *Computer Graphics for cos 2x and 2 cos x:* Use the program PLOT SINUSOID or a similar plotting program to draw on the same set of

axes the graphs of

$$y = \cos 2x \quad \text{and} \quad y = 2 \cos x.$$

Tell the difference in effect the 2 has as a coefficient of the x and as a coefficient of the cosine. Repeat the procedure to show that $\sin 2x$ does *not* equal 2 $\sin x$.

For Problems 3 through 8, show that the double argument property really works by substituting the given measures of angles or arcs into the formula and showing that you get the right answer.

3. $\sin 2A$, $A = 30°$ 4. $\cos 2A$, $A = 30°$

5. $\cos 2A$, $A = \dfrac{\pi}{4}$ 6. $\sin 2A$, $A = \dfrac{\pi}{4}$

7. $\tan 2A$, $A = 60°$ 8. $\tan 2A$, $A = \dfrac{\pi}{4}$

For Problems 9 through 16,

a. Find *exact* values for $\sin 2A$, $\cos 2A$, and $\tan 2A$ if A terminates in the given quadrant.
b. Find decimal approximations for $\sin 2A$, $\cos 2A$, and $\tan 2A$ by finding the measure of A (between $0°$ and $360°$), doubling it, and finding the functions by calculator.
c. Show that your answers to parts (a) and (b) agree with each other.

9. $\sin A = \dfrac{3}{5}$, Quadrant I   10. $\cos A = \dfrac{-3}{5}$, Quadrant II

11. $\tan A = \dfrac{-3}{4}$, Quadrant IV   12. $\tan A = \dfrac{4}{3}$, Quadrant III

13. $\cos A = \dfrac{-6}{7}$, Quadrant II   14. $\sin A = \dfrac{-2}{7}$, Quadrant IV

15. $\csc A = -3$, Quadrant III   16. $\sec A = 4$, Quadrant I

For Problems 17 through 22, solve the equation for x or θ. You should use the appropriate double argument property first to transform the left member to a *single* function. Then take the inverse cosine, sine, or tangent of each member as you did in Section 2–11. For each equation, find

a. the *general* solution for x or θ, in terms of a multiple of n.
b. the particular values of x or θ in the domain $\le x < 2\pi$ or $0° \le 360°$.
Leave the answers in *exact* form, involving π, if necessary.

17. $4 \sin x \cos x = \sqrt{3}$ 18. $4 \sin x \cos x = -\sqrt{2}$

19. $\cos^2 \theta - \sin^2 \theta = -1$

20. $1 - 2 \sin^2 \theta = \dfrac{1}{2}$

21. $\dfrac{2 \tan x}{1 - \tan^2 x} = \sqrt{3}$

22. $\dfrac{2 \tan x}{1 - \tan^2 x} = -1$

23. *Computer Verification of Solutions:* Use the program PLOT FUNC-TION or a similar program to verify that your solutions to Problem 17 are correct. To do this, draw $y = 4 \sin x \cos x$ and then draw a horizontal line at $y = \sqrt{3}$. Draw vertical lines at several of your solutions. How do the results show that your answers are right?

24. Repeat Problem 23 for $4 \sin x \cos x = -\sqrt{2}$, which is Problem 18 above.

For Problems 25 through 34, prove that the given equation is an identity.

25. $\sin 2x = \dfrac{2 \tan x}{1 + \tan^2 x}$

26. $\sec 2x = \dfrac{\sec^2 x}{2 - \sec^2 x}$

27. $\cos 2\phi = \dfrac{1 - \tan^2 \phi}{1 + \tan^2 \phi}$

28. $\sin 2\phi = 2 \cot \phi \sin^2 \phi$

29. $\dfrac{\cos 2D}{\cos D - \sin D} = \cos D + \sin D$

30. $(1 + \tan x) \tan 2x = \dfrac{2 \tan x}{1 - \tan x}$

31. $\tan r = \dfrac{1 - \cos 2r}{\sin 2r}$

32. $\tan y = \dfrac{\sin 2y}{1 + \cos 2y}$

33. $\sin^2 \theta = \dfrac{1}{2}(1 - \cos 2\theta)$

34. $\cos^2 \theta = \dfrac{1}{2}(1 + \cos 2\theta)$

The composite argument properties can be combined with the double argument properties to derive triple, quadruple, etc., argument properties. For example, $\sin 3x = \sin (2x + x)$, which is a sine of a composite argument.

For Problems 35 through 38, derive multiple argument properties for the given functions.

35. $\sin 3x$ in terms of $\sin x$ alone.
36. $\cos 3x$ in terms of $\cos x$ alone.
37. $\cos 4x$ in terms of $\cos x$ alone.
38. $\sin 4x$ in terms of $\sin x$ and $\cos x$.

The double argument properties work whenever one of the arguments is twice as large as the other. For Problems 39 through 46, write equations expressing:

39.   tan $14x$ in terms of tan $7x$.
40.   cot $14x$ in terms of cot $7x$.
41.   cos $6x$ in terms of sin $3x$ and cos $3x$.
42.   sin $6x$ in terms of sin $3x$ and cos $3x$.
43.   cos $10x$ in terms of cos $5x$ *alone.*
44.   cos $10x$ in terms of sin $5x$ *alone.*
45.   cos x in terms of cos $\frac{1}{2}x$ *alone.*
46.   cos x in terms of sin $\frac{1}{2}x$ *alone.*

Problems 47 and 48 allow you to discover something about the next section.

47.   Use the answer to Problem 43 to write an equation expressing cos $\frac{1}{2}x$ in terms of cos x.

48.   Use the answer to Problem 44 to write an equation expressing sin $\frac{1}{2}x$ in terms of cos x.

49.   A right triangle has legs of length 7 varas and 11 varas. Find the measure of the smaller acute angle. How long is a vara?

50.   Sketch the graph of $y = \sec \theta$.

51.   Write the exact value of $\tan\left(-\dfrac{\pi}{3}\right)$.

52.   *Increase in Sine Problem:*   By what percent does sin θ increase when θ increases from $10°$ to $11°$? From $80°$ to $81°$? From $88°$ to $89°$?

3–5 HALF-ARGUMENT PROPERTIES

In the expression $\cos \frac{1}{2}x$, the $\frac{1}{2}$ cannot be commuted to the left. In $\frac{1}{2} \cos x$, the $\frac{1}{2}$ is the amplitude, while in $\cos \frac{1}{2}x$, the $\frac{1}{2}$ affects the period. The graphs in Figure 3–5a, drawn by the program PLOT SINUSOID, show the different effects.

In this section you will derive properties expressing functions of half an argument in terms of functions of that argument alone.

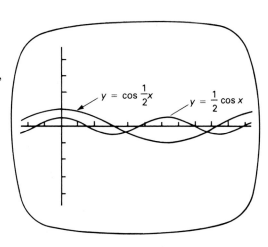

Figure 3–5a

Objective:

Be able to express cos ½x, sin ½x, and tan ½x in terms of functions of x. The desired properties can be derived simply by performing algebra on the various forms of the cosine double-argument property. To find cos ½x, you start with the form that has *cosine* alone in the right member.

$\cos 2A = 2 \cos^2 A - 1$	Double argument property
$1 + \cos 2A = 2 \cos^2 A$	Adding 1 to each member
$\frac{1}{2}(1 + \cos 2A) = \cos^2 A$	Dividing by 2
$\therefore \boxed{\cos^2 A = \frac{1}{2}(1 + \cos 2A)}$	Symmetry

This equation expresses a *power* of a function in terms of a function of a *multiple* angle or arc. Solving $\cos 2A = 1 - 2 \sin^2 A$ for $\sin^2 A$ gives:

$$\boxed{\sin^2 A = \frac{1}{2}(1 - \cos 2A)}$$

In these two properties the argument A on the left is *half* the argument $2A$ on the right. Letting $A = \frac{1}{2}x$ and substituting gives

$$\cos^2 \tfrac{1}{2}x = \tfrac{1}{2}(1 + \cos x) \qquad \text{and} \qquad \sin^2 \tfrac{1}{2}x = \tfrac{1}{2}(1 - \cos x)$$

Taking the square root of each member of both equations gives:

$$\boxed{\begin{aligned} \cos \tfrac{1}{2}x &= \pm\sqrt{\tfrac{1}{2}(1 + \cos x)} \\ \sin \tfrac{1}{2}x &= \pm\sqrt{\tfrac{1}{2}(1 - \cos x)} \end{aligned}}$$

These are called half-argument properties since they express functions of ½x in terms of functions of x. There are corresponding properties for trigonometric functions, where x is replaced by an angle measure, θ.

The ambiguous sign ± is determined by the quadrant in which ½x or ½θ terminates (*not* by where x or θ terminates!). For example, if $\theta = 120°$ then ½θ = 60°, which terminates in Quadrant I. So,

$$\sin \tfrac{1}{2}\theta = +\sqrt{\tfrac{1}{2}(1 - \cos \theta)}.$$

But if $\theta = 480°$, which is coterminal with 120° as shown in Figure 3–5b, then ½θ = 240°. Since 240° terminates in Quadrant III,

$$\sin \tfrac{1}{2}\theta = -\sqrt{\tfrac{1}{2}(1 - \cos \theta)}.$$

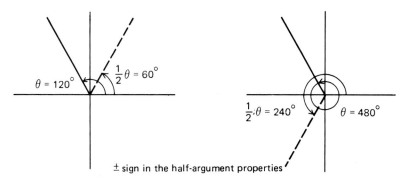

± sign in the half-argument properties

Figure 3–5b

The half-argument property for the tangent is obtained from the sine and cosine half-argument properties by using the quotient property.

$$\tan \tfrac{1}{2}x = \frac{\sin \tfrac{1}{2}x}{\cos \tfrac{1}{2}x} \qquad\qquad \text{Quotient property}$$

$$= \frac{\pm\sqrt{\tfrac{1}{2}(1 - \cos x)}}{\pm\sqrt{\tfrac{1}{2}(1 + \cos x)}} \qquad \text{Half-argument properties}$$

$$= \pm\sqrt{\frac{1 - \cos x}{1 + \cos x}} \qquad\qquad \text{Properties of radicals and fractions}$$

$$\therefore \quad \boxed{\tan \tfrac{1}{2}x = \pm\sqrt{\frac{1 - \cos x}{1 + \cos x}}} \qquad \text{Transitivity}$$

This tangent half-argument property can be simplified by rationalizing the denominator.

$$\tan \tfrac{1}{2}x = \pm\sqrt{\frac{1 - \cos x}{1 + \cos x} \cdot \frac{1 + \cos x}{1 + \cos x}} \qquad \text{Multiplication property of 1}$$

$$= \pm\sqrt{\frac{1 - \cos^2 x}{(1 + \cos x)^2}} \qquad\qquad \text{Multiplication property of fractions}$$

$$= \pm\frac{\sqrt{1 - \cos^2 x}}{|1 + \cos x|} \qquad\qquad \sqrt{n^2} = |n|$$

$$= \pm\frac{\sqrt{1 - \cos^2 x}}{1 + \cos x} \qquad\qquad 1 + \cos x \geq 0 \text{ for all } x$$

An added benefit appears immediately, since the radicand $1 - \cos^2 x$ in the numerator is equal to $\sin^2 x$, a perfect square. So the tangent half-argument property may be written:

$$\tan \tfrac{1}{2}x = \frac{\sin x}{1 + \cos x}$$

In Problem 33 that follows, you will be asked to explain why the ± sign can be dropped.

A still more interesting form of the property can be obtained by rationalizing the *numerator* instead of the denominator.

$$\tan \tfrac{1}{2}x = \frac{1 - \cos x}{\sin x}$$

Since the denominator in this last form has only *one* term, it is useful for proving identities that involve fractions. In Problem 34 of the following exercise, you will be asked to prove this form of the tangent half-argument property.

Example: If $\cos \theta = 15/17$, and θ is in the domain $270° < \theta < 360°$,
a.   Find *exact* values of $\sin \tfrac{1}{2}\theta$, $\cos \tfrac{1}{2}\theta$, and $\tan \tfrac{1}{2}\theta$.
b.   Find decimal approximations for $\sin \tfrac{1}{2}\theta$, $\cos \tfrac{1}{2}\theta$, and $\tan \tfrac{1}{2}\theta$ by finding the measure of θ, dividing by 2, and pressing the appropriate function keys on the calculator.
c.   Show that the answers to parts (a) and (b) agree.

a. $270° < \theta < 360°$ Given domain

   $135° < \tfrac{1}{2}\theta < 180°$ Dividing by 2

   $\therefore \tfrac{1}{2}\theta$ terminates in Quadrant II.

$\sin \tfrac{1}{2}\theta = +\sqrt{\dfrac{1}{2}\left(1 - \dfrac{15}{17}\right)}$ Substitution into half-argument property

   $= \dfrac{1}{\sqrt{17}}$ Simplifying

$\cos \tfrac{1}{2}\theta = -\sqrt{\dfrac{1}{2}\left(1 + \dfrac{15}{17}\right)}$ Substitution into half-argument property

   $= -\dfrac{4}{\sqrt{15}}$ Simplifying

$$\tan \tfrac{1}{2}\theta \;=\; \frac{\sin \tfrac{1}{2}\theta}{\cos \tfrac{1}{2}\theta} \qquad\qquad \text{Quotient properties}$$

$$=\; \frac{1}{\sqrt{17}} \cdot \left(-\frac{\sqrt{17}}{4}\right) \qquad \text{Substitution, and definition of}$$
$$\text{division}$$

$$=\; -\frac{1}{4} \qquad\qquad \text{Simplifying}$$

b. $\theta_{\text{ref}} \;=\; \cos^{-1}\dfrac{15}{17}$

$\qquad\quad =\; 28.07\ldots^{\circ}$

$\therefore\ \theta \;=\; 360^{\circ} - 28.07^{\circ}\ldots \text{(Figure 3-5c)}$

$\qquad\quad =\; 331.92\ldots^{\circ}$

$\therefore\ \tfrac{1}{2}\theta \;=\; 165.96\ldots^{\circ}$

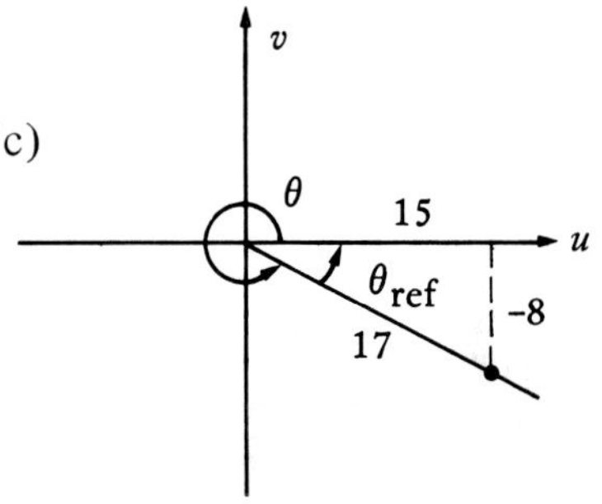

$\sin \tfrac{1}{2}\theta \;\approx\; \underline{0.2425}$

$\cos \tfrac{1}{2}\theta \;\approx\; \underline{-0.9701}$

$\tan \tfrac{1}{2}\theta \;=\; \underline{-0.25}$

Figure 3-5c

c. $\dfrac{1}{\sqrt{17}} \;\approx\; \underline{0.2425}$

$-\dfrac{4}{\sqrt{17}} \;\approx\; \underline{-0.9701}$

$-\dfrac{1}{4} \;=\; \underline{-0.25}$

The exercise that follows is designed to give you enough practice using the half-argument properties so that you will learn them.

Exercise 3-5

1. *Computer Verification Half-Argument Properties:*   Use the program PLOT TWO or a similar plotting program to draw on the same set of axes the graphs of

$$y = \cos \tfrac{1}{2}x \quad\text{and}\quad y = \sqrt{\tfrac{1}{2}(1 + \cos x)}.$$

Explain how the result verifies the cosine double-argument property only for certain values of x. How could the property be verified for other values of x? Repeat the procedure to verify the property

$$\sin \tfrac{1}{2}x = \sqrt{\tfrac{1}{2}(1 - \cos x)}.$$

Explain why the title of this problem is computer *verification*, not computer proof.

2. *Computer Graphics for sin ½ x and ½ sin x:* Use the program PLOT SINUSOID or a similar plotting program to draw on the same set of axes the graphs of

$$y = \sin \tfrac{1}{2}x \ \text{ and } \ y = \tfrac{1}{2} \sin x.$$

Tell the difference in effect the ½ has as a coefficient of the x and as a coefficient of the sine. Repeat the procedure to show that cos (½)x does *not* equal (½) cos x.

For Problems 3 through 12, verify that the half-argument properties actually work by substituting the given measure of the angle or arc into the formula and showing that you get the right answer.

3. cos ½θ,	$\theta = 60°$	4. sin ½θ,	$\theta = 60°$
5. sin ½x,	$x = \pi/2$	6. cos ½x,	$x = \pi/2$
7. tan ½x,	$x = 2\pi/3$	8. tan ½x,	$x = \pi$
9. cos ½θ,	$\theta = 420°$	10. sin ½θ,	$\theta = 420°$
11. sin ½θ,	$\theta = -60°$	12. cos ½θ,	$\theta = -60°$

For Problems 13 through 18,

a. Find *exact* values for sin ½θ, cos ½θ, and tan ½θ if θ terminates in the given domain.
b. Find decimal approximations for sin ½θ, cos ½θ, and tan ½θ by finding the measure of θ, dividing by 2, and pressing the appropriate function keys on the calculator.
c. Show that the answers to parts (a) and (b) agree with each other.

13. $\cos \theta = \dfrac{3}{5}, \quad 0° < \theta < 90°$

14. $\cos \theta = \dfrac{3}{5}, \quad 270° < \theta < 360°$

15. $\cos \theta = -\dfrac{3}{5}, \quad 180° < \theta < 270°$

16. $\cos \theta = -\dfrac{3}{5}, \quad 90° < \theta < 180°$

17. $\cos \theta = \dfrac{3}{5}, \quad 630° < \theta < 720°$

18. $\cos \theta = -\dfrac{3}{5}, \quad 450° < \theta < 540°$

19. Solve the equation $\sqrt{\frac{1}{2}(1 + \cos x)} = \frac{\sqrt{3}}{2}$ two ways:

    a. by replacing the left member with cos ½x, and
    b. by squaring each member. By plotting the graphs of

$$y = \sqrt{\frac{1}{2}(1 + \cos x)} \quad \text{and} \quad y = \cos \tfrac{1}{2}x,$$

        show why you *lose* half of the solutions by the replacement.

20. Repeat Problem 19 for the equation $\sqrt{\frac{1}{2}(1 - \cos x)} = 1$.

For Problems 21 through 24, solve the equation for values of x or θ. You should replace the left member with a single function using the appropriate half-argument or double-argument property. Then you should take the inverse sine, cosine, or tangent of each member, as in Section 2–11.

21. $\dfrac{\sin x}{1 + \cos x} = -1$ 22. $\dfrac{1 - \cos \theta}{\sin \theta} = \dfrac{\sqrt{3}}{3}$

23. $\sin x \cos x = 1$ 24. $\cos^2 \theta - \sin^2 \theta = -\dfrac{\sqrt{3}}{2}$

For Problems 25 through 32, prove that the given equation is an identity.

25. $\tan \tfrac{1}{2}x + \cot \tfrac{1}{2}x = 2 \csc x$

26. $\tan x \tan \tfrac{1}{2}x = \sec x - 1$

27. $\dfrac{2 \tan \tfrac{1}{2}x}{1 + \tan^2 \tfrac{1}{2}x} = \sin x$

28. $\tan \tfrac{1}{2}x (2 \cot x + \tan \tfrac{1}{2}x) = 1$

29. $\dfrac{\cos \tfrac{1}{2}\theta - \sin \tfrac{1}{2}\theta}{\cos \tfrac{1}{2}\theta + \sin \tfrac{1}{2}\theta} = \dfrac{\cos \theta}{1 + \sin \theta}$

30. $\dfrac{\cos \tfrac{1}{2}\phi + \sin \tfrac{1}{2}\phi}{\cos \tfrac{1}{2}\phi - \sin \tfrac{1}{2}\phi} = \sec \phi + \tan \phi$

31. $\tan \tfrac{1}{2}A = \csc A - \cot A$

32. $\tan \left(\dfrac{\pi}{4} + \dfrac{x}{2} \right) = \sec x + \tan x$

33. The property

$$\tan \tfrac{1}{2}x = \dfrac{\sin x}{1 + \cos x} \quad \text{comes from} \quad \dfrac{\pm \sqrt{1 - \cos^2 x}}{1 + \cos x}.$$

        By considering the quadrants in which x and $\frac{1}{2}x$ may terminate, explain why the ambiguous sign $\pm$ disappears in this property.

34. Prove that

$$\tan \tfrac{1}{2}x = \pm \sqrt{\frac{1 - \cos x}{1 + \cos x}}$$

can be transformed to

$$\tan \tfrac{1}{2}x = \frac{1 - \cos x}{\sin x},$$

and explain what happens to the $\pm$ sign.

Problems 35 and 36 allow you to discover something about the next section.

35. The right-hand members of the composite argument properties for $\sin (A + B)$ and $\sin (A - B)$ are *conjugates* of each other. When you add or subtract conjugates, one of the two terms drops out, leaving twice the other term.

   a. Write an equation expressing $\sin (A + B) + \sin (A - B)$ in terms of functions of A and B.
   b. Write an equation expressing $\sin (A + B) - \sin (A - B)$ in terms of functions of A and B.

36. Repeat Problem 35 for $\cos (A + B)$ and $\cos (A - B)$.

Problem 37 is meant to challenge the most diligent students!

37. *Sin 18°, etc.:* You have learned how to find exact values of functions of multiples of $15°$. It is possible to find exact values for functions of certain other angles, too. In this problem, you will combine trigonometric properties with algebraic techniques and a little ingenuity to find the exact value of $\sin 18°$.

   a. Use the double argument property for sine to write an equation expressing $\sin 72°$ in terms of $\sin 36°$ and $\cos 36°$.
   b. Transform the equation in part a so that $\sin 72°$ is expressed in terms of $\sin 18°$ and $\cos 18°$. You should find that the *sine* form of the double argument property for $\cos 36°$ is best.
   c. You recall by the cofunction property that $\sin 72° = \cos 18°$. Replace $\sin 72°$ in your equation from part b with $\cos 18°$. Then simplify the resulting equation. If you have done everything correctly, the $\cos 18°$ should disappear from the equation, leaving a *cubic* (third degree) equation in $\sin 18°$.

d. Solve the equation in part c for $\sin 18°$. It may help to let $x = \sin 18°$ and solve for x. If you transform the equation so that the right member is 0, you should find that $(2x - 1)$ is a factor of the left member. The other factor may be found by long division. To solve the equation, recall the multiplication property of zero and the quadratic formula.

e. You should get *three* solutions for the equation in part d. Only *one* of these could possibly be $\sin 18°$. *Which* one?

f. A pattern shows up for some exact values of $\sin \theta$:

$$\sin 15° = \frac{\sqrt{6} - \sqrt{2}}{4}$$

$$\sin 18° = \frac{\sqrt{5} - 1}{4} = \frac{\sqrt{5} - \sqrt{1}}{4}$$

$$\sin 30° = \frac{1}{2} = \frac{2}{4} = \frac{\sqrt{4} - \sqrt{0}}{4}$$

See if you can figure out what the pattern is!!

38. *Radian Drawing Problem:*   Sketch an angle you think is about 1 radian. Then measure it in degrees either with a protractor or by right triangle techniques. Within what percent of the right number of degrees did your angle come?

39. Write the exact value of $\sin 120°$.

40. Write the exact value of $\tan \dfrac{5\pi}{6}$.

3–6   SUM AND PRODUCT PROPERTIES

The composite argument properties for sine are

$$\sin (A + B) = \sin A \, \cos B + \cos A \, \sin B,$$

$$\sin (A - B) = \sin A \, \cos B - \cos A \, \sin B.$$

By *adding* respective members of the two equations, you get:

$$\boxed{\sin (A + B) + \sin (A - B) = 2 \sin A \, \cos B}$$

This property is of interest because the left member is a *sum* of two sines, and the right member is a *product* of a sine and a cosine.

Objectives:

1. Be able to transform a *sum* (or difference) of two sines or two co-sines into a *product* of sines and cosines.
2. Be able to transform a *product* of two sines, two cosines, or a sine and cosine into a *sum* (or difference) of two sines or cosines.
3. Confirm by computer graphics that the sum and product are equivalent.

By subtracting respective members of the composite argument proper-ties for sine, above, you get:

$$\sin (A + B) - \sin (A - B) = 2 \cos A \sin B$$

The other two "sum and product" properties needed to accomplish the ob-jectives come from adding and subtracting the composite argument proper-ties for the cosine:

$$\cos (A + B) = \cos A \cos B - \sin A \sin B$$

$$\cos (A - B) = \cos A \cos B + \sin A \sin B$$

$$\cos (A + B) + \cos (A - B) = 2 \cos A \cos B$$

By subtracting instead of adding:

$$\cos (A + B) - \cos (A - B) = -2 \sin A \sin B$$

The reverse process, expressing a sum as a product, is more easily ac-complished by first replacing the $A + B$ and $A - B$ by other *single* variables.

For instance, let

$$A + B = x,$$

$$A - B = y.$$

Adding respective members of these equations gives

$$2A = x + y,$$

$$A = \tfrac{1}{2}(x + y),$$

and subtracting respective members gives

$$2B = x - y,$$

$B = \frac{1}{2}(x - y).$

Replacing A and B with $\frac{1}{2}(x + y)$ and $\frac{1}{2}(x - y)$, respectively, leads to the following forms of the sum and product properties:

$$\begin{array}{l} \sin x + \sin y = 2 \sin \frac{1}{2}(x + y) \cos \frac{1}{2}(x - y) \\ \sin x - \sin y = 2 \cos \frac{1}{2}(x + y) \sin \frac{1}{2}(x - y) \\ \cos x + \cos y = 2 \cos \frac{1}{2}(x + y) \cos \frac{1}{2}(x - y) \\ \cos x - \cos y = -2 \sin \frac{1}{2}(x + y) \sin \frac{1}{2}(x - y) \end{array}$$

These properties are difficult to remember correctly, since they are all so similar to one another. Therefore, it is usually more reliable for you to remember how you derived them from the composite argument properties (which you *should* remember by now!). Then you can *derive* the sum and product properties whenever you need them.

Example 1:   Express $2 \sin 13° \cos 48°$ as a sum.
Using the first form of the sum and product properties,

$2 \sin 13° \cos 48°$

$= \sin (13° + 48°) + \sin (13° - 48°)$	Sum and product properties
$= \sin 61° + \sin (-35°)$	Arithmetic
$= \sin 61° - \sin 35°$	Sine is an *odd* function

If you want $\sin 13° \cos 48°$ instead of $2 \sin 13° \cos 48°$, you can simply divide both members by 2, getting

$\sin 13° \cos 48° = \frac{1}{2} \sin 61° - \frac{1}{2} \sin 35°.$

Example 2:   Express $\cos 47° + \cos 59°$ as a *product*.
Using the second forms of the sum and product properties,

$\cos 47° + \cos 59°$

$= 2 \cos \frac{1}{2}(47° + 59°) \cos \frac{1}{2}(47° - 59°)$	Sum and product properties
$= 2 \cos \frac{1}{2}(106°) \cos \frac{1}{2}(-12°)$	Arithmetic
$= 2 \cos 53° \cos (-6°)$	Arithmetic
$= 2 \cos 53° \cos 6°$	Cosine is an *even* function

Example 3:   The sum and product properties may be used to express more complicated products in terms of sums of functions. For example,

$\sin^2 x \cos x$

$= \frac{1}{2}(1 - \cos 2x) \cos x$	See Section 3-5
$= \frac{1}{2}(\cos x - \cos x \cos 2x)$	Distributing $\cos x$
$= \frac{1}{2}(\cos x - \frac{1}{2}(\cos(x + 2x)$ $+ \cos(x - 2x)))$	Sum and product properties
$= \frac{1}{2}(\cos x - \frac{1}{2}(\cos 3x + \cos(-x)))$	Arithmetic
$= \frac{1}{2}(\cos x - \frac{1}{2}\cos 3x - \frac{1}{2}\cos x)$	Distributing $-\frac{1}{2}$, and cosine is *even*
$= \frac{1}{2}(\frac{1}{2}\cos x - \frac{1}{2}\cos 3x)$	Associativity
$= \frac{1}{4}\cos x - \frac{1}{4}\cos 3x$	Distributing $\frac{1}{2}$

The answer is an expression which is *linear* (first degree) in functions of multiples of x.

Example 4:   Solve the equation $\sin 5x + \sin x = 0$ for values of x in the domain $0 < x < 2\pi$.
   If the left member were a *product* instead of a sum, then the equation would have the form "product = 0." In that case, each factor could be set equal to 0, since a product is 0 if and only if one of its factors is 0. So you write

$\sin 5x + \sin x = 0$	Given equation
$2 \sin \frac{1}{2}(5x + x) \cos \frac{1}{2}(5x - x) = 0$	Sum and product properties
$2 \sin 3x \cos 2x = 0$	Arithmetic
$\sin 3x \cos 2x = 0$	Dividing by 2
$\sin 3x = 0$ or $\cos 2x = 0$	Setting each factor = 0
$3x = 0 + 2\pi n$ or $2x = \pm\frac{\pi}{2} + 2\pi n$ or $\pi + 2\pi n$	Taking $\sin^{-1}$ and $\cos^{-1}$
$x = 0 + \frac{2\pi n}{3}$ or $x = \pm\frac{\pi}{4} + \pi n$ or $\frac{\pi}{3} + \frac{2\pi n}{3}$	Dividing by 3 or by 2

$$x = 0, \frac{2\pi}{3}, \frac{4\pi}{3}, 2\pi, \ldots,$$

$$\frac{\pi}{3}, \pi, \frac{5\pi}{3}, \frac{7\pi}{3}, \ldots,$$

$$\frac{\pi}{4}, \frac{5\pi}{4}, \frac{9\pi}{4}, \ldots,$$

$$-\frac{\pi}{4}, \frac{3\pi}{4}, \frac{7\pi}{4}, \ldots \qquad \text{Setting } n = 0, 1, 2, \ldots$$

$$\therefore S = \left\{ 0, \frac{\pi}{4}, \frac{\pi}{3}, \frac{2\pi}{3}, \frac{3\pi}{4}, \pi, \frac{5\pi}{4}, \frac{4\pi}{3}, \frac{5\pi}{3}, \frac{7\pi}{4} \right\}$$

Selecting values in the domain.

Example 5:   Transform cos x + cos 5x to a product. Verify your result by computer graphics. Describe the pattern the graph forms.

By the second form of the sum
and product properties,

cos x + cos 5x

= 2 cos ½(x + 5x) cos ½(x – 5x)

= 2 cos 3x cos (–2x)

= <u>2 cos 3x cos 2x.</u>

The last step is valid because
cosine is an even function.
Using the program PLOT TWO
or a similar program you find
that both y = cos x + cos 5x
and y = 2 cos 3x cos 2x have the
graph shown in Figure 3–6a. The
pattern is a *sinusoid with a varying*

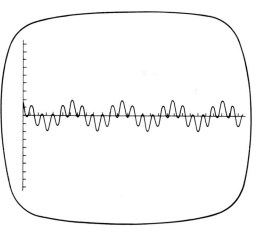

Figure 3–6a

sinusoidal axis. In Section 4–1 you will learn how to draw these graphs by
adding or multiplying ordinates of the individual sinusoids.

In the following exercise you will use these properties to transform sums
to products, and vice versa.

Exercise 3-6

For Problems 1 through 12, transform the indicated product to a *sum* (or difference) of sines or cosines of *positive* arguments.

1. $2 \sin 41° \cos 24°$
2. $2 \cos 73° \sin 62°$
3. $2 \cos 53° \cos 49°$
4. $2 \sin 29° \sin 16°$
5. $2 \cos 3.8 \sin 4.1$
6. $2 \cos 2 \cos 3$
7. $2 \sin 4.6 \sin 7.2$
8. $2 \sin 1.8 \cos 6.2$
9. $2 \sin 3x \cos 5x$
10. $2 \sin 8x \sin 2x$
11. $2 \cos 4x \cos 7x$
12. $2 \cos 11x \sin 9x$

For Problems 13 through 24, transform the indicated sum (or difference) into a *product* of sines and cosines of *positive* arguments.

13. $\cos 46° + \cos 12°$
14. $\cos 56° - \cos 24°$
15. $\sin 54° + \sin 22°$
16. $\sin 29° - \sin 15°$
17. $\cos 2.4 - \cos 4.4$
18. $\sin 1.8 + \sin 6.4$
19. $\sin 2 - \sin 6$
20. $\cos 3.2 + \cos 4.8$
21. $\sin 3x + \sin 9x$
22. $\sin 9x - \sin 11x$
23. $\cos 8x - \cos 10x$
24. $\cos 5x + \cos 13x$

For Problems 25 through 28, solve the equations by first transforming it to a product equal to zero. Use values of x or θ in the given domain.

25. $\sin 3x - \sin x = 0, \quad 0 \le x < 2\pi$
26. $\sin 3\theta + \sin \theta = 0, \quad 0° \le \theta < 360°$
27. $\cos 5\theta + \cos 3\theta = 0, \quad 0° \le \theta < 180°$
28. $\cos 5x - \cos x = 0, \quad 0 \le x < \pi$

For Problems 29 through 40, prove that the given equation is an identity.

29. $\cos x - \cos 5x = 4 \sin 3x \sin x \cos x$
30. $\sin 5x + \sin 3x = 4 \sin 2x \cos 2x \cos x$
31. $\dfrac{\sin 3x + \sin x}{\sin 3x - \sin x} = \dfrac{2 \cos^2 x}{\cos 2x}$
32. $\dfrac{\sin 5x + \sin 7x}{\cos 5x + \cos 7x} = \tan 6x$
33. $\sin x + \sin 2x + \sin 3x = \sin 2x(1 + 2 \cos x)$
34. $\cos x + \cos 2x + \cos 3x = \cos 2x(1 + 2 \cos x)$
35. $1 + \cos x = \dfrac{1}{2} + \dfrac{\sin \frac{3}{2}x}{2 \sin \frac{1}{2}x}$

36. $1 + \cos x + \cos 2x = \dfrac{1}{2} + \dfrac{\sin \frac{5}{2}x}{2 \sin \frac{1}{2}x}$

37. $\sin (x + y) \sin (x - y) = \sin^2 x - \sin^2 y$
38. $\sin (x + y) \sin (x - y) = \cos^2 y - \cos^2 x$
39. $\cos (x + y) \cos (x - y) = \cos^2 x - \sin^2 y$
40. $\sin (x + y) \cos (x - y) = \tfrac{1}{2} \sin 2x + \tfrac{1}{2} \sin 2y$

For Problems 41 through 46, transform the given product or power to a *sum* (or difference) of terms that are *linear* (first degree) in functions of multiples of x.

41. $\cos^2 x \sin x$ 42. $\sin^2 x \cos^2 x$
43. $\sin^3 x$ 44. $\cos^3 x$
45. $\cos^2 x \sin^3 x$ 46. $\sin^2 x \cos^3 x$

For Problems 47 through 50, transform the sum to a product, or the product to a sum. Then plot the original expression and the transformed expression using PLOT TWO or a similar plotting program to verify that your answer is correct. In each case, describe the pattern the graph forms.

47. $\sin x + \sin 7x$ 48. $\cos 8x - \cos 7x$
49. $\cos x \cos 8x$ 50. $\sin 6x \cos 7x$

51. The expression $\sin 2x \cos 3x$ is a *product* of functions of *multiple* arguments. In this problem you will transform the expression in two opposite directions.

   a. Transform $\sin 2x \cos 3x$ so that it involves only sines and cosines of x.
   b. Transform $\sin 2x \cos 3x$ so that it involves no products or powers of trigonometric functions.
   c. What relationship do you notice among the *degree* of your answer to part a, the *highest multiple* of x in your answer to part b, and the *multiples* of x in the original expression?

52. Repeat Problem 51 for $\sin 3x \cos 2x$.

Problem 53 allows you to discover something about the next section.

53. Given the expression $C \cos (x - D)$, where C and D stand for constants:

a. Expand the expression using the composite argument properties.
b. Show that there are constants A and B for which

$$C \cos (x - D) = A \cos x + B \sin x.$$

c. What do C and D equal in terms of A and B?

Problem 54 is meant to be a challenge!

54. In Problem 36 you proved an identity expressing $1 + \cos x + \cos 2x$ in terms of sines of fractional arguments. In this problem you will attempt to generalize this property to

$$1 + \cos x + \cos 2x + \cos 3x + \ldots + \cos nx = \frac{1}{2} + \frac{\sin \frac{2n + 1}{2} x}{2 \sin \frac{1}{2} x},$$

where n is *any* positive integer.

a. By a clever use of the double argument property for sine, express $\sin x$ in terms of sines and cosines of $\frac{1}{2}x$.
b. By a clever use of the composite argument property for sine, express $\sin (3/2)x$ in terms of functions of x and $(1/2)x$.
c. Prove that

$$1 + \cos x = \frac{1}{2} + \frac{\sin \frac{3}{2}x}{2 \sin \frac{1}{2}x}.$$

d. Prove that

$$1 + \cos x + \cos 2x = \frac{1}{2} + \frac{\sin \frac{5}{2}x}{2 \sin \frac{1}{2}x}$$

by starting with the identity you proved in part c and adding $\cos 2x$ to both members. You will find that after you add $\cos 2x$ to the big fraction by use of a common denominator, the sum and product properties can be used to transform a *product* in the numerator to a very interesting *sum*!

e. Prove that

$$1 + \cos x + \cos 2x + \cos 3x = \frac{1}{2} + \frac{\sin \frac{7}{2}x}{2 \sin \frac{1}{2}x}$$

using the same technique as in part d.

f. Prove that if

$$1 + \cos x + \cos 2x + \ldots + \cos 37x = \frac{1}{2} + \frac{\sin \frac{75}{2}x}{2 \sin \frac{1}{2}x},$$

then

$$1 + \cos x + \cos 2x \ldots + \cos 37x + \cos 38x = \frac{1}{2} + \frac{\sin \frac{77}{2}x}{2 \sin \frac{1}{2}x}.$$

g. If you have studied mathematical induction, prove that the property stated at the beginning of this problem is true for *any* positive integer value of n.

3–7   LINEAR COMBINATION OF COSINE AND SINE WITH EQUAL ARGUMENTS

If r and s are variables, then an expression such as $3r - 5s$ is called a *linear combination* of r and s. In this section you will study expressions such as $7 \cos x + 2 \sin x$, which are linear combinations of a cosine and a sine with equal arguments. These expressions differ from those of the previous section because the sum involves both a sine and cosine. The sum and product properties have sums of two cosines or two sines.

Objective:
Be able to express $A \cos x + B \sin x$ in the form $C \cos (x - D)$, where A, B, C, and D stand for constants.

Starting with the expression $C \cos (x - D)$ and using the composite-argument properties, you can write

$$C \cos (x - D) = C(\cos x \cos D + \sin x \sin D).$$

Upon distributing, commuting, and associating, this equation becomes

$$C \cos (x - D) = (C \cos D) \cos x + (C \sin D) \sin x.$$

Since D is a constant, $\cos D$ and $\sin D$ are also constants. The objective may be accomplished by making

$$A = C \cos D,$$
$$B = C \sin D.$$

By a clever combination of algebra and trigonometry, C and D can be expressed in terms of A and B. Squaring and then adding gives

$$A^2 = C^2 \cos^2 D$$

$$B^2 = C^2 \sin^2 D$$

$$A^2 + B^2 = C^2 \cos^2 D + C^2 \sin^2 D$$
$$= C^2 (\cos^2 D + \sin^2 D)$$
$$= C^2$$

$$\therefore \quad C = \boxed{\sqrt{A^2 + B^2}}$$

The positive square root is used simply as a matter of convenience. Once C is known, D is the argument that satisfies:

$$\boxed{\cos D = \frac{A}{C} \quad \text{and} \quad \sin D = \frac{B}{C}}$$

Example 1: To transform $3 \cos 2x - 4 \sin 2x$ to the form $C \cos (2x - D)$, you first observe that the sine and cosine have equal arguments. Also, $A = 3$ and $B = -4$. Therefore,

$$C = \sqrt{3^2 + (-4)^2} = 5.$$

Consequently,

$$\cos D = \frac{3}{5} \quad \text{and} \quad \sin D = -\frac{4}{5}.$$

The reference arc is approximately 0.927. Since $\cos D$ is positive and $\sin D$ is negative, D must terminate in Quadrant IV. Therefore $D \approx 2\pi - 0.927 \approx 5.356$. In summary,

$$3 \cos 2x - 4 \sin 2x = 5 \cos (2x - 5.356)$$
$$= 5 \cos 2(x - 2.678)$$

Note that the two terms on the left have graphs that are sinusoids with the same period (π) but different amplitudes (3 and 4). The expression on the right is another sinusoid with the *same* period (π), but a *different* amplitude (5) and phase displacement, 2.678. It is this property that explains why two sound waves of the same pitch will add together to form another sound wave of the same pitch. Only the amplitude and phase are changed. Note also that the amplitudes do not simply add together. This explains why a choir of 100 members all singing the same note is not 100 times as loud as only one member singing the note.

Example 2:   Solve the equation $2 \cos \theta - 3 \sin \theta = 1$ for values of θ in the domain $0° \leq \theta \leq 360°$. Round off to the nearest degree.

To get *one* function on the left side, you can use the linear combination property of this section. The sum and product properties of Example 4 in the last section will not help since the sum involves two *different* functions, and since the right member of the equation does not equal 0.

$2 \cos \theta - 3 \sin \theta = 1$	Given equation
$\sqrt{13} \cos (\theta - 303.69 \ldots°) = 1$	$\sqrt{2^2 + 3^2} = \sqrt{13}$, and
	$D = \cos^{-1} \dfrac{2}{\sqrt{13}}$
	$= \sin^{-1} \left(-\dfrac{3}{\sqrt{13}} \right)$
	$= 303.69 \ldots°$
$\theta - 303.69 \ldots° = \cos^{-1} \left(\dfrac{1}{\sqrt{13}} \right)$	Dividing by $\sqrt{13}$ and taking $\cos^{-1}$.
$\theta = 303.69 \ldots° \pm 73.89 \ldots° + 360n°$	Adding $303.69 \ldots°$ and using a calculator.
$\theta = 377.58 \ldots° + 360n°$, or $229.79 \ldots° + 360n°$	Arithmetic
$S = \{\, 18°, 230° \,\}$	Letting $n = -1$ or 0, and rounding off.

Note: You should keep the intermediate values in decimal form as you solve the equation and round off only the final answers.

In the following exercise you will get practice expressing linear combinations of sine and cosine in terms of a single cosine.

Exercise 3–7

For Problems 1 through 10, transform the given expression to the form $C \cos (x - D)$, assuming that the functions are:

a.   trigonometric
b.   circular

1. $\cos x + \sqrt{3} \sin x$
2. $\sqrt{3} \cos x + \sin x$
3. $5 \cos x - 5 \sin x$
4. $\sqrt{2} \cos x - \sqrt{2} \sin x$
5. $5 \sin x - 12 \cos x$
6. $4 \sin x - 3 \cos x$
7. $-15 \cos 3x - 8 \sin 3x$
8. $-12 \cos 7x - 5 \sin 7x$
9. $(\sqrt{6} + \sqrt{2}) \cos x + (\sqrt{6} - \sqrt{2}) \sin x$
10. $0.6561 \cos x + 0.7547 \sin x$

For Problems 11 through 14, sketch at least one cycle of the graph of the given equation.

11. $y = 5 \sqrt{3} \cos 2\theta - 5 \sin 2\theta$
12. $y = 6 \cos 3\theta + 6 \sin 3\theta$
13. $y = 4 \cos \pi x + 4 \sin \pi x$
14. $y = -\cos \frac{\pi}{6} x + \sqrt{3} \sin \frac{\pi}{6} x$

For Problems 15 through 18, solve the equation for x or θ in the domain $0 \le x < 2\pi$ or $0° \le \theta < 360°$. Round off values of x to 2 decimal places, and values of θ to the nearest degree.

15. $5 \cos \theta + 7 \sin \theta = 3$
16. $2 \cos x + 5 \sin x = 4$
17. $8 \cos x - 3 \sin x = 5$
18. $7 \cos \theta - 4 \sin \theta = 6$

19.   *Computer Graphics Verification of Property:*   In Problem 5 you were to transform $5 \sin x - 12 \cos x$ to a single sinusoid. Plot the graph of $y = 5 \sin x - 12 \cos x$ as well as the answer you got on the same set of axes. You may use a program such as PLOT TWO. Explain how the result verifies the linear combination property.

20.   Repeat Problem 19 with $4 \sin x - 3 \cos x$ from Problem 5.

21.   How many degrees are there in $\frac{\pi}{5}$ radians?

22.   Write the exact value of $\sec^{-1} (-2)$.

23.   *Roof Problem:*   Builders specify the slope of a roof by rise and run. For instance, a "six-twelve" roof rises 6 inches for each run of 12 inches. What angle does a six-twelve roof make with a horizontal ceiling joist?

24.   Sketch the graph of $y = \csc \theta$.

3-8 SIMPLIFICATION OF TRIGONOMETRIC EXPRESSIONS

The ultimate objective of this chapter is for you to be able to solve trigono-metric equations. Doing this requires that you be able to transform a trig-onometric expression to an equivalent, specified form, possibly simplifying it. Unfortunately, merely stating "simplify" a given trigonometric expres-sion is not enough. As with any mathematical expression, "simple" means "simpler to use in subsequent work." For example, if $\sin 3x + \sin 5x$ ap-pears in an equation, the equation may be easier to solve if the expression is transformed to a product. But in more advanced mathematics such as calculus, it may be simpler to use if left as a sum. It is for this reason that the desired form of the answer will always be specified.

In this section you will be given the desired algebraic form (sum, prod-uct, etc.) or trigonometric form (sines, double arguments, etc.), but not the answer itself. The transformations will give you skills you must have for solving trigonometric equations in the next section. There, *you* must decide which form is most desirable.

Objective:

Given a trigonometric expression, transform it to a specified algebraic or trigonometric form.

For your convenience, the properties you have learned so far are sum-marized on pages 168 and 169. You should, of course, try to work the problems *without* reference to the table.

Exercise 3-8

For Problems 1 through 26, write an equation with the quantity on the left of the comma expressed in terms involving only the trigonometric functions or algebraic form on the right. Note that you should work *all* these problems, rather than just the odd- or even-numbered ones.

1. $\sin 2x$, $\sin x$ *and* $\cos x$
2. $\sin^2 x$, $\cos 2x$
3. $\sin^2 x$, $\cos x$
4. $\cos^2 x$, $\sin x$
5. $\cos^2 x$, $\cos 2x$
6. $\cos 2x$, $\cos x$
7. $\cos 2x$, $\sin x$
8. $\cos 2x$, $\cos x$ *and* $\sin x$

9. $\tan 2x$, $\tan x$
10. $\sin \frac{1}{2}x$, $\cos x$
11. $\cos \frac{1}{2}x$, $\cos x$
12. $\tan \frac{1}{2}x$, $\cos x$
13. $\tan \frac{1}{2}x$, $\cos x$ *and* $\sin x$
14. $\sin 3x$, $\sin x$
15. $\cos 4x$, $\cos 2x$
16. $\cos 6x$, $\cos 3x$
17. $\sin x \cos x$, $\sin 2x$
18. $\sin x \cos y$,   sum of sines or cosines
19. $\cos x \cos y$,   sum of sines or cosines
20. $\cos x + \cos y$,   product of sines and/or cosines
21. $\sin x + \sin y$,   product of sines and/or cosines
22. $\sin x + \cos x$,   *single* cosine
23. $\sin 3x \sin 7x$,   sum of sines or cosines of positive multiples of x
24. $\sin 3x + \sin 7x$,   product of sines and/or cosines of positive multiples of x
25. $\sqrt{3} \cos x - \sin x$,   cosine with phase displacement
26. $-4 \cos x - 4 \sin x$,   cosine with phase displacement

SUMMARY OF PROPERTIES OF TRIGONOMETRIC FUNCTIONS

1. *Reciprocal*

   $\cot x = 1/\tan x$ or $\tan x \cot x = 1$
   $\sec x = 1/\cos x$ or $\cos x \sec x = 1$
   $\csc x = 1/\sin x$ or $\sin x \csc x = 1$

2. *Quotient*

   $\tan x = \sin x/\cos x = \sec x/\csc x$
   $\cot x = \cos x/\sin x = \csc x/\sec x$

3. *Pythagorean*

   $\cos^2 x + \sin^2 x = 1$
   $1 + \tan^2 x = \sec^2 x$
   $\cot^2 x + 1 = \csc^2 x$

4. *Odd-Even*

$\sin (-x)$ =	$-\sin x$	(odd)	$\cot (-x)$ =	$-\cot x$	(odd)
$\cos (-x)$ =	$\cos x$	(even)	$\sec (-x)$ =	$\sec x$	(even)
$\tan (-x)$ =	$-\tan x$	(odd)	$\csc (-x)$ =	$-\csc x$	(odd)

5. *Cofunction*

$$\cos(90° - \theta) = \sin\theta \qquad \text{or} \qquad \cos(\pi/2 - x) = \sin x$$
$$\cot(90° - \theta) = \tan\theta \qquad \text{or} \qquad \cot(\pi/2 - x) = \tan x$$
$$\csc(90° - \theta) = \sec\theta \qquad \text{or} \qquad \csc(\pi/2 - x) = \sec x$$

6. *Composite Argument*

$$\cos(A - B) = \cos A \cos B + \sin A \sin B$$
$$\cos(A + B) = \cos A \cos B - \sin A \sin B$$
$$\sin(A - B) = \sin A \cos B - \cos A \sin B$$
$$\sin(A + B) = \sin A \cos B + \cos A \sin B$$
$$\tan(A - B) = \frac{\tan A - \tan B}{1 + \tan A \tan B}$$
$$\tan(A + B) = \frac{\tan A + \tan B}{1 - \tan A \tan B}$$

7. *Double Argument*

$$\sin 2x = 2\sin x \cos x$$
$$\cos 2x = \cos^2 x - \sin^2 x = 1 - 2\sin^2 x = 2\cos^2 x - 1$$
$$\tan 2x = \frac{2\tan x}{1 - \tan^2 x}$$

8. *Half Argument*

$$\sin \tfrac{1}{2}x = \pm\sqrt{\tfrac{1}{2}(1 - \cos x)}$$
$$\cos \tfrac{1}{2}x = \pm\sqrt{\tfrac{1}{2}(1 + \cos x)}$$
$$\tan \tfrac{1}{2}x = \pm\sqrt{\frac{1 - \cos x}{1 + \cos x}} = \frac{\sin x}{1 + \cos x} = \frac{1 - \cos x}{\sin x}$$

9. *Sum and Product*

$$2\cos A \cos B = \cos(A + B) + \cos(A - B)$$
$$2\sin A \sin B = -\cos(A + B) + \cos(A - B)$$
$$2\sin A \cos B = \sin(A + B) + \sin(A - B)$$
$$2\cos A \sin B = \sin(A + B) - \sin(A - B)$$

$$\cos x + \cos y = 2\cos\tfrac{1}{2}(x + y)\cos\tfrac{1}{2}(x - y)$$
$$\cos x - \cos y = -2\sin\tfrac{1}{2}(x + y)\sin\tfrac{1}{2}(x - y)$$
$$\sin x + \sin y = 2\sin\tfrac{1}{2}(x + y)\cos\tfrac{1}{2}(x - y)$$
$$\sin x - \sin y = 2\cos\tfrac{1}{2}(x + y)\sin\tfrac{1}{2}(x - y)$$

10. *Linear Combination of Sine and Cosine*

$$A\cos x + B\sin x = C\cos(x - D),$$

where $C = \sqrt{A^2 + B^2}$, and $\cos D = \dfrac{A}{C}$ and $\sin D = \dfrac{B}{C}$.

For Problems 27 through 30, a definition of "simple form" is given. Use the definition to "simplify" the expressions.

27. Simple form involves no multiple or composite arguments. Simplify:

   a. $\cos (x - 37°)$
   b. $\cos (x + y + z)$
   c. $\cos 3x$

28. Simple form consists of *one* term, which may be composed of several factors. Simplify:

   a. $\cos 37° \cos \theta + \sin 37° \sin \theta$
   b. $\cos 37° + \cos \theta$
   c. $\cos \theta + \cos 2\theta + \cos 3\theta$

29. Simple form involves *no* products or powers of trigonometric functions, but may involve functions of multiple arguments. That is, the expression should be *linear* (first degree) in functions of multiple arguments. Simplify:

   a. $\sin x \cos x$ c. $\cos^2 x \sin x$
   b. $\cos^2 x$ d. $\sin^4 x$

30. Simple form involves a *single* cosine or sine term (no products, powers, or sums of functions!), but may involve multiple or composite arguments. Simplify:

   a. $\cos x + \sin x$ c. $\cos x - \sin x$
   b. $\cos x \sin x$ d. $\sin x - \cos x$

For Problems 31 through 38, write the general or principal value of the inverse relation or function.

31. $x = \cos^{-1} \dfrac{\sqrt{3}}{2}$ 32. $x = \sin^{-1} \dfrac{-1}{2}$

33. $\theta = \tan^{-1} (-1)$ 34. $\theta = \cot^{-1} \sqrt{3}$

35. $x = \cot^{-1} \left(\dfrac{-1}{\sqrt{3}} \right)$ 36. $x = \mathrm{Sec}^{-1} (-\sqrt{2})$

37. $\theta = \mathrm{Csc}^{-1} 2$ 38. $\theta = \mathrm{Cos}^{-1} (-1)$

39. *Triangle Problem:*   Bill Dupp lifts one end of a 14-foot-long board. The other end remains on the ground. Bill holds his end of the board 8 feet up, the highest he can reach. What angle does the other end of the

board make with the ground? How far are Bill's feet from that other end of the board?

40. *Sinusoid Problem:*   Graph one complete cycle of

$$y = 3 + 4 \cos \frac{\pi}{8} (x - 5).$$

3–9   GENERAL TRIGONOMETRIC EXPRESSIONS

In Sections 3–3 through 3–7 you used the properties of that particular section to solve trigonometric equations. Now it is time for you to collect your knowledge and solve such equations when you are not told which property to use.

The following is a formal definition of a solution of a trigonometric equation.

DEFINITION

A *solution* of a trigonometric equation is a value of the variable in the argument that makes the equation true.

That is, if an expression such as cos 3(x - 5) appears in the equation, a solution is a value of x and not a value of the entire argument 3(x - 5).

Objective:

Given a trigonometric equation and a domain of the variable, find all solutions of the equation in the domain.

A compact way to write a domain such as $180° \le \theta \le 360°$ is $[180°, 360°]$. This is read, "the closed interval between $180°$ and $360°$." Other interval notations are as follows:

INTERVAL NOTATION

Written	*Meaning*	*Name*
$\theta \in [180°, 360°]$	$180° \le \theta \le 360°$	Closed interval
$\theta \in (180°, 360°)$	$180° < \theta < 360°$	Open interval
$\theta \in [180°, 360°)$	$180° \le \theta < 360°$	Half-open interval
$\theta \in (180°, 360°]$	$180° < \theta \le 360°$	Half-open interval

The following examples show you some techniques for solving equations in various domains.

Example 1:   Solve $2 \sin \theta - 1 = 0$ for
a. $\theta \in \{$real numbers of degrees$\}$
b. $\theta \in [0°, 360°]$
c. $\theta \in [180°, 360°]$

a.   The procedure is to isolate the sine on one side of the equation so that you can take the inverse sine of each member.

$2 \sin \theta - 1 = 0$ Given equation

$\sin \theta = \frac{1}{2}$ Adding 1, then dividing by 2

$\theta = 30° + 360n°$ or $150° + 360n°$ Taking $\sin^{-1}$

$\therefore S = \{30° + 360n°, 150° + 360n°\}$ Writing the solution set.

b.   If the domain is $\theta \in [0°, 360°]$, the solutions are found by picking values of n. If $n = 0$, then $\theta = 30°$ or $150°$. All other integer values of n give solutions that are out of the domain. So you write

$S = \{30°, 150°\}$

c.   There are *no* solutions in the domain $[180°, 360°]$. So you write

$S = \phi$

Note:
The values of θ in part (a), namely, $\theta = 30° + 360n°$ or $150° + 360n°$ form what is called the *general solution* of the equation. Values of θ in a particular domain are called *particular solutions.* You should always write the general solution for an equation first, then pick the particular solutions. As you will see in the next few examples, you might leave out some solutions if you do not write down the general solution.

Example 2:   Solve $\sin 2x \cos x + \cos 2x \sin x = 1$ for $x \in [0, 2\pi)$.

$\sin 2x \cos x + \cos 2x \sin x = 1$ Given equation
$\sin (2x + x) = 1$ Composite argument properties
$\sin 3x = 1$ Combining like terms
$3x = \pi/2 + 2\pi n$ $\sin \pi/2 = 1$
$x = \pi/6 + 2\pi/3n$ Dividing by 3
$x = \pi/6, 5\pi/6, 3\pi/2$ Picking those integer values of n
$\therefore S = \{\pi/6, 5\pi/6, 3\pi/2\}$ for which $x \in [0, 2\pi)$

The most difficult part of solving an equation is getting started. The thing that gets you started this time is recognizing a familiar property, the composite argument property, that can be used on the left-hand member.

Example 3:   Solve $\cos 2\theta - \cos 4\theta = \sqrt{3} \sin 3\theta$ for $\theta \in [0°, 360°)$.

This problem is complicated because there are three different arguments, 2θ, 4θ, and 3θ. Luckily, the number of arguments can be reduced by applying the sum and product properties to the left member, getting

$$-2 \sin 3\theta \sin (-\theta) = \sqrt{3} \sin 3\theta.$$

This has the advantage of reducing the number of *functions*, too. Now everything is in terms of sines. Since sin is an *odd* function,

$$2 \sin 3\theta \sin \theta = \sqrt{3} \sin 3\theta.$$

At this point it is tempting to divide each member by $\sin 3\theta$. But you recall that dividing by a variable that can equal zero might *lose* solutions. So you resist the temptation and try something else.

$2 \sin 3\theta \sin \theta - \sqrt{3} \sin 3\theta = 0$	Subtracting $\sqrt{3} \sin 3\theta$
$\sin 3\theta (2 \sin \theta - \sqrt{3}) = 0$	Factoring
$\sin 3\theta = 0$ or $2 \sin \theta - \sqrt{3} = 0$	Multiplication property of 0
$\sin 3\theta = 0$ or $\sin \theta = \sqrt{3}/2$	Addition and multiplication properties of equality

$\therefore$ $3\theta = 0° + 360n°$, $180° + 360n°$;   or
        $\theta = 60° + 360n°$, $120° + 360n°$
$\therefore$ $\theta = 0° + 120n°$, $60° + 120n°$, $60° + 360n°$,
        or $120° + 360n°$
$\therefore$ $S = \{0°, 60°, 120°, 180°, 240°, 300°\}$

Again, the solution set is determined by picking all values of n that give solutions in the domain.

Example 4:   Solve $\cos (\theta - 57°) = -1$ for $\theta \in (-180°, 180°)$.

The composite argument $(\theta - 57°)$ suggests use of the composite argument properties. However, the equation is already in the form of *one* function of *one* argument equal to a *constant*. Thus, the composite argument properties would take you in the wrong direction! So you simply write

$\theta - 57° = 180° + 360n°$	$\cos 180° = -1$
$\theta = 237° + 360n°$	Adding $57°$ to both members
$\theta = -123°$	Letting $n = -1$

This is the only solution in the domain.

$\therefore$ $S = \{-123°\}$

Example 5:   Solve $\cos^2 \theta + \sin \theta + 1 = 0$ for $\theta \in [-90°, 270°)$.

There are two different functions, sine and cosine. $\cos^2 \theta$ is easily transformed to sines using the Pythagorean properties. This transformation will *reduce* the number of functions and thus simplify the equation.

$1 - \sin^2 \theta + \sin \theta + 1 = 0$	Pythagorean properties
$\sin^2 \theta - \sin \theta - 2 = 0$	Commutativity, associativity, and multiplication by -1
$(\sin \theta - 2)(\sin \theta + 1) = 0$	Factoring
∴ $\sin \theta = 2$ or $\sin \theta = -1$	Multiplication property of zero

The equation $\sin \theta = 2$ has no real solutions.

∴ $\sin \theta = -1$ Only other choice
    $\theta = 270° + 360n°$ $\sin 270° = -1$

The only solution in the domain occurs when $n = -1$, for which $\theta = -90°$. The $270°$ you get when $n = 0$ is out of the domain, since the interval is *open* at the upper end.

∴ $S = \{-90°\}$.

Example 6:   Solve $\dfrac{\sin \theta}{1 + \cos \theta} = 1$ for $\theta \in (0°, 360°)$.

There are two ways of approaching this problem. The first is to eliminate the fraction by multiplying both members by $1 + \cos \theta$.

$\sin \theta = 1 + \cos \theta$

This equation contains two different functions. Since it is easier to transform *squares* of sines into cosines, you can square both members.

$\sin^2 \theta = 1 + 2 \cos \theta + \cos^2 \theta$	Squaring each member
$1 - \cos^2 \theta = 1 + 2 \cos \theta + \cos^2 \theta$	Pythagorean properties
$0 = 2 \cos \theta + 2 \cos^2 \theta$	Addition property of equality
$0 = \cos \theta (1 + \cos \theta)$	Division by 2, then factoring
$\cos \theta = 0$ or $1 + \cos \theta = 0$	Multiplication property of zero
$\cos \theta = 0$ or $\cos \theta = -1$	Subtracting 1
$\theta = 90° + 360n°, 270° + 360n°,$	
$\quad$ or $180° + 360n°$	

The solutions in the domain are $90°$, $270°$, and $180°$. However, substituting these into the original equation reveals that only $90°$ works. The $180°$ is an *extraneous* solution introduced by multiplying both members by $1 + \cos \theta$

and the 270° is another extraneous solution introduced by squaring both members. Your next step should look something like this:

extraneous

$\theta = 90°, \cancel{270°}, \cancel{180°}$
$\therefore S = \{90°\}.$

You should remember that whenever you square both members or multiply by a variable that can equal zero, you must check *all* the solutions. Any which do not satisfy the original equation should be marked "extraneous" and should not be put in the solution set.

A clever application of trigonometric properties can sometimes avoid steps that give extraneous solutions. In this example, $\sin\theta/(1 + \cos\theta)$ is recognizable as the half-argument property for tangent. Therefore, the original equation becomes

$\tan \frac{1}{2}\theta = 1$ Half-argument properties
$\frac{1}{2}\theta = 45° + 180n°$ $\tan 45° = 1$, and period of tangent is 180°
$\theta = 90° + 360n°$ Multiplying by 2
$\therefore S = \{90°\}$

The preceding examples were selected to show you many of the useful techniques that exist for solving trigonometric equations and some of the pitfalls you might stumble into. The table on page 177 summarizes these techniques.

The following exercise will give you practice solving trigonometric equations.

Exercise 3-9

For Problems 1 through 40, solve the equation in the indicated domain.

1. $\tan\theta + \sqrt{3} = 0$, $\theta \in [0°, 360°)$
2. $2\cos\theta + \sqrt{3} = 0$, $\theta \in [0°, 360°)$
3. $2\sin(\theta + 47°) = 1$, $\theta \in [0°, 360°)$
4. $\sec(\theta + 81°) = 2$, $\theta \in [0°, 360°)$
5. $4\cos^2\theta = 1$, $\theta \in [-180°, 180°]$
6. $4\sin^2\theta = 3$, $\theta \in [-180°, 180°]$
7. $2\sin\theta\cos\theta = \sqrt{2}\cos\theta$, $\theta \in \{\text{real numbers of degrees}\}$
8. $\tan\theta\sec\theta = \tan\theta$, $\theta \in \{\text{real numbers of degrees}\}$
9. $\tan x - \sqrt{3} = 2\tan x$, $x \in \{\text{real numbers}\}$
10. $\cos x + 2 = 3\cos x$, $x \in \{\text{real numbers}\}$

11. $2 \sin^2 \theta + \sin \theta = 0,$ $\qquad\qquad\quad \theta \in (-180°, 180°)$

12. $\tan^2 \theta + \tan \theta = 0,$ $\qquad\qquad\quad \theta \in [-90°, 90°)$

13. $2 \cos^2 x - 5 \cos x + 2 = 0,$ $\qquad\quad x \in [0, 2\pi)$

14. $2 \sec^2 x - 3 \sec x - 2 = 0,$ $\qquad\quad x \in [0, 2\pi)$

15. $\sin^2 \theta + 5 \sin \theta + 6 = 0,$ $\qquad\quad \theta \in [0°, 360°)$

16. $4 \csc^2 \theta + 4 \csc \theta + 1 = 0,$ $\qquad\quad \theta \in [0°, 360°)$

17. $\tan^2 x - \sec x - 1 = 0,$ $\qquad\qquad x \in [-\pi, \pi)$

18. $3 - 3 \sin x - 2 \cos^2 x = 0,$ $\qquad\quad x \in [-\pi, \pi]$

19. $1 - \cos \theta = -\sin \theta,$ $\qquad\qquad \theta \in [-180°, 180°)$

20. $\dfrac{1 + \cos \theta}{\sin \theta} = -1,$ $\qquad\qquad\qquad \theta \in [-180°, 180°)$

21. $4 \sin x \cos x = \sqrt{3},$ $\qquad\qquad\quad x \in [0, 2\pi)$

22. $\sin x = \sin 2x,$ $\qquad\qquad\qquad\quad x \in [0, 2\pi)$

23. $\dfrac{\sin (90° - \theta)}{\sin \theta} = -\sqrt{3},$ $\qquad\qquad \theta \in (-270°, 270°)$

24. $\tan (90° - \theta) = -1,$ $\qquad\qquad \theta \in (-180°, 180°)$

25. $\sin 2\theta \cos 64° + \cos 2\theta \sin 64° = \sqrt{3}/2,$ $\theta \in [0°, 360°)$

26. $\cos 3\theta \cos 12° - \sin 3\theta \sin 12° = \frac{1}{2},$ $\theta \in [-120°, 120°)$

27. $\cos 4\theta - \sin 2\theta = 0,$ $\qquad\qquad \theta \in (-90°, 90°)$

28. $\cos 4\theta - \sin 2\theta = 1,$ $\qquad\qquad \theta \in [-90°, 90°)$

29. $\cos 3\theta + \cos 5\theta = 0,$ $\qquad\qquad \theta \in (-90°, 90°)$

30. $\sin 5\theta + \sin 7\theta = 0,$ $\qquad\qquad \theta \in [-90°, 90°)$

31. $\cos x - \sqrt{3} \sin x = 1,$ $\qquad\qquad x \in (0, 2\pi]$

32. $\sin x - \sqrt{3} \cos x = 1,$ $\qquad\qquad x \in [-\pi, \pi]$

33. $\dfrac{\tan 10\theta + \tan 50°}{1 - \tan 10\theta \tan 50°} = \dfrac{\sqrt{3}}{3},$ $\qquad \theta \in (0°, 90°)$

34. $\tan \theta - \tan 10° = 1 + \tan \theta \tan 10°,$ $\quad \theta \in [-180°, 180°]$

35. $\tan \frac{1}{2}x + 1 = \cos x,$ $\qquad\qquad\quad x \in [0, 4\pi]$

36. $2 \cos^2 \frac{1}{2}x - 2 = 2 \cos x,$ $\qquad\quad x \in [-\pi, \pi)$

37. $2 \cos (\theta + 30°) \cos (\theta - 30°) = 1,$ $\quad \theta \in [-180°, 180°]$

38. $4 \sin (\theta + 75°) \cos (\theta - 75°) = 1,$ $\quad \theta \in [-180°, 180°)$

39. $\cos^2 \frac{1}{2}x - \frac{1}{2} \cos x = \frac{1}{2},$ $\qquad\qquad x \in \{\text{real numbers}\}$

40. $\sin x \tan \frac{1}{2}x = 1 - \cos x,$ $\qquad\qquad x \in \{\text{real numbers}\}$

For Problems 41 through 50, solve the equation in the domain $\theta \in [0, 360°)$ or $x \in [0, 2\pi)$, obtaining approximate values by calculator or from Tables I or II.

41. $5 \sec^2 \theta + 2 \tan \theta - 8 = 0$

42. $3 \tan^2 \theta - 5 \sec \theta - 9 = 0$

43. $3 \cos \theta - 4 \sin \theta = 1$

44. $5 \cos \theta + 12 \sin \theta = 13$

45. $3 \sin^2 x - \sin x = 0$
46. $4 \cos^2 x + \cos x = 0$
47. $\sin^2 x + \sin x - 1 = 0$
48. $\cos^2 x - 2 \cos x - 2 = 0$
49. $4 \sin (-x) = 3$
50. $5 \cos (-x) = 2$

For Problems 51 through 53, solve the equation for the indicated values of
x. Note that this is what you did with sinusoids in Section 2-7.

51. $3 + 4 \cos 2(\theta - 10°) = 5,$ $\theta \in [0°, 360°)$
52. $4 + 3 \cos 2(\theta - 10°) = 5,$ $\theta \in [0°, 360°)$
53. $4 + 3 \cos 2(x - 1) = 2,$ x is the smallest positive real number
                                              satisfying the equation.
54. $5 + 2 \sin 3(x - 4) = 6,$ x is the smallest positive real number
                                              satisfying the equation.

Techniques for Solving Trigonometric Equations

1. Get an equation (or equations) in which *one* function of *one*
    argument equals a *constant*. Some ways are:

    a. Reduce the number of different arguments (Examples 2 and
        3).
    b. Reduce the number of different functions (Examples 5 and
        6).
    c. Do any obvious algebra (Example 1).
    d. *Do not divide* both members by a variable (Example 3).
    e. Use any obvious trigonometric properties (Examples 2, 6).
    f. Get a product equal to zero (Examples 3, 5, 6).

2. Get the *general* solution by finding the argument.

    a. If it is a *special* angle, write the *exact* value.
    b. If it is *not* a special angle, use the tables.

3. Do whatever algebra you need to find the *variable* in the argu-
    ment (Examples 2, 3, 4, and 6).

4. Write the solution set.

    a. Find all solutions in the domain by picking integer values of
        n in the general solution.
    b. Check for extraneous solutions if you have multiplied by a
        variable.

55. *Computer Check of Solutions:* Use the program EVALUATE FUNCTION or a similar program to check the solutions you found for Problems 51 through 54. You should type the left member of the equation as the function to be evaluated. Then you should type the solutions, one at a time, and verify that you get the proper value for the right member of the equation.

56. *Computer Graphics Verification of Solutions:* Use the program PLOT TWO or a similar plotting program to verify the solutions of the following equations. To do this, enter one member of the equation as one function and the other member as the second function. How do you verify your solutions?

   a. Problem 10, $\cos x + 2 = 3 \cos x$
   b. Problem 22, $\sin x = \sin 2x$
   c. Problem 36, $2 \cos^2 \tfrac{1}{2}x - 2 = 2 \cos x$
   d. Problem 40, $\sin x \tan \tfrac{1}{2}x = 1 - \cos x$

3–10 CHAPTER REVIEW AND TEST

In this chapter you have learned properties with which you can *transform* trigonometric expressions to forms that look simpler or are simpler to use in a given problem. The properties are particularly useful for solving trigonometric equations.

At the beginning of the chapter are listed eight specific objectives. Briefly stated, these are:

1. Use the quotient, reciprocal, and Pythagorean properties to transform expressions containing functions with the *same* argument.
2. Use the odd–even properties to transform functions with *negative* arguments.
3. Use the composite argument properties and cofunction properties to transform functions whose arguments contain a *sum*.
4. Use the double argument and half-argument properties to transform to functions of *half* or *twice* the argument.
5. Use the sum and product properties to express sums of sines or cosines as products of sines and cosines, and vice versa.
6. Use the linear combination of sinusoid properties to transform to a cosine with a phase displacement.
7. Transform a trigonometric expression using any combination of the above properties.
8. Solve trigonometric equations.

This section contains review problems and a chapter test. The six review problems are numbered according to the first six of the objectives above. By working these problems, you can be sure you know what to do when you are told the objective being tested. The chapter test consists of expressions to transform and equations to solve. These problems will measure your ability to draw together the necessary techniques when you are *not* told which objective is being tested.

Review Problems

The following problems are numbered according to the objective being tested.

1. a. Express $\tan x$ and $\cot x$ in terms of $\sin x$ and $\cos x$.
    b. Express $\tan x$ and $\cot x$ in terms of $\sec x$ and $\csc x$.
    c. Write three different equations in which a product of two trigonometric functions equals 1.
    d. Write equations expressing $\sin^2 x$ in terms of $\cos x$, $\tan^2 x$ in terms of $\sec x$, and $\csc^2 x$ in terms of $\cot x$.

2. Express $\sin(-x)$, $\cos(-x)$, $\tan(-x)$, $\cot(-x)$, $\sec(-x)$, and $\csc(-x)$ as the *same* function of (positive) x.

3. Write equations expressing:

    a. $\sin(x + y)$ in terms of sines and cosines of x and y
    b. $\cos(x + y)$ in terms of sines and cosines of x and y
    c. $\sin(x - y)$ in terms of sines and cosines of x and y
    d. $\cos(x - y)$ in terms of sines and cosines of x and y
    e. $\tan(x + y)$ in terms of $\tan x$ and $\tan y$
    f. $\tan(x - y)$ in terms of $\tan x$ and $\tan y$
    g. $\cos(90° - \theta)$ in terms of $\sin \theta$
    h. $\cot(\pi/2 - x)$ in terms of $\tan x$
    i. $\sec(\pi/2 - x)$ in terms of $\csc x$

4. Write equations expressing:

    a. $\sin 2x$ in terms of sines and cosines of x
    b. $\cos 2x$ in terms of

      (i) sines and cosines of x
      (ii) $\sin x$
      (iii) $\cos x$

    c. $\tan 2x$ in terms of $\tan x$
    d. $\sin \frac{1}{2}x$ in terms of $\cos x$
    e. $\cos \frac{1}{2}x$ in terms of $\cos x$

    f. tan $\frac{1}{2}x$ in terms of

        (i) sin x and cos x, with a single-term denominator
        (ii) sin x and cos x, with a single-term numerator
        (iii) cos x alone

5. a. Write the following as *sums* of functions:

        (i) sin x sin y
        (ii) cos x cos y
        (iii) sin x cos y
        (iv) cos x sin y

    b. Write the following as *products* of functions:

        (i) sin x + sin y
        (ii) cos x + cos y
        (iii) sin x – sin y
        (iv) cos x – cos y

6. Express 5 cos x – 7 sin x as a cosine with a phase displacement.

Chapter Test

The following problems require you to draw upon your knowledge of the trigonometric function properties in Objectives 1 through 6. The problems are either transforming expressions or solving equations, as in Objectives 7 and 8. Work each problem. Then tell by number which of Objectives 1 through 8 you used in that problem. Since there may be several ways of working the problem, your list of objectives may differ from that in the answers at the back of the book.

1. Solve the following equations in the indicated domain.

    a. sin $2x$ = cos x, $x \in [\pi/4, 3\pi/4]$
    b. tan $2(\theta + 41°)$ = 1, $\theta \in$ {real numbers of degrees}
    c. $\sqrt{3}$ sin x – cos x = 1, $x \in$ {real numbers}
    d. csc x tan x cos x = 1, $x \in [-\pi, \pi]$
    e. sin θ + sin 3θ + sin 5θ = 0, $\theta \in [0°, 360°]$
    f. sin θ cos $37°$ = cos θ sin $37°$, $\theta \in (-180°, 180°)$

2. Prove that the following are identities.

   a. $\sin (x + y) \sin (x - y) = \sin^2 x - \sin^2 y$

   b. $\cot^2 x - \cos^2 x = \cot^2 x \cos^2 x$

   c. $\dfrac{\sin x + \sin y}{\cos x + \cos y} = \tan \dfrac{1}{2}(x + y)$

3. Find *exact* values of:

   a. $\cos 15°$

   b. $\sin \dfrac{\pi}{8}$

4. a. Transform $\cos 2(x + y)$ to functions of x and y.

   b. Transform $\sin 58° + \sin 33°$ to a *single* term.

   c. Transform $\sin^2 x \cos x$ to a *sum* of functions of *multiples* of x, which involves *no* products of functions.

   d. Transform $\cos 38x$ to

      (i) functions of $19x$,

      (ii) functions of $76x$.

   e. Simplify $\sin 37° \cos 53° + \cos 37° \sin 53°$.

   f. Transform $\cos 23° + \sin 23°$ to a *multiple* of a *cosine* of a *positive* angle.

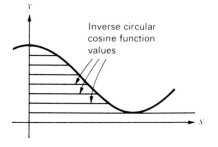

Inverse circular cosine function values

Inverting a function $y = f(x)$ gives a convenient way to express x in terms of y. The lengths of the horizontal timbers supporting the roller coaster track could be values of an inverse circular cosine function.

Often in the real world a periodic function is composed of two or more sinusoids. For example, when two people are singing harmonizing notes, the resulting sound wave might have a graph like that below.

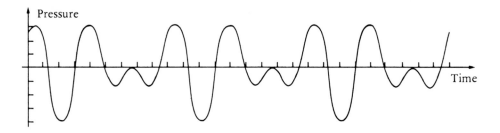

In this chapter you will learn how to draw such graphs from their equations, first by hand, and then by computer graphics. The results will allow you to illustrate some of the properties you learned in the last chapter. You will also study functions derived from inverse sines, cosines, etc. The properties of these inverse circular functions will allow you to calculate quickly the values of x corresponding to given values of y in a sinusoidal function. Applications you will study include problems about rotary motion, for which you will learn the concept of angular velocity.

Specific objectives for this chapter are:

1. Be able to draw a graph composed of several trigonometric or other functions, either
   a. with pencil and paper, or
   b. on a computer screen or plotter.
2. Confirm by graphing that certain properties of trigonometric functions are true.
3. Given a real-world situation involving rotating objects, find linear and angular velocities of various parts of the objects.
4. Given an equation of an inverse circular function, draw its graph.
5. Given an expression containing inverse circular functions, evaluate it, or transform it to a simpler form.
6. Given a real-world situation involving sinusoidal variation, find quickly the values of x corresponding to a given value of y.

4–1 COMPOSITION OF ORDINATES

You have been studying one kind of periodic function, the sinusoid. It turns out that other types of periodic functions can be formed by adding, subtracting, multiplying, or dividing sinusoidal functions. For example, musical notes are composed of a *sum* of many sinusoids. When music is carried over a radio, its sound waves are *multiplied* by another sinusoidal function called the "carrier wave." In this section you will draw graphs of functions that are composed of sinusoids.

Objective:

Given a function involving a sum or product of other functions, at least one of which is a sinusoid, be able to sketch the graph quickly.

This topic is called "composition of ordinates," because the ordinates of the desired function are composed of sums and products of the ordinates of other functions. In your later mathematical career, you may have a chance to do the reversed problem, finding sinusoids that lead to a given periodic function. This reverse problem is called "harmonic analysis." It is used for such things as analyzing earthquake waves to tell what kind of material they have traveled through. It is also used to analyze sound waves picked up from the ocean to tell whether they are being generated by fish or submarines!

Example: To sketch a graph of the sum of two sinusoids in which one has twice the period of the other, suppose that

$$f(x) = \cos x + \sin 2x.$$

The first thing to do is sketch two *auxiliary* graphs, one of $y = \cos x$, and the other of $y = \sin 2x$. A portion of these graphs is shown in Figure 4-1a. To find the point at $x = \pi/4$, measure the *ordinates* (the y-values) of the two graphs and add these together. The graph of $y = \sin 2x$ is at 1, and the graph of $y = \cos x$ is at about 0.7. So the composed graph will have a point at about $y = 1.7$. For the purposes of this section, you can measure the distances accurately enough by eye, without needing to use a ruler.

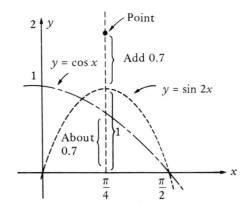

Figure 4-1a

You repeat this process for other values of x, such as 0, $\pi/2$, $3\pi/4$, etc.

The resulting critical points are shown in Figure 4–1b. The final graph is made by connecting the critical points with a smooth curve, as in Figure 4–1c.

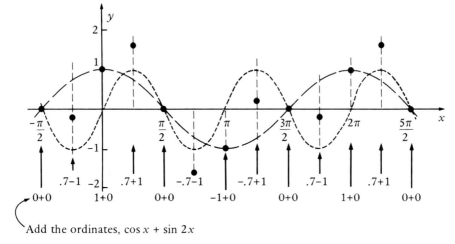

Add the ordinates, $\cos x + \sin 2x$

Figure 4–1b

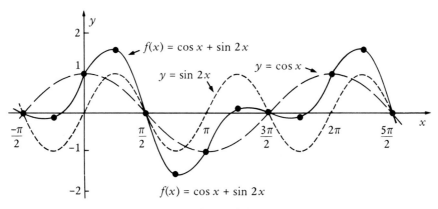

Figure 4–1c

A sound wave generated by playing the notes middle C and high (tenor) C at the same time would have a pressure wave that looks like the graph in Figure 4–1c.

In the exercise that follows, you are to draw graphs by composition of ordinates. Some of the graphs are related to real-world phenomena.

Exercise 4–1

For problems 1 through 20, sketch at least one complete cycle of the graph. Choose some way of making the final graph clearly distinguishable from the auxiliary graphs, such as by drawing it darker or in color.

1. $f(x) = \cos x + \sin x$

2. $f(x) = \cos x - \sin x$

3. $f(x) = 2 \cos x - \sin x$

4. $f(x) = \cos x + 3 \sin x$

5. $f(x) = 2 \cos x \sin x$

6. $f(x) = 2 \cos^2 x$ (Use $y = 2 \cos x$ and $y = \cos x$.)

7. $f(x) = \frac{1}{2}x + \sin \frac{\pi}{2} x$

8. $f(x) = \frac{1}{5}x + 2 \cos \frac{\pi}{4} x$

9. $f(x) = \left(\frac{1}{2}x\right)\left(\sin \frac{\pi}{2} x\right)$

10. $f(x) = \left(\frac{1}{5}x\right)\left(2 \cos \frac{\pi}{4} x\right)$

11. $f(x) = \left| \sin \frac{\pi}{4} x \right|$

12. $f(x) = \left| \cos \frac{\pi}{4} x \right|$

13. $f(x) = 4 \sin \frac{\pi}{10} x + \sin \pi x$

14. $f(x) = \sin \frac{\pi}{10} x + \sin \pi x$

15. $f(x) = \dfrac{\sin x}{\cos x}$

16. $f(x) = \dfrac{\cos x}{\sin x}$

17. $f(x) = \dfrac{1}{\sin x}$

18. $f(x) = \dfrac{1}{\cos x}$

19. $f(x) = \left(4 \sin \frac{\pi}{10} x\right)(\sin \pi x)$

20. $f(x) = [|\cos \pi x|]$

(In Problem 20, the symbol [number] means "the greatest integer less than or equal to the number." For instance, $[7.9] = 7$, $[-4.1] = -5$, $[\pi] = 3$, $[6] = 6$, etc.)

21. *Identity Problem:*   Prove that $\cos x \sec^2 x = \cos x + \sin x \tan x$.

22. *Identity Problem:*   Prove that $\sin 2x = 2 \tan x \cos^2 x$.

23. *Equation Problem:*   Solve for $x \in [-1, 1]$: $\cos 2\pi x = \cos \pi x$.

24. *Graphing Problem:*   Sketch two cycles: $y = \tan \frac{1}{2}\theta$.

25. Write the exact value of $\sin 3000°$.

26. *Triangle Problem:*   Mae Danerror thinks that a 3–4–5 right triangle is the same as a 30°–60° right triangle. What is the measure of the larger acute angle in a 3–4–5 right triangle? By what percent does this measure differ from 60?

27. How many degrees in $\dfrac{\pi}{5}$ radians?

28. *Rotary Motion Problem:*   A wheel turns 100 revolutions. How many degrees does it turn? How many radians?

4–2 COMPOSITION OF ORDINATES BY COMPUTER GRAPHICS

The difficulty with composition of ordinates by hand-sketching is that minor inaccuracies in the auxiliary graphs can cause big errors in the composed graph. In this section you will use the programs PLOT COMP, PLOT COMP GEN, and PLOT FUNCTION or similar programs to draw auxiliary graphs and the composed graph.

Objective:

Use computer graphics to draw graphs by composition of ordinates.

Example: Plot $f(x) = 5 \sin \dfrac{\pi}{12} x \cos \pi x$ using $y = 5 \sin \dfrac{\pi}{12} x$ and $y = \cos \pi x$ as auxiliary graphs. Describe the shape of the composed graph.

The output for this example should be a graph similar to that in Figure 4–2a.

These instructions are for the program PLOT COMP on the accompanying disk. Consult instruction manuals for other plotting programs you may be using.

After you type RUN, the computer asks if you want to change scales. Type N (for "no"). Then it asks you to type the first function, its amplitude and period. Since the coefficients of x are $\dfrac{\pi}{12}$ and π, the periods of the two sinusoids will be 24 and 2 units, respectively. Type SIN,5,24 for the first function and press RETURN. Type COS,1,2 for the second function and press RETURN.

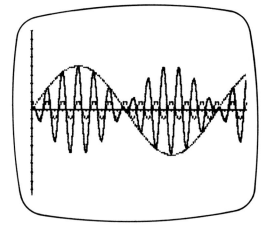

$$f(x) = 5 \sin \frac{\pi}{12} x \cos \pi x$$

Figure 4–2a

The composed graph is *sinusoid with a variable amplitude,* as shown in Figure 4–2a.

In the following exercise you will compose coordinates by computer graphics.

Exercise 4-2

For Problems 1 through 12, plot the graph by composing ordinates of appropriate auxiliary graphs. Describe the shape of the composed graph.

1. $f(x) = 4 \cos \frac{\pi}{6} x + 4 \sin \frac{\pi}{3} x$ 2. $f(x) = 2 \sin \cdot \frac{\pi}{2} x + 2 \cos \frac{\pi}{6} x$

3. $f(x) = 6 \sin \frac{\pi}{12} x \cos \frac{\pi}{3} x$ 4. $f(x) = 6 \sin \frac{\pi}{10} x \sin \frac{\pi}{2} x$

5. $f(x) = 4 \sin \frac{\pi}{10} x - \sin \pi x$ 6. $f(x) = 3 \sin \pi x - 2 \sin \frac{\pi}{10} x$

(The functions in Problems 5 and 6 can be thought of as sinusoids with sinusoidal axes that *vary* instead of being constant. The Sun Elevation Problem of Exercise 2–12, Problem 19, has a function like this. See *Scientific American,* August, 1982, page 39, for another sinusoid with a variable axis, representing the concentration of carbon dioxide in the atmosphere as a function of time.)

7. $f(x) = 4 \sin \frac{\pi}{10} x \cos \pi x$ 8. $f(x) = 6 \sin \cdot \frac{\pi}{24} x \sin \pi x$

(The functions in Problems 7 and 8 can be thought of as sinusoids with variable amplitudes. AM radio waves behave this way, the amplitude of a high-frequency carrier wave being *modulated* with just the right frequency for the sound being carried. The initials "AM" stand for *amplitude modulation.*)

9. $f(x) = 2 \sin \frac{2\pi}{3} x + 2 \sin \frac{2\pi}{3.6} x$ 10. $f(x) = 2 \cos \frac{2\pi}{3} x + 2 \sin \frac{2\pi}{3.6} x$

(In these functions, two sinusoids with nearly equal periods combine to form a function with a relatively *long* period. This phenomenon occurs, for example, when your car is going alongside another on the highway. The "beats" that you hear occur because the two engines are going *almost* the same speed. See the October 1973 issue of *Scientific American,* page 95, for another example.)

11. $f(x) = (\sin \frac{\pi}{6} x)/(\cos \frac{\pi}{6} x)$ 12. $f(x) = (\cos \frac{\pi}{10} x)/(\sin \frac{\pi}{10} x)$

(You should recognize Problems 11 and 12 as being tangent and cotangent graphs.)

13. *Variable Phase Displacement Problem:*   In earlier problems of this section you saw the effects of varying the sinusoidal axis and the

amplitude of a sinusoid. In this problem you will investigate what happens when the phase displacement varies. Let

$$f(x) = 2 \cos \left(x - \frac{\pi}{6} \cos x \right)$$

a. Use the program PLOT TWO or similar program to plot $y = 2 \cos x$ and $y = f(x)$ on the same set of axes.
b. Compare the graph of f with the time-of-sunrise graph in Figure 2-12o. You should find an interesting resemblance!

14. *Fourier Series Problem:* About 150 years ago, the French mathematician Fourier investigated infinite series of sines and cosines. In this problem you will see one thing he discovered. Let

$$f(x) = \cos x - \frac{1}{3} \cos 3x + \frac{1}{5} \cos 5x - \frac{1}{7} \cos 7x + \ldots .$$

a. Let $g(x)$ be the first three terms of $f(x)$. That is,

$$g(x) = \cos x - \frac{1}{3} \cos 3x + \frac{1}{5} \cos 5x.$$

Plot the graph of g using PLOT FUNCTION, or similar program.

b. Let $h(x)$ be the first 100 terms of $f(x)$. You can modify PLOT FUNCTION by setting up a loop at the beginning of the program to calculate successive terms and add or subtract them, as appropriate.
c. Use the program EVALUATE FUNCTION or similar program to print the *values* (not the graph) of $h(x)$ for each 0.1 unit of x, from 0 to 3.
d. Calculate the value of $\pi/4$. How does this number seem to be related to the values of $h(x)$?

15. *Biorhythm Problem:* Scientists have put forth a theory that a person's biological functioning is controlled by three independent phenomena that vary sinusoidally with time. These rhythms are

physical: period = 23 days,
emotional: period = 28 days,
intellectual: period = 33 days.

When the physical cycle is near a high point, the person can do well in physical activities, and so forth. In this problem you will explore the biorhythms due to the combined effects of these three cycles.

a.   Suppose that on a particular day all three of your cycles are at a high point. Assume that each sinusoid has an amplitude of 1 unit, and that the sinusoidal axes are along the time axis. Draw all three cycles for the next 100 days. You may use PLOT SINUSOID for this.

b.   The scientists claim that when all three cycles are at or near a low point, a person's overall performance is very poor. When, during the next 100 days, will your performance be the poorest?

c.   The scientists also claim that when all three cycles are at or near the time axis, you are most susceptible to accidents, disease, and making bad decisions. When, during the next 100 days, is this most likely to happen?

d.   When will all three cycles again reach a high point on the same day? Is this phenomenon likely to happen very often during a person's life?

e.   Use PLOT FUNCTION, or similar program, to plot the composed graph which is the sum of all three sinusoids. You must make the appropriate modifications so that all 100 days will fit on the computer screen.

16. *Variable Amplitude Pendulum Problem:*   In Problem 21 of Exercise 2-12 you encountered an equation expressing the position of a swinging pendulum as a function of time. The amplitude of the pendulum decreased exponentially with time. The equation was

$$f(x) = 30 + 20 \times 10^{-0.0233x} \times \cos \frac{\pi}{1.1} (x - 1.1)$$

Use the program PLOT COMP GEN, or similar program, to plot a graph of this function on the screen.

For Problems 17 and 18, surprising things happen to the functions near $x = 0$. Plot these graphs using PLOT FUNCTION or similar program. Put the vertical axis near mid-screen.

17. $f(x) = \dfrac{\sin x}{x}$ 18. $f(x) = \sin \dfrac{1}{x}$

19. *Identity Problem:*   Prove that $y = 5 \cos x + 12 \sin x$ is a sinusoid with amplitude 13 units. What are its period and phase displacement?

20. *Identity Problem:*   Transform $10 \cos 3x \sin 6x$ to a sum of two sinusoids.

21. Write the exact value of tan 150°.

22. Write the exact value of csc $\frac{2\pi}{3}$.

23. *Rotary Motion Problem:* An ice skater turns through 20 revolutions in 5 seconds. How many degrees per second does she turn?

24. *Triangle Problem:* Calvin Butterball walks along Alamo Street toward its intersection with Heights Street (Figure 4-2b). When he is still 30 yards from the corner, he cuts off at an angle of 35° to Alamo, taking a shortcut. How far from the corner does he emerge on Heights Street? How many yards does he save by using the shortcut?

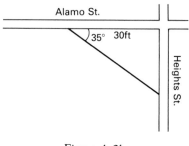

Figure 4-2b

4-3 PROPERTIES VERIFIED BY COMPUTER GRAPHING

In Chapter 3 you learned properties of trigonometric and circular functions such as

$$3 \cos x + 4 \sin x = 5 \cos (x - 0.927 \ldots)$$

This identity says, "If you add two sinusoids with equal periods, the result is another sinusoid with the same period, but with a different amplitude and a phase displacement." The meaning of these words becomes clear if you draw a graph of the left member, $y = 3 \cos x + 4 \sin x$, by composition of ordinates (Figure 4-3a).

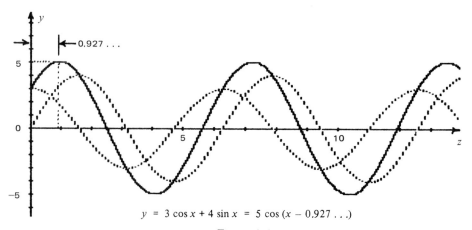

$$y = 3 \cos x + 4 \sin x = 5 \cos (x - 0.927 \ldots)$$

Figure 4-3a

The composed graph has the same period, 2π, as the two auxiliary graphs. Its amplitude is 5 units, which equals $\sqrt{3^2 + 4^2}$. Its phase displacement is about 0.927, which is $\cos^{-1}\left(\frac{3}{5}\right)$ or $\sin^{-1}\left(\frac{4}{5}\right)$. So this graph illustrates the property of a linear combination of two sinusoids with equal periods, from Section 3–7.

In this section you will verify other properties by drawing their graphs using composition of ordinates. The computer graphics program on the accompanying disk will help.

Objective:

Be able to verify trigonometric identities by plotting graphs of one or both members.

The following exercise has problems to guide you in accomplishing this objective.

Exercise 4–3

1. Plot the graph of $y = 8 \sin\frac{\pi}{6}x \cos\frac{\pi}{6}x$ by composition of ordinates.

    Then do the following things:
    a. Tell the amplitude and period of the composed graph.
    b. Write an equation for the composed graph as a *single* sinusoidal function. Use as simple an equation as possible.
    c. Use the appropriate properties of circular functions to prove that the expression in part (b) is identical to the expression in the original equation.

2. Repeat Problem 1 for $y = 2 \sin x \cos x$.

3. Plot the graph of $y = 9 \cos^2 \frac{\pi}{6}x$ by plotting auxiliary graphs of

    $y = 9 \cos\frac{\pi}{6}x$ and $y = \cos\frac{\pi}{6}x$, and multiplying the ordinates. Then:
    a. Tell the amplitude, period, and vertical displacement of the composed graph.
    b. Write an equation for the composed graph as a *single* sinusoidal function. Use as simple an equation as possible.
    c. Prove that your equation in part (b) is identical to the original equation.

4. Repeat Problem 3 for $y = 2 \cos^2 x$, using $y = 2 \cos x$ and $y = \cos x$ as auxiliary graphs.

5. Plot the graph of $y = 6 \sin^2 \frac{\pi}{4} x$ using $y = 6 \sin \frac{\pi}{4}$ and $y = \sin \frac{\pi}{4} x$ as auxiliary graphs. Then

    a. Tell the amplitude, period, and vertical displacement of the composed graph.

    b. Write a sinusoidal equation for the composed graph that has *zero* phase displacement.

    c. Prove that your equation in part (b) is identical to the original equation.

6. Repeat Problem 5 for $y = 2 \sin^2 x$ using $y = 2 \sin x$ and $y = \sin x$ as auxiliary graphs.

7. Plot the graph of $y = 3 \cos \frac{\pi}{6} x + 3 \sin \frac{\pi}{6} x$ by composition of ordinates. Then:

    a. Tell the amplitude, period, and phase displacement (for the cosine function) of the composed graph.

    b. Write a sinusoidal equation for the composed graph.

    c. Prove that your equation in part (b) is identical to the original equation.

8. Repeat Problem 7 for $y = 4 \cos x - 3 \sin x$.

9. Repeat Problem 7 for $y = -5 \cos \frac{\pi}{10} x + 7 \sin \frac{\pi}{10} x$.

10. Repeat Problem 7 for $y = \cos x + \sin x$.

11. a. Plot the graph of $y = \cos \frac{\pi}{3} x + \cos \frac{\pi}{6} x$ by composition of ordinates.

    b. The graph in part (a) has various high points, some higher than others. Write the x- and y-coordinates for the first four high points with non-negative values of x.

    c. Use the Sum and Product Properties of Section 3–6 to transform the equation in part (a) so that y equals a *product*.

    d. Plot the graph of the equation in part (c) by composition of ordinates. What do you notice about this graph?

12. Repeat Problem 11 for $y = \sin \frac{\pi}{2} x + \sin \frac{\pi}{6} x$.

13. a. Plot the graph of $y = 2 \sin \frac{\pi}{12} x \cos \pi x$ by composition of ordinates.

    b. Describe in words what the graph looks like.

    c. Use the Sum and Product Properties of Section 3–6 to transform the equation in part (a) so that y equals a *sum*.

    d. To three decimal places, what are the periods of the two sinusoids in part (c)? Plot the equation in part (c) by composition of ordinates.

    e. What can you conclude about a *product* of two sinusoids with greatly *differing* periods, and a *sum* of two sinusoids with nearly *equal* periods?

14. Repeat Problem 13 for $y = 2 \cos \frac{\pi}{10} x \cos \pi x$.

15. *Rotating Motion Problem:* Suppose that you are on a merry-go-round that is rotating at a constant number of revolutions per minute. Will you be moving faster or slower if you sit 6 feet from the center than if you sit 2 feet from the center? How much faster or slower?

16. *Triangle Problem:* A 50-foot-high flagpole casts a horizontal shadow on the ground. At a certain time of day the sun's rays make an angle of 73° with the ground. How long will the shadow be at this time?

17. Write the exact value of sin 30°.

18. Write the exact values of $x = \sec^{-1} 0.5$.

19. *Identity Problem:* Prove that $\dfrac{\sec x - 2}{\sec x - 1} = 1 - \cos x \csc^2 x - \cot^2 x$.

20. *Identity Problem:* Prove that $\cos 2x - \cos^2 x = \cos^2 x - 1$. Verify the result by computer graphics using PLOT TWO or a similar plotting program.

21. Quick! About how many radians in a complete revolution?

22. *Equation Problem:* Write the general solution for

$$\cos 3\pi x + \cos \pi x = 0.$$

4–4   ANGULAR VELOCITY

If you have ever ridden on a merry-go-round on a playground or at a carnival, you realize that you go faster when you sit near the outside. This happens because as the merry-go-round turns through a certain angle, you travel farther when you are at the outside (Figure 4–4a).

    However, all points on the merry-go-round turn through the *same* number of degrees in a given time. There are two different kinds of speed associated with a point on a rotating object, the number of degrees per unit time and the distance per unit time.

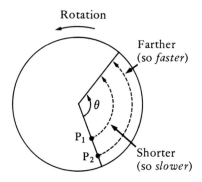

Figure 4–4a

DEFINITIONS

The *angular velocity* of a point on a rotating object is the number of *degrees* (radians, revolutions, etc.) per unit time through which the point turns.

The *linear velocity* of a point on a rotating object is the *distance* per unit time that the point travels along its circular path.

Objective:

Given information about one or more rotating objects, be able to calculate linear and angular velocities.

Note that the angular velocity of all points on a rotating object is the *same.* However, the linear velocity depends on how far the point is from the axis of rotation.

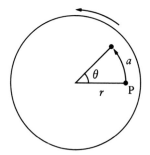

Figure 4–4b

To see how linear velocity depends on the distance from the center, suppose that point P is r units from the center, as shown in Figure 4–4b. Suppose, too, that the object turns through an angle of measure θ in t units of time. Let ω (Greek letter "omega," lower case) stand for the angular velocity of P and let v stand for its linear velocity. By the definitions of angular and linear velocity:

$$\omega = \frac{\theta}{t}$$ and $$v = \frac{a}{t}$$

There is a simple relationship between angular and linear velocity. If θ is the radian measure of an angle, then the length of the corresponding arc on a unit circle is also θ (Figure 4–4c). By the properties of similar geometric figures,

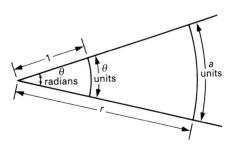

$$\frac{a}{r} = \frac{\theta}{1}.$$

Figure 4-4c

Multiplying by r gives the relationship

$$a = r\theta$$ for θ in radians.

Dividing each member of this equation by t gives

$$\frac{a}{t} = \frac{r\theta}{t}$$

By definition, $a/t = v$ and $\theta/t = \omega$. Therefore,

$$v = r\omega$$ for ω in radians per unit time.

These two equations, and the definitions of angular and linear velocity, can be used to accomplish the objective.

Example 1:   An LP record rotates at $33\frac{1}{3}$ revolutions per minute (rpm).

a. How many radians per minute is this?
b. Find the angular and linear velocities at the needle when it is just starting the record, about 14.5 centimeters from the center.
c. Find the angular and linear velocities of the center of the turn table.

Figure 4-4d

a. There are 2π radians per revolution. Therefore,

$$\omega = (2\pi)(33\tfrac{1}{3})$$

$$= 66\tfrac{2}{3}\pi \text{ radians per minute}$$

Note: There is a way to check your answers by finding their *units.* Since *per* . . . means *divided by* . . . , you write

$$\frac{33\tfrac{1}{3}\text{ revolutions}}{\text{minute}} \times \frac{2\pi \text{ radians}}{\text{revolution}}$$

The revolutions cancel out, leaving the units radians per minute.

b. All points on the same rotating object have the same angular velocity. Therefore

$$\omega = 66\tfrac{2}{3}\pi \text{ radians per minute}$$

$$\nu = r\omega$$

$$= (14.5)(66\tfrac{2}{3}\pi)$$

$$\approx 3030 \text{ cm/min} \text{ (rounding off to 3 significant digits, as was the } 14.5 \text{ you started with.)}$$

c. The turn table and the record rotate as a single object. So all points on the turn table have the same angular velocity as the record, even the *center* of the turn table. Therefore,

$$\omega = 66\tfrac{2}{3}\pi \text{ radians per minute.}$$

$$\nu = r\omega$$

$$= (0)(66\tfrac{2}{3}\pi)$$

$$= 0 \text{ cm/min}$$

Example 2:   The pedals on a bicycle turn the front sprocket at 8 radians per second. The sprocket has a diameter of 20 centimeters. The back sprocket, connected to the wheel, has a diameter of 6 centimeters.

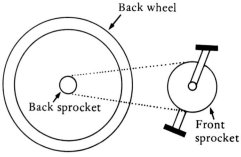

Figure 4-4e

a.   Find the linear velocity of the chain.
b.   Find the angular velocity of the back sprocket.

a.   The chain is connected to the rim of the front sprocket. Therefore, its
     linear velocity is the same as the linear velocity of the rim of the
     sprocket.

$$v = r\omega$$
$$= (10)(8) \qquad \text{(The radius is } \frac{20}{2} = 10 \text{ cm.)}$$
$$= \underline{80 \text{ cm/sec}}$$

b.   The chain is also connected to the rim of the back sprocket. So that rim
     must have the same linear velocity as the chain. Solving $v = r\omega$ for ω and
     substituting gives

$$\omega = \frac{v}{r}$$
$$= \frac{80}{3} \qquad \text{(The radius is } \frac{6}{2} = 3 \text{ cm.)}$$
$$= 26\frac{2}{3} \text{ radians per second}$$

Note that the wheels of a bicycle rotate *faster* than the pedals, in this case
26-2/3 radians per second for a pedal angular velocity of 8 radians per
second.

From these examples you can reach the following conclusions.

Conclusions:

1.   If two rotating objects are connected by their *rims*, as in the bicycle
     example, then their rims have the same *linear* velocity.
2.   All points on the same rotating object have the *same angular* velocity.
3.   If two rotating objects are connected so that they rotate as a single
     object, such as by an *axle* or as in the record example, then they have
     the same *angular* velocity.

Exercise 4-4

1. *Ship's Propeller Problem:* The propellers on an average freighter have a radius of 4 feet (Figure 4-4f). At full speed ahead, the propellers turn at 150 revolutions per minute.

   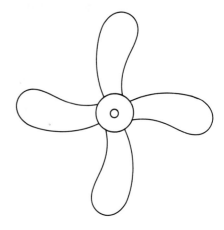

   a. What is the angular velocity in radians per minute at the tip of the blades? at the center of the propeller?
   b. What is the linear velocity in feet per minute at the tip of the blades? at the center of the propeller?

   Figure 4-4f

2. *Ferris Wheel Problem:* Dan Druff and Ella Funt are riding on a Ferris wheel. Dan observes that it takes 20 seconds to make a complete revolution. Their seat is 25 feet from the axle of the wheel.

   a. What is their angular velocity in revolutions per minute? Degrees per minute? Radians per minute?
   b. What is their linear velocity?

3. *David and Goliath Problem:* David puts a rock in his sling and starts whirling it around. He realizes that in order for the rock to reach Goliath, it must leave the sling at a speed of 60 feet per second. So he swings the sling in a circular path of radius 4 feet. What must the angular velocity be in order for David to achieve his objective?

4. *Lawn Mower Blade Problem:* In order for a lawn mower blade (Figure 4-4g) to cut grass, it must strike the grass with a speed of at least 900 inches per second.

   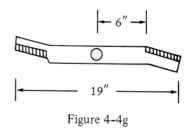

   Figure 4-4g

   a. If the innermost part of the cutting edge is 6 inches from the center of the blade, how many radians per second must the blade turn? How many revolutions per minute is this?
   b. The blade has a diameter of 19 inches. If the outermost tip of the blade hits a rock while turning as in part (a), how fast could the rock be hurled from the mower?

5. *Lawn Mower Cord Problem:* Yank Hardy pulls the cord on his power mower. In order for the engine to start, the pulley must turn at 180 revolutions per minute. The pulley has a radius of 0.2 feet (Figure 4–4h).

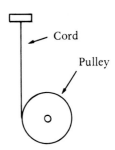

a. How many radians per second must the pulley turn?

b. How fast must Yank pull the cord to start the mower?

c. When Yank pulls this hard, what is the angular velocity of the center of the pulley?

Figure 4-4h

6. *Train Problem:* A train wheel has a diameter of 30 inches to the rim, which rests on the track. The flange, which keeps the wheel from slipping off the track, projects 1 inch beyond the rim (Figure 4–4i). When the train is traveling 60 mph, what is the linear velocity of a point on the outer edge of the flange?

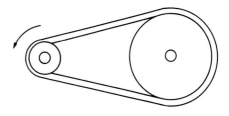

Figure 4-4i

7. *Pulley Problem No. 1:* A small pulley 6 centimeters in diameter is connected by a belt to a larger pulley 15 centimeters in diameter, as shown in Figure 4–4j. The small pulley is turning at 120 rpm.

a. Find the angular velocity of the small pulley in radians per second.

b. Find the linear velocity of the rim of the small pulley.

c. What is the linear velocity of the rim of the large pulley? Explain.

d. Find the angular velocity of the large pulley in radians/ second.

e. How many rpm is the large pully turning?

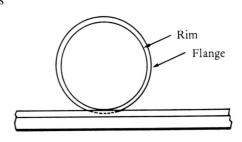

Figure 4-4j

8. *Pulley Problem No. 2:* A large pulley 20 cm in diameter drives a small pulley 6 cm in diameter by a pulley belt that goes over the rim of each (Figure 4–4j). The large pulley has an angular velocity of 150 radians per minute.

    a. What is the linear velocity of the large pulley's rim?
    b. What is the linear velocity of the small pulley's rim?
    c. What is the angular velocity of the small pulley?

9. *Gear Problem No. 1:* A small gear of radius 5 cm is turning with an angular velocity of 20 radians per second. It drives a large gear of radius 15 cm (Figure 4–4k).

    a. What is the linear velocity of the teeth on the large gear?
    b. What is the angular velocity of the teeth on the large gear?
    c. What is the angular velocity of a point at the center of the large gear?

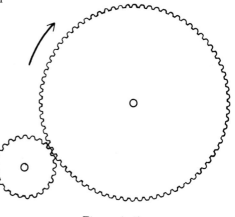

10. *Gear Problem No. 2:* A large gear of diameter 30 centimeters is revolving at 45 rpm. It drives a small gear of diameter 8 centimeters, as shown in Figure 4–4j.

Figure 4–4k

    a. How many radians per minute is the large gear turning?
    b. What is the linear velocity of the teeth on the large gear?
    c. What is the linear velocity of the teeth on the small gear?
    d. How many radians per minute is the small gear turning?
    e. How many revolutions per minute is the small gear turning?

11. *Cockroach Problem:* A cockroach is sitting 4 cm from the center of a lazy Susan. Unaware of its presence, Phoebe Small spins the lazy Susan through an angle of 120 degrees.

    a. Through how many radians did the roach turn?
    b. What distance did it travel?
    c. If Phoebe turned the lazy Susan 120 degrees in ½ second, what was the roach's angular velocity?
    d. What was its linear velocity?

12. *See Saw Problem:*   Stan Dupp and his brother Ben play on a see saw.
Stan sits at a point 8 feet from the pivot. Ben, being heavier, sits just
5 feet from the pivot. As Ben goes down and Stan goes up, the see saw
rotates through an angle of 37 degrees in 0.7 seconds.

   a.   What are Ben's angular velocity in radians per second, and his linear
velocity in feet per second?
   b.   What are Stan's angular and linear velocities?

13. *Bicycle Problem:*   Della Casee is riding a racing bike at a speed of 50.4
kilometers per hour. The wheels have a diameter of 70 centimeters.
Find the angular velocity of the wheels in radians per second.

14. *Tractor Problem:*   The rear
wheels of a tractor (Figure
4–4ℓ) are 4 feet in diameter,
and turn at 20 rpm.

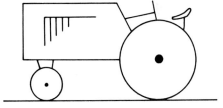

   a.   How fast is the tractor
going (feet per second)?
   b.   The front wheels have a

Figure 4-4ℓ.

diameter of only 1.8 feet.
What is the linear velocity of a point on their tire treads?
   c.   What is the angular velocity of the front wheels in rpm?

15. *Three Gear Problem:*   Three gears
are shown in Figure 4–4m.

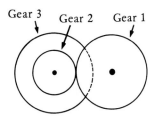

Figure 4-4m

   a.   Gear 1 turns at 200 rpm. What
is its angular velocity in radians
per second?
   b.   What is the linear velocity of
the teeth on gear 1, 13 millimeters from its axle?
   c.   Gear 1's teeth mesh with gear
2's teeth. Gear 2 has a radius of
3 millimeters. What is the linear velocity of gear 2's teeth?
   d.   What is gear 2's angular velocity in radians per second?
   e.   Gear 2 and gear 3 are connected to the same axle. What is the
linear velocity of gear 3's teeth? (Its radius is 10 millimeters.)

16. *Wheel and Grindstone Problem:* A waterwheel of diameter 12 feet turns at 0.3 radian per second.

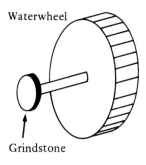

Waterwheel

Grindstone

Figure 4-4n

   a. What is the linear velocity of the rim?
   b. The wheel is connected by an axle to a grindstone of diameter 3 feet (Figure 4-4n). What is the angular velocity of a point on the rim of the grindstone?

17. *Truck Problem:* Old-fashioned trucks used a chain to transmit power from the engine to the wheels (Figure 4-4o). Suppose that the drive sprocket had a diameter of 6 inches and the wheel sprocket had a diameter of 20 inches. If the drive sprocket goes 300 rpm, find:

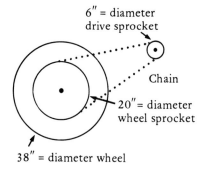

6" = diameter drive sprocket

Chain

20" = diameter wheel sprocket

38" = diameter wheel

Figure 4-4o

   a. The angular velocity of the drive sprocket in radians per minute.
   b. The linear velocity of the 20-inch wheel sprocket in inches per minute.
   c. The angular velocity of the wheel in radians per minute.
   d. The speed of the truck to the nearest mile per hour.

18. *Car Wheel Problem:* A car's wheel turns at 200 revolutions per minute. The radius of each wheel is 1.3 feet.

   a. To the nearest radian per minute, what is the angular velocity of a point
       i. on the tire tread?
       ii. on the hubcap, 0.4 feet from the center?
       iii. right at the center?
   b. To the nearest foot per minute, what is the linear velocity of a point
       i. on the tire tread?
       ii. on the hubcap, 0.4 feet from the center?
       iii. right at the center?
   c. To the nearest mile per hour, how fast is the car going?

19. *Clock Minute Hand Problem:* If the minute hand of a clock is long
    enough, the human eye can perceive the motion of its tip. The shortest
    minute hand you can see moving is about 10 inches long. What is the
    slowest linear motion the human eye can perceive (inches per minute)?

20. *Clock Second Hand Problem:* An
    electric clock transmits rotation from
    its motor to the clock hands through
    a series of small gears driving larger
    gears. The second hand must make
    one revolution every minute
    (obviously!)

    a. What is the angular velocity of
        the second hand in radians per
        minute?
    b. The second hand is fastened to
        gear 1, whose diameter is 3.8
        centimeters (Figure 4–4p). What
        is gear 1's angular velocity?
    c. Gear 2, of diameter 0.6 centi-
        meter, meshes with gear 1's
        teeth. What is the linear velocity
        of gear 2's teeth?
    d. Gear 3, of diameter 4 centimeters,
        is connected to the same axle as gear 2. What is the linear velocity of
        gear 3's teeth?

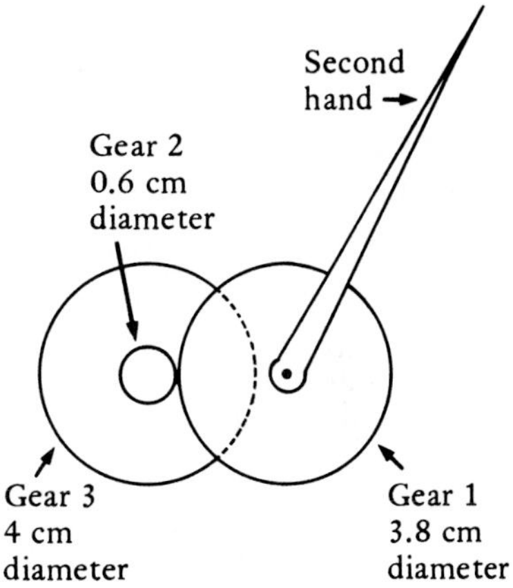

Second
hand →

Gear 2
0.6 cm
diameter

Gear 3
4 cm
diameter

Gear 1
3.8 cm
diameter

Figure 4–4p

21. *Projector Problem 1:* When
    you are showing a movie,
    the film goes through the
    projector with a constant
    linear velocity of about
    30 centimeters per second.
    The film winds off Reel 1
    and onto Reel 2 (Figure
    4–4q). As the projector
    runs, the radius of the film
    rolled up on Reel 1 de-
    creases, and the radius on
    Reel 2 increases. When the
    radius of film on Reel 1 is
    8 centimeters and that on Reel 2 is 18 centimeters, find

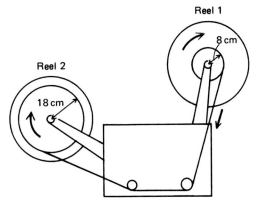

Reel 1

8 cm

Reel 2

18 cm

Figure 4–4q

a. the angular velocity of Reel 1 in

(i)   radians/second,
(ii) revolutions/second,
(iii) degrees/second,

b. the angular velocity of Reel 2,
c. the linear velocity of a point on the rim of Reel 2 if the diameter of the reel is 40 centimeters,
d. the linear and angular velocities of a point at the center of Reel 2.

22. *Projector Problem 2:* When you have finished showing a film, you rewind it as shown in Figure 4–4r. During rewinding, Reel 1 turns with a constant angular velocity of about 13 radians/second.

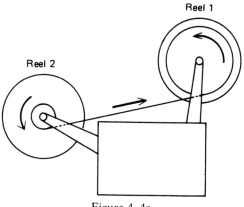

Figure 4–4r

a. Find the linear velocity of the film at the beginning of rewinding, when the diameter of film on Reel 1 is 10 centimeters.

b. Find the linear velocity of the film at the end of rewinding, when the diameter of film on Reel 1 is 40 centimeters.
c. If the diameter of film on Reel 2 is 10 centimeters at the end of rewinding, what is its angular velocity then?
d. Explain why the end of the film flaps around uncontrollably as it comes off Reel 2.

23. *Earth's Rotation Problem 1:* The Earth revolves once on its axis every 24 hours. For parts a through d, find

a. the angular velocity of the Earth in radians per hour,
b. the linear velocity of a point on the equator, 4000 miles from the axis,
c. the linear velocity at the North Pole,
d. the linear velocity in San Antonio, latitude 30°. (You must first find the perpendicular distance from San Antonio to the Earth's axis.)
e. Spacecraft from Cape Kennedy are always fired into orbit from west to east. Based on your answers above, tell *why* they are fired that way.

24. *Earth's Rotation Problem 2:* The Earth orbits the Sun once every 365 days. It is about 93,000,000 miles from the Sun to the Earth.

   a. What is the Earth's angular velocity about the Sun in radians per hour?
   b. What is the Earth's linear velocity in miles per hour?

25. *Record Player Problem No. 1:* The turntable on a record player rotates at 33-1/3 rpm.

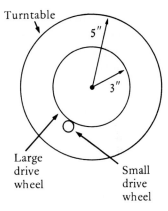

   a. What is the linear velocity of a point on its rim?
   b. A large drive wheel is attached to the turntable's axle, below the turntable (Figure 4–4s). What is the linear velocity of its rim?
   c. A motor drives a small drive wheel at 600 rpm. What must the radius of the small drive wheel be so that the turntable will rotate at 33-1/3 rpm with no slippage between the two drive wheels?

Figure 4-4s

26. *Record Player Problem No. 2:* A record rotates with an angular velocity of 33-1/3 revolutions per minute. The grooves are spaced so that there are 83.25 grooves per centimeter. As the needle moves toward the center of the record, each groove is slightly shorter than the preceding one because its radius is smaller. The radius of the outer groove is 15 centimeters and that of the innermost groove is 7 centimeters. To the nearest centimeter, what is the total distance which the needle travels while the record is being played?

27. *Angular Velocity and Sinusoids:* A water wheel 14 meters in diameter is rotating as shown in Figure 4–4t. You start a stopwatch and observe the motion of point *P* on the rim of the wheel. When the stopwatch reads 3 seconds, *P* is at its maximum distance from the water. When the stopwatch reads 8 seconds, the point *P* is at its maximum depth below the water.

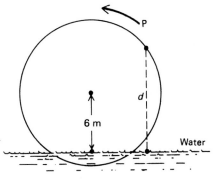

Figure 4-4t

a. Find the angular velocity of P in

   (i) revolutions per second,
   (ii) radians per second.

b. The distance d of P from the water's surface varies sinusoidally with time. Using a *circular* function, write an equation expressing d in terms of t, the number of seconds on the stopwatch.

c. The general sinusoidal equation is $y = C + A \cos B(x - D)$. You have learned that A is the amplitude, C is the axis location, and D is the phase displacement. Up till now, you have learned only that B "tells you" what the period is. By comparing your value of B with the answers above, tell *what* the constant B actually is.

28. *Rotating Beacon Problem:* A police car pulls up alongside a long brick wall. While the police are away from the car, the red beacon light continues to rotate, shining a spot of red light that moves along the wall (Figure 4–4u). As you watch, you decide to make a mathematical model of the position of the light spot as a function of time.

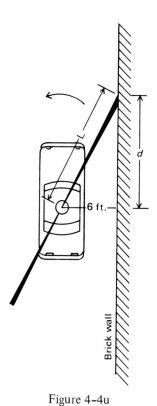

a. You start your stopwatch when the beam of light is perpendicular to the wall. You find that the light makes one complete revolution in exactly 2 seconds. The perpendicular distance from the light to the wall is 6 feet. Write equations expressing the distances d and L in terms of the number of seconds t, that the stopwatch reads.

b. Calculate d and L when t equals

   (i)   0.1,
   (ii)   0.3,
   (iii) 0.5,
   (iv)   0.8.

Figure 4–4u

c. What is the first positive value of t for which $d = 5$?

d. Sketch graphs of d and L versus time t.

29. *Nauseating Ride Problem:* One of
the more nauseating rides at an
amusement park is a merry-go-
round that rotates at a constant
angular velocity while rings of seats
rotate at a different (but constant)
angular velocity (Figure 4–4v).
Suppose that the seats rotate at 30
rpm while the merry-go-round is
rotating at 12 rpm.

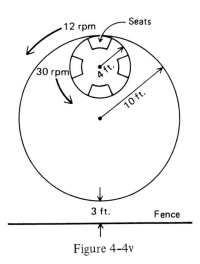

Figure 4–4v

a. Find your linear velocity in feet
per second due to the *combined*
rotations of the seats and merry-
go-round when your seat is

   (i) farthest from the center of the merry-go-round,
   (ii) closest to the center of the merry-go-round.

b. In what direction are you actually moving when your seat is closest
to the merry-go-round's center?

c. As your seat turns, your distance from the fence varies sinusoidally
with time. As the merry-go-round turns, the axis of this sinusoid also
varies sinusoidally with time but with a different period. Suppose
that your seat is 23 feet from the fence at time $t = 0$ seconds. Write
an equation expressing your distance from the fence in terms of t.

d. By composition of ordinates, sketch one complete cycle of the
graph of the function in part c above.

e. From the answers to the questions above, you should be able to
figure out why the ride is so nauseating. Why?

30. *Identity Problem:*   Prove that $\sin 3x + \sin x = 4 \sin x \cos^2 x$.

31. *Triangle Problem:*   Draw a diagram representing a triangle with base
10 cm, one side 3 cm, and angle 27° between the base and the 3-cm side.
What is the altitude of the triangle from the other end of the 3-cm side
to the base?

32. *Equation Problem:*   Write the general solution for

   $$2 \sin (\theta - 67°) = \cos (\theta - 67°).$$

4–5 INVERSE CIRCULAR FUNCTION GRAPHS

In earlier chapters you have used $\sin^{-1}$, $\cos^{-1}$, and so forth to solve equations and to find angles of right triangles. In this section you will study functions derived from these inverse relations.

The equation

$$y = \tan^{-1} x$$

means that

$$x = \tan y.$$

This equation says that y is an arc whose tangent is x. For this reason the abbreviation

$$y = \arctan x$$

is sometimes used. Similarly, the names arcsin, arccos, arccot, arcsec, and arccsc are used for $\sin^{-1}$, $\cos^{-1}$, $\cot^{-1}$, $\sec^{-1}$, and $\csc^{-1}$, respectively.

The graph of $y = \tan^{-1} x$ can be plotted by using $x = \tan y$, selecting values of y, and finding x.

y	x
$-\pi/2$	undef.
$-\pi/4$	-1
0	0
$\pi/4$	1
$\pi/2$	undef.

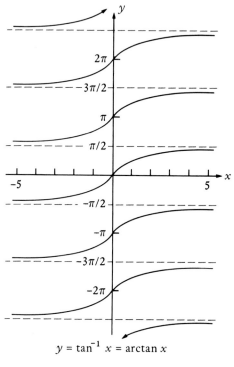

$y = \tan^{-1} x = \arctan x$

Figure 4–5a

The result (Figure 4–5a) is similar to the tangent graph, but the cycles go along the y-axis rather than the x-axis. As you can see, the relation is not a function. There are *many* values of y for each value of x. However, any one branch of the graph *is* a function. The branch between $\dfrac{-\pi}{2}$ and $\dfrac{\pi}{2}$ is called the *inverse tangent function*, or the *principal branch of the inverse*

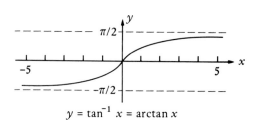

$y = \tan^{-1} x = \arctan x$

Figure 4–5b

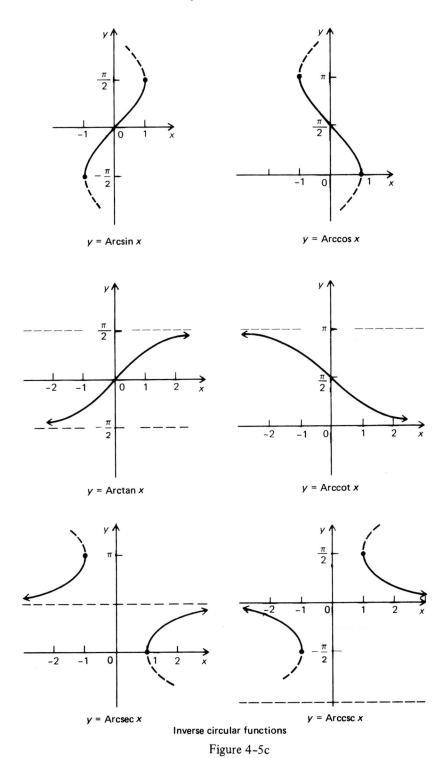

Inverse circular functions

Figure 4-5c

tangent relation. Its graph (Figure 4–5b) has the following features:

1. It is a *function.*
2. It uses the *entire domain* (all real numbers, for $\tan^{-1}$).
3. It is one, *continuous* graph.
4. It is *centrally located* near the origin.

To distinguish the function from the corresponding relation, the initial letter of the name is capitalized,

$$y = \text{Tan}^{-1} x \qquad \text{or} \qquad y = \text{Arctan } x.$$

Functions can be derived from the other inverse circular relations by selecting appropriate branches of their graphs. The branches in Figure 4–5c (preceding page) have as many as possible of the features listed above.

From Figure 4–5c you can read off the following ranges for the inverse circular functions.

Ranges of Inverse Circular Functions

$y = \text{Arcsin } x = \text{Sin}^{-1} x, \quad y \in [-\pi/2, \pi/2]$

$y = \text{Arccos } x = \text{Cos}^{-1} x, \quad y \in [0, \pi]$

$y = \text{Arctan } x = \text{Tan}^{-1} x, \quad y \in (-\pi/2, \pi/2)$

$y = \text{Arccot } x = \text{Cot}^{-1} x, \quad y \in (0, \pi)$

$y = \text{Arcsec } x = \text{Sec}^{-1} x, \quad y \in [0, \pi] \text{ and } y \neq \pi/2$

$y = \text{Arccsc } x = \text{Csc}^{-1} x, \quad y \in [-\pi/2, \pi/2] \text{ and } y \neq 0$

Objective:

Draw graphs of inverse circular functions, including translations or dilations.

Example 1: Sketch the graph of $y = 2 \text{ Arcsin } x$.

The graph of $y = \text{Arcsin } x$ is shown in the first sketch of Figure 4–5d. For $y = 2 \text{ Arcsin } x$, each ordinate will be *double* its previous value. So the graph is "stretched out" in the y-direction, as shown in the second sketch of Figure 4–5d.

Note that transforming a function $y = f(x)$ to $y = A \cdot f(x)$ by multiplying by a constant A is called a *vertical magnification* or *vertical dilation*, of the function. The amplitude A of a sinusoid in $y = A \cos x$ is actually just a vertical magnification. If A is between 0 and 1, the graph gets *smaller* in the y-direction, and the transformation is sometimes called a *vertical reduction*.

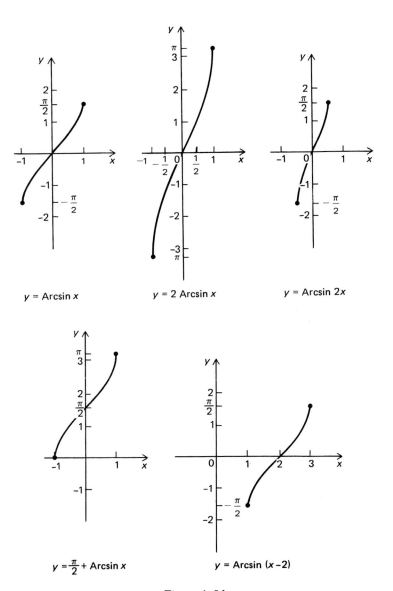

Figure 4–5d

Example 2: Sketch the graph of $y = $ Arcsin $2x$.

Since the argument of Arcsin must be between –1 and 1, inclusive, you can write

$$-1 \leq 2x \leq 1.$$

Dividing all three members of this inequality by 2 produces

$$-\frac{1}{2} \leq x \leq \frac{1}{2}.$$

So the entire graph is *compressed* in the x-direction so that it is only half as wide as the graph of $y = $ Arcsin x. The graph is shown in the third sketch of Figure 4–5d.

Transforming a function $y = f(x)$ by multiplying its *argument* x by a constant B, getting $y = f(Bx)$, causes a *horizontal reduction* by a factor of $1/B$. This phenomenon is what occurs with $y = \cos Bx$, where the period of the sinusoid was reduced from 2π by a factor of $1/B$ and became $2\pi/B$.

Example 3: Sketch the graph of $y = (\pi/2) + $ Arcsin x.

Adding $\pi/2$ to each ordinate of the graph of $y = $ Arcsin x has the effect of *raising* the graph by $\pi/2$ units, as shown in the fourth sketch of Figure 4–5d. Such a transformation is called a *vertical translation*. It does not affect the shape or size of the graph, only its vertical position. You used the same transformation when you plotted $y = C + \cos x$ and found that the sinusoidal axis was raised by C units.

Example 4: Sketch the graph of $y = $ Arcsin $(x - 2)$.

As in Example 2, the argument of the Arcsin function must be between –1 and 1, inclusive. So you can write

$$-1 \leq x - 2 \leq 1.$$

Adding 2 to all three members of this inequality gives

$$1 \leq x \leq 3.$$

So the entire graph appears between $x = 1$ and $x = 3$, instead of between –1 and 1. It has undergone a *horizontal translation* of 2 units, as shown in the last sketch of Figure 4–5d. This shift is exactly what happened with $\cos (x - D)$, which has a horizontal phase displacement of D units.

A summary of the effects of the four constants A, B, C, and D on the graph of a function $y = f(x)$ is shown below.

> If $y = C + A\, f(B(x - D))$, then the graph of $y = f(x)$ is
>
> a. *magnified* in the y-direction by a factor of A,
> b. *reduced* in the x-direction by a factor of $1/B$,
> c. *translated* in the y-direction by a distance C,
> d. *translated* in the x-direction by a distance D.

In the following exercise, you will use these conclusions to sketch graphs of various transformed inverse circular functions. You will also find an important mathematical reason why the circular functions are preferable to trigonometric functions with degree arguments.

Exercise 4–5

For Problems 1 through 6, sketch both graphs on the *same* set of axes. Be sure to label each graph.

1. $y = \text{Arcsin } x$ and $y = 3 \text{ Arcsin } x$
2. $y = \text{Arctan } x$ and $y = \text{Arctan } 3x$
3. $y = \text{Arcsec } x$ and $y = \pi + \text{Arcsec } x$
4. $y = \text{Arccsc } x$ and $y = \text{Arccsc } (x - 3)$
5. $y = \text{Arccot } x$ and $y = 3 \text{ Arccot } 2x$
6. $y = \text{Arccos } x$ and $y = \dfrac{\pi}{2} + \text{Arccos } (x - 3)$

For Problems 7 through 16, sketch a graph of the inverse circular function.

7. $y = \dfrac{\pi}{3} + \text{Arctan } x$ 8. $y = 2 \text{ Arccsc } x$

9. $y = \text{Arcsin } \dfrac{1}{10}x$ 10. $y = \text{Arcsec } 4x$

11. $y = \text{Arccot } (x + 3)$ 12. $y = \dfrac{1}{2} \text{ Arccos } x$

13. $y = 2\pi + 3 \text{ Arcsin } \dfrac{1}{4}x$ 14. $y = 4 \text{ Arccos } \dfrac{1}{2}(x + 3)$

15. $y = \dfrac{\pi}{3} + \dfrac{1}{2} \text{ Arccos } 3(x - 1)$ 16. $y = -\pi + 2 \text{ Arcsin } \dfrac{1}{4}(x - 3)$

17. *Inverse of a Linear Function:* Let function f be defined by
$$f = \{(x, y): y = 3x + 2\}.$$
The inverse of f, f^{-1} , is found by interchanging the variables x and y in the equation.

$$f^{-1} = \{(x, y): x = 3y + 2\}$$

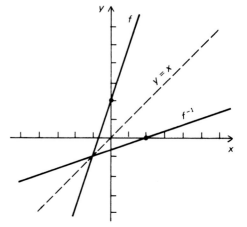

a.   Tell the slope and the y-intercept of the graph of f.

b.   Transform the equation for f^{-1}, $x = 3y + 2$, so that y is expressed in terms of x.

c.   Tell the slope and the y-intercept of the graph of f^{-1}.

d.   Figure 4-5e shows the graphs of f and f^{-1}. What is the relationship between these graphs and the line, $y = x$?

Figure 4-5e

e.   The equation for f can be written $f(x) = 3x + 2$, and the equation for f^{-1} can be written $f^{-1}(x) = (1/3)x - 2/3$. By appropriate substitution, show that $f(f^{-1}(x)) = x$, and that $f^{-1}(f(x)) = x$.

18. *Inverse of a Quadratic Function:* Let

$$g = \{(x, y): y = x^2\}, \text{ and let}$$
$$g^{-1} = \{(x, y): x = y^2\}.$$

a.   Transform the equation for g^{-1} so that y is in terms of x.

b.   Plot carefully the graphs of g and g^{-1} on the same set of axes. Use the same scales for both axes.

c.   Demonstrate that the graphs are *reflections* of each other through the line $y = x$, as in Figure 4-5c.

d.   Is g^{-1} a *function*? Explain.

e.   By appropriate substitutions, show that $g(g^{-1}(x)) = x$.

19. *Accurate Inverse Cosine Graph:*

a.   Plot an accurate graph of $y = \mathrm{Cos}^{-1} x$ by finding y for each 0.1 unit of x from $x = -1$ through $x = 1$. Use a fairly large scale, and use the same scale on both axes.

b.   On the same set of axes as in part (a), plot an accurate graph of $y = \cos x$ from $x = 0$ to $x = \pi$.

c.   Demonstrate that the two graphs are reflections of each other through the line $y = x$.

20. *Accurate Inverse Sine Graph:* Repeat Problem 19 for $y = \mathrm{Sin}^{-1} x$ and for $y = \sin x$ between $x = -\pi/2$ and $x = \pi/2$.

21. *Computer Graphics Problem:*   Use the program PLOT INVERSE from the accompanying disk or a similar plotting program to confirm that your answers to Problems 1, 15, and 16, above, are correct.

22. *Inverse Value Problem:*   Suppose that θ = Arcsin (3/7). Find exact values of:

    a. $\cos \theta$ b. $\tan \theta$ c. $\sec \theta$

23. *Identity Problem:*   Prove that the following is an identity:

    $\sin x \cos x \tan x \cot x \sec x \csc x = 1$.

24. *Identity Problem:*   What is the amplitude of the function

    $f(x) = 7 \cos 3x + 24 \sin 3x$?

25. Find by calculator θ = Arcsin 0.7. Then find $\sin \theta$. What do you notice?

26. *Triangle Problem:*   A triangle is to be drawn with base 20 cm, one side 15 cm, and altitude 13 cm from the other end of the 15-cm side to the base. How long will the third side of the triangle be?

27. *Rotary Motion Problem:*   Mars orbits the Sun once every 687 days. Its average distance from the Sun is 141 million miles.

    a.   What is its angular velocity in radians per hour?
    b.   What is its linear velocity in miles per hour?

28. Write the exact value of $\cos \dfrac{5\pi}{6}$.

4–6   EXACT VALUES OF INVERSE FUNCTIONS

In Sections 1–4 and 2–5 you found exact values of functions for special arguments. In this section you will do the same sort of thing for inverse circular functions.

Objective:

Be able to find exact values of special inverse circular functions.

The most important thing for you to know is the *range* of each inverse function. For this purpose it helps to think of the inverse function as an arc or angle in a uv-coordinate system (Figure 4–6a). If the argument of the inverse function is positive, such as Arcsin 0.8, then the arc or angle is in Quadrant I. If the argument is negative, the arc or angle is in Quadrant II for Arccos, Arccot, and Arcsec, and in Quadrant IV for Arcsin, Arctan, and Arccsc. None of the inverse circular functions corresponds to an angle in Quadrant III.

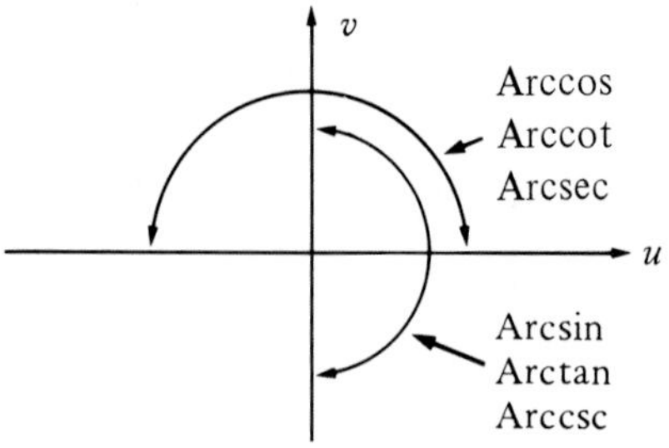

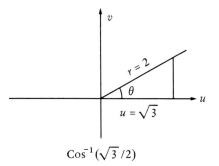

Inverse circular function ranges

Figure 4–6a

Example 1:   Evaluate $\text{Cos}^{-1}(\sqrt{3}/2)$.

Let $\theta = \text{Cos}^{-1}(\sqrt{3}/2)$.

Then θ terminates in Quadrant I (Figure 4–6b). From the diagram, $\theta = \pi/6$ radians, corresponding to 30°. Therefore,

$$\text{Cos}^{-1}(\sqrt{3}/2) = \underline{\pi/6}.$$

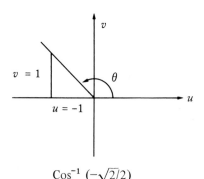

$\text{Cos}^{-1}(\sqrt{3}/2)$

Figure 4–6b

Example 2:   Evaluate $\text{Cos}^{-1}(-\dfrac{\sqrt{2}}{2})$.

Let $\theta = \text{Cos}^{-1}(-\dfrac{\sqrt{2}}{2})$.

Then θ terminates in Quadrant II (Figure 4–6c). From the diagram, $\theta = \dfrac{3\pi}{4}$ radians, corresponding to 135°. Therefore,

$$\text{Cos}^{-1}(-\dfrac{\sqrt{2}}{2}) = \underline{\dfrac{3\pi}{4}}$$

$\text{Cos}^{-1}(-\sqrt{2}/2)$

Figure 4–6c

Example 3:   Evaluate $\tan (\text{Arcsin} (-\frac{2}{3}))$.

Arcsin $(-\frac{2}{3})$ terminates in

Quadrant IV (Figure 4–6d). From
the diagram, $v = -2$, and $r = 3$. By
the Pythagorean Theorem,
$u = \sqrt{5}$. Therefore,

$$\tan (\text{Arcsin} (-\frac{2}{3})) = -\frac{2}{\sqrt{5}}$$

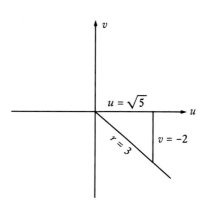

The answers to problems such as
Example 3 are *exact* values in radical
form. The answers can be checked
by finding approximations by calculator. Evaluating the expression

directly, you would enter $-\frac{2}{3}$ into

Figure 4-6d

the calculator, then press the inverse
sine key, getting

$$\text{Arcsin} (-\frac{2}{3}) = -0.729727 \ldots .$$

Then, without clearing the calculator, you press the tangent key, getting

$$\tan (\text{Arcsin} (-\frac{2}{3})) = -0.894427 \ldots .$$

Evaluating $-\frac{2}{\sqrt{5}}$ by calculator gives

$$-\frac{2}{\sqrt{5}} = -0.884427 \ldots .$$

which agrees with the value above.

Example 4:   Evaluate $\text{Cos}^{-1} (\cos \frac{\pi}{3})$.

This expression can be evaluated by starting inside the parentheses.

$$\text{Cos}^{-1} (\cos \frac{\pi}{3}) = \text{Cos}^{-1} (\frac{1}{2})$$

$$= \frac{\pi}{3}$$

Note that the answer to Cos^{-1} $(\cos x)$ turned out to be x. This happens if x is in the range or the inverse cosine function. For a value outside the range, such as Cos^{-1} $(\cos 2\pi)$, the answer would be Cos^{-1} (1), which equals 0, not 2π. In general,

$$f(f^{-1}(x)) = x \quad \text{and} \quad f^{-1}(f(x)) = x$$

provided x is in the *range* of the outside function, and in the *domain* of the inside function.

You will prove this property in Exercise 4–7.

Exercise 4-6

For Problems 1 through 24, find the *exact* value of the inverse circular function. The answer should be expressed in terms of π, if necessary. You may check the answers by calculator.

1. $\text{Arcsin } \dfrac{1}{2}$

2. $\text{Sin}^{-1} \dfrac{\sqrt{3}}{2}$

3. $\text{Cos}^{-1} 0$

4. $\text{Arccos } 1$

5. $\text{Arctan } 1$

6. $\text{Tan}^{-1} \sqrt{3}$

7. $\text{Cot}^{-1} \sqrt{3}$

8. $\text{Arccot } 1$

9. $\text{Arcsec } 2$

10. $\text{Sec}^{-1} \dfrac{2}{\sqrt{3}}$

11. $\text{Csc}^{-1} \sqrt{2}$

12. $\text{Arccsc } 2$

13. $\text{Sin}^{-1} (-\dfrac{\sqrt{3}}{2})$

14. $\text{Arcsin } (-\dfrac{1}{2})$

15. $\text{Arccos } (-1)$

16. $\text{Cos}^{-1} (-\dfrac{\sqrt{2}}{2})$

17. $\text{Tan}^{-1} (-1)$

18. $\text{Arctan } (-\sqrt{3})$

19. $\text{Arccot } (-1)$

20. $\text{Cot}^{-1} (-\sqrt{3})$

21. $\text{Sec}^{-1} (-\sqrt{2})$

22. $\text{Arcsec } (-1)$

23. $\text{Arccsc } (-\sqrt{2})$

24. $\text{Csc}^{-1} (-1)$

For Problems 25 through 48, find the *exact* value of the expression, using radicals or π if necessary. You may check the answers by calculator.

25. $\tan{(\cos^{-1}{\frac{4}{5}})}$

26. $\cos{(\arctan{\frac{4}{3}})}$

27. $\sin{(\tan^{-1}{\frac{5}{12}})}$

28. $\sec{(\arcsin{\frac{15}{17}})}$

29. $\cos{(\arcsin{(-\frac{8}{17})})}$

30. $\cot{(\csc^{-1}{(-\frac{13}{12})})}$

31. $\sec{(\arccos{\frac{2}{3}})}$

32. $\sin{(\cot^{-1}{4})}$

33. $\cot{(\sin^{-1}{(-\frac{\sqrt{2}}{2})})}$

34. $\tan{(\operatorname{arcsec}{(-\sqrt{2})})}$

35. $\csc{(\operatorname{arccot}{3})}$

36. $\csc{(\tan^{-1}{\frac{1}{2}})}$

37. $\csc{(\operatorname{arccsc}{5})}$

38. $\sin{(\sin^{-1}{\frac{2}{3}})}$

39. $\cos{(\sin^{-1}{2})}$

40. $\tan{(\operatorname{arcsec}{0})}$

41. $\arctan{(\tan{\frac{\pi}{6}})}$

42. $\cos^{-1}{(\cos{\frac{\pi}{4}})}$

43. $\sin^{-1}{(\sin{(-\frac{\pi}{4})})}$

44. $\operatorname{arcsec}{(\sec{(-\frac{\pi}{3})})}$

45. $\sec^{-1}{(\sec{\frac{7\pi}{6}})}$

46. $\operatorname{arccsc}{(\csc{\frac{2\pi}{3}})}$

47. $\operatorname{arccot}{(\tan{\frac{\pi}{3}})}$

48. $\sin^{-1}{(\cos{\frac{\pi}{6}})}$

49. *Angular Velocity Problem:*   Find the angular velocity in radians per second for a point 8 cm from the center of a wheel that is rotating at 40 rpm.

50. *Identity Problem:*   Prove that $\cos{2x}\sec{x} = 2\cos{x} - \sec{x}$.

51. *Triangle Problem:*   Lena Genst leans a 20-foot-long ladder against the wall. She knows that the angle the ladder makes with the ground should be no more than 70°. What is the highest the top of the ladder can be from the ground?

52. *Graphing Problem:*   Sketch the graph of $y = 7 + 2\sin{3(\theta - 40°)}$.

53. If $f(x) = 4 + 9\cos{\pi(x + 11)}$, what is the first positive value of x for which the graph crosses the x-axis?

54. By what percent does cos θ change when θ increases from $10°$ to $11°$? From $85°$ to $86°$?

4–7 PROPERTIES OF INVERSE CIRCULAR FUNCTIONS

Many computers have only the inverse tangent function available. If you write a program that needs other inverse circular functions, you must express these in terms of an Arctangent. In this section you will learn properties that allow you to do this. You will also learn properties related to the cofunction and reciprocal properties of the circular functions.

Objective:

Be able to express one inverse circular function in terms of another, and use this ability to simplify expressions.

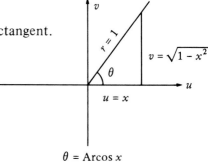

Example 1:   Express Arccos x as an Arctangent.
     The technique is similar to the problems of the last section. First, let θ equal Arccos x, and then draw the angle in a uv-coordinate system (Figure 4–7a).

$\theta = \text{Arccos } x$

$\therefore x = \cos\theta$, and $\theta \in [0, \pi]$.

Since $\cos\theta = u/r$, label $u = x$ and $r = 1$.

$\theta = \text{Arcos } x$

Figure 4–7a

By the Pythagorean Theorem,

$$v = \sqrt{1 - x^2}.$$

From the definition of tangent,

$$\tan\theta = \frac{\sqrt{1 - x^2}}{x}$$

Therefore,

$$\theta = \arctan\frac{\sqrt{1 - x^2}}{x}$$

where the lower case "a" is used until the ranges are checked. If x is negative,

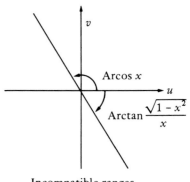

Incompatible ranges or arcos and arctan

Figure 4–7b

then Arccos x is between $\pi/2$ and π, while Arctan x is between $-\pi/2$ and 0. To get the correct value for Arccos x in this case you must add π to the Arctangent. Figure 4–7b shows that these two angles are π radians apart.

The property resulting from Example 1 is listed in the table below, along

$$\text{Arcsin } x = \text{Arctan } \frac{x}{\sqrt{1-x^2}}, \quad x \in (-1, 1)$$

$$\text{Arccos } x = \text{Arctan } \frac{\sqrt{1-x^2}}{x}, \quad \text{for } x \in (0, 1]$$

$$= \pi + \text{Arctan } \frac{\sqrt{1-x^2}}{x}, \quad \text{for } x \in [-1, 0)$$

$$\text{Arccot } x = \text{Arctan } \frac{1}{x}, \quad \text{for } x > 0$$

$$= \pi + \text{Arctan } \frac{1}{x}, \quad \text{for } x < 0$$

$$\text{Arcsec } x = \text{Arctan } \sqrt{x^2 - 1}, \quad \text{for } x \geq 1$$

$$= \pi + \text{Arctan } (-\sqrt{x^2 - 1}), \quad \text{for } x \leq -1$$

$$\text{Arccsc } x = \text{Arctan } \left(\frac{1}{\sqrt{x^2 - 1}} \right), \quad \text{for } x > 1$$

$$= \text{Arctan } \left(-\frac{1}{\sqrt{x^2 - 1}} \right), \quad \text{for } x < -1$$

with the other four inverse circular functions in terms of the Arctangent. In the following exercise you will derive some of these properties.

The properties of circular functions which you learned in Chapter 3 can be used to find exact values of expressions containing inverse circular functions.

Example 2:   Find the *exact* value of $\sin (2 \text{ Arctan } \frac{8}{15})$. Check your answer by calculator.

Using the Double Argument Properties,

$$\sin\left(2 \text{ Arctan } \frac{8}{15}\right)$$

$$= 2 \sin\left(\text{Arctan } \frac{8}{15}\right) \cos\left(\text{Arctan } \frac{8}{15}\right)$$

Arctan $\frac{8}{15}$ can be drawn on a uv-Coordinate

system, as in Figure 4–7c.

The Pythagorean Theorem gives

$$r = \sqrt{15^2 + 8^2} = 17$$

Therefore,

$$\sin\left(2 \text{ Arctan } 8/15\right)$$

$$= 2 \cdot \frac{8}{17} \cdot \frac{15}{17}$$

$$= 240/289$$

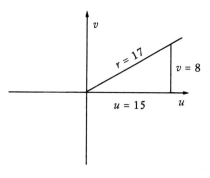

Figure 4–7c

To check the answer by calculator, first evaluate Arctan 8/15, which is 0.48995 . . . . Then, without clearing the calculator, double the result, getting 0.97991 . . . , and press the sin key. The result, 0.830449 . . . agrees with the value you get by dividing 240 by 289.

Exercise 4–7

For Problems 1 through 6, write an equation expressing the given inverse function in terms of the other.

1. Express Arcsec x as an Arctangent.
2. Express Arcsin x as an Arctangent.
3. Express Arccos x as an Arcsine.
4. Express Arcsin x as an Arccosine.
5. Express Arcsec x as an Arccosine.
6. Express Arccsc x as an Arcsine.

For Problems 7 through 18, use the properties of functions and inverse functions to find *exact* values of the expressions, using radicals, if necessary. You may check your answers by calculator.

7. $\cos\left(2 \text{ Arctan } \frac{4}{3}\right)$

8. $\cos\left(2 \text{ Arcsin } \frac{1}{3}\right)$

9. $\sin\left(2 \text{ Arcsec }\left(-\frac{25}{7}\right)\right)$

10. $\tan\left(2 \text{ Arcsin }\left(-\frac{8}{17}\right)\right)$

11. $\sin (\text{Tan}^{-1} \dfrac{1}{2} + \text{Tan}^{-1} \dfrac{1}{3})$ 12. $\tan (\text{Tan}^{-1} \dfrac{1}{4} + \text{Tan}^{-1} \dfrac{3}{5})$

13. $\cos (\text{Sin}^{-1} \dfrac{2}{3} + \text{Sin}^{-1} \dfrac{1}{5})$ 14. $\cos (\text{Sec}^{-1} \dfrac{3}{2} - \text{Cos}^{-1} \dfrac{1}{5})$

15. $\sin (\dfrac{\pi}{2} - \text{Arccos} \dfrac{11}{13})$ 16. $\csc (\dfrac{\pi}{2} - \text{Arcsec } 19)$

17. $\tan (\dfrac{\pi}{2} - \text{Arccot } 2)$ 18. $\cos (\dfrac{\pi}{2} - \text{Arcsin } 0.7)$

19. *Function of an Inverse Function Property:*
   a. Prove that $f^{-1}(f(x)) = x$ by letting $y = f(x)$, using the definition of f^{-1}, and using a clever substitution.
   b. Prove that $f(f^{-1}(x)) = x$ by letting $y = f^{-1}(x)$, using the definition of f^{-1}, and using a clever substitution.

20. *Cofunction Properties Problem:* Prove that the following cofunction properties are true:

   a. $\text{Cos}^{-1} x = \dfrac{\pi}{2} - \text{Sin}^{-1} x$

   b. $\text{Cot}^{-1} x = \dfrac{\pi}{2} - \text{Tan}^{-1} x$

   c. $\text{Csc}^{-1} x = \dfrac{\pi}{2} - \text{Sec}^{-1} x$

21. *Reciprocal Properties Problem:* Prove that the following reciprocal properties are true, and tell what modification must be made if the argument is negative.

   a. $\text{Arctan } x = \text{Arccot } \dfrac{1}{x}$

   b. $\text{Arcsec } x = \text{Arccos } \dfrac{1}{x}$

   c. $\text{Arccsc } x = \text{Arcsin } \dfrac{1}{x}$

22. Write a computer program and use it to print a short table of values of Arcsin x, Arccos x, Arctan x, and Arccot x for each 0.1 unit from $x = -1$ through $x = 1$. The formulas of this section should help if your computer has only the Arctangent function available.

23. *Computer Graphics Problem:* Sketch what you think the graph of

$$y = 1 + \frac{10}{\pi} \text{ Arctan } \frac{1}{2}(x + 3)$$

will look like. Then use the program PLOT INVERSE from the accompanying disk or a similar plotting program to draw the graph. Did the computer confirm your work?

24. *Tangent Function Doubling Problem:* Show that tan 89° is approximately twice tan 88°. Show that tan 89.9° is even closer to being twice tan 89.8°. Explore tangents of other angles close to 90°. Then state a conjecture about a relationship between θ and tan θ as θ gets very close to 90°.

25. *Equation Problem:* Find the first four non-negative values of x that satisfy the equation

   $\sin 2\pi x = \cos \pi x$.

Check your solutions using the program PLOT SINUSOID or a similar plotting program to draw the graph of each member of the equation, and find out where they cross.

26. *Triangle Problem:* A ship is 3720 feet away from the base of a 100-foot-tall lighthouse. The people in the lighthouse want to turn on their searchlight and illuminate the ship instantly, without having to move the light after it is turned on. At what angle below the horizontal should they aim the light to accomplish their objective?

27. *Rotary Motor Problem:* A big gear, 11 cm in diameter, is connected through an axle to a small gear 7 cm in diameter. The big gear rotates with an angular velocity of 13 radians per second. What is the angular velocity of the outermost points of the teeth of the small gear?

28. *Identity Problem:* Prove that

$$\cos (x + \frac{\pi}{3}) \cos (x - \frac{\pi}{3}) = \cos^2 x - 0.75.$$

Confirm the identity by computer graphics. You may use PLOT TWO from the accompanying disk.

29. Sketch the graph of $y = \text{Arccos } x$.

30. Sketch the graph of $y = \text{Arcsec } x$.

4–8   REAL-WORLD APPLICATIONS OF INVERSE CIRCULAR FUNCTIONS

In Section 2–12 you used sinusoidal functions as mathematical models of real-world phenomena. The general equation is

$$y = C + A \cos B(x - D).$$

Finding values of y for given values of x was relatively easy. All you needed to do was substitute for x and evaluate the resulting expression. But finding x for given values of y was more complicated. You had to do quite a bit of algebra after substituting for y. In this section you will take advantage of what you have learned about inverse circular relations to make the job easier.

Objective:

Given an equation of the form $y = C + A \cos B(x - D)$, solve it for x in terms of y, and use the resulting equation to calculate values of x for given values of y.

Example: Suppose that you have found, from some real-world situation, that variables x and y are related by the equation

$$y = 3 + 5 \cos \frac{\pi}{10} (x + 4).$$

A graph of this function is shown in Figure 4–8a. You wish to get values of x for several different values of y. You decide to solve the equation for x in terms of y, so that you will not have to repeat these algebraic steps for every value of y you substitute.

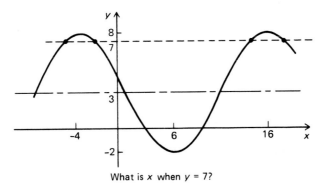

What is x when y = 7?

Figure 4–8a

Since x is deeply buried on the right side of the equation, it will take quite a bit of algebra to peel away the other numbers and leave x by itself. The transformation would go as follows:

$$y - 3 = 5 \cos \frac{\pi}{10} (x + 4) \qquad \text{Subtracting 3}$$

$$\frac{1}{5}(y - 3) = \cos \frac{\pi}{10} (x + 4) \qquad \text{Multiplying by } \frac{1}{5}$$

$$\arccos \frac{1}{5} (y - 3) = \frac{\pi}{10} (x + 4) \qquad \text{arccos of each member}$$

Note that in this step you use the arccosine *relation*. This way you will get all possible values of x, rather than just one value. The rest of the transformation is straightforward algebra.

$$\frac{10}{\pi} \arccos \frac{1}{5} (y - 3) = x + 4 \qquad \text{Multiplying by } \frac{10}{\pi}$$

$$-4 + \frac{10}{\pi} \arccos \frac{1}{5} (y - 3) = x \qquad \text{Adding } -4$$

$$\therefore x = -4 + \frac{10}{\pi} \arccos \frac{1}{5} (y - 3) \qquad \text{Symmetry}$$

Once you get the equation, you realize that it has the same form as the equations whose graphs you plotted in Section 4–3.

Now suppose that you are asked to calculate the values of x for which $y = 7$. Substituting 7 for y gives:

$$x = -4 + \frac{10}{\pi} \arccos \frac{1}{5}(7 - 3) \qquad \text{Substitution}$$

$$= -4 + \frac{10}{\pi} \arccos \frac{4}{5} \qquad \text{Arithmetic}$$

$$\approx -4 + \frac{10}{\pi} (\pm 0.6435 + 2\pi n) \qquad \text{Calculator}$$

$$\approx -4 \pm 2.048 + 20n \qquad \text{Distributing } \frac{10}{\pi}$$

$$= -1.952 + 20n \ \text{ or } \ -6.048 + 20n \qquad \text{Arithmetic}$$

If you want a particular value of x, such as the first positive value, you simply substitute integers for n. If $n = 0$, both values of x are still negative. If $n = 1$, then $x \approx 18.048$ or 13.952. So the smallest positive value of x is

$$x \approx 13.952.$$

In the exercise that follows, you will use the technique above to analyze some problems from the real world.

Exercise 4-8

1. *Inverse Values by Computer:* Write a computer program to find values of x for given values of y for a general sinusoidal function,

$$y = C + A \cos \frac{2\pi}{P} (x - D).$$

The program should allow you to input values of the constants C, A, P (the period) and D. Then it should let you put in various values of y, and print the 14 values of x from $n = -3$ to $n = 3$ (see Example). Test your program using the particular equation

$$y = 3 + 5 \cos \frac{\pi}{10} (x + 4)$$

from the example. The output should be as follows:

```
]RUN
FOR Y = C + A COS 2PI/P(X – D),
TYPE C,A,P,D: 3,5,20,–4
TYPE Y: 7
```

N	X VALUE
−3	−66.05
−3	−61.95
−2	−46.05
−2	−41.95
−1	−26.05
−1	−21.95
0	−6.05
0	−1.95
1	13.95
1	18.05
2	33.95
2	38.05
3	53.95
3	58.05

```
ANOTHER Y-VALUE? Y/N
?N
```

2. *Piston Problem:* A piston in an auto-
mobile engine goes up and down inside
the cylinder as shown in Figure 4–8b,
causing the crankshaft to rotate. Suppose
that at time = 0.1 second the piston is at
its maximum distance from the top of
the cylinder, y = 13 cm. The crankshaft
has a radius of 6 cm and makes one revolution every 0.5 second.

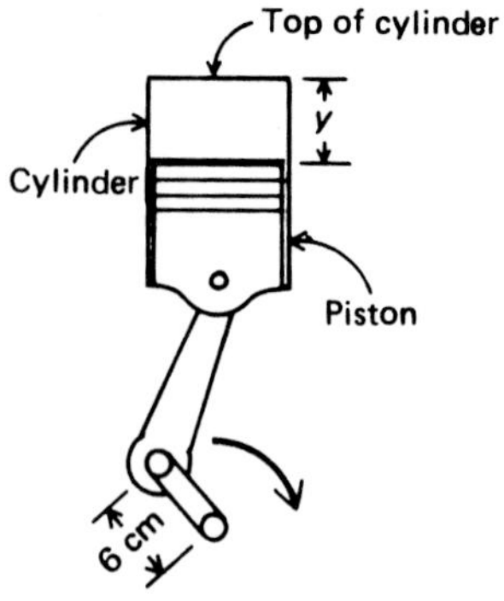

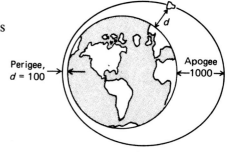

Figure 4–8b

a. Use the techniques of Section 2–12
to write an equation expressing y in
terms of t.

b. Solve the equation for t in terms of y.

c. Find the first three positive values of t for which y is 2 centimeters.
You may use the program of Problem 1, above.

d. For how long each cycle is y *less* than 2 cm?

3. *Spaceship Problem:* A spacecraft is
in an elliptical orbit around the
Earth (Figure 4–8c). At time $t = 0$
hours, it is at its apogee (highest
point) d = 1000 kilometers above
the Earth's surface. Fifty minutes
later, it is at its perigee d = 100
kilometers above the surface.

Perigee,
d = 100

Apogee
←1000→

Figure 4–8c

a. Assuming that d varies sinusoidally with time, use the techniques of
Section 2–12 to write an equation expressing d in terms of t.
b. Solve the equation for t in terms of d.
c. Predict the first three positive values of t for which the spacecraft is
200 kilometers from the surface.
d. In order to transmit information back to Earth, the spacecraft must
be within 700 kilometers of the surface. For how many consecutive
minutes will the spacecraft be able to transmit?

4. *Tide Problem:* At a certain point on the beach, a post sticks out of the
sand, its top being 76 centimeters above the beach (Figure 4–8d). The
depth of the water at the post varies sinusoidally with time due to the

motion of the tides. Using the techniques of Section 2–12, you find that the depth d in centimeters is

$$d = 40 + 60 \cos \frac{\pi}{6}(t - 2),$$

where t is the time in hours since midnight.

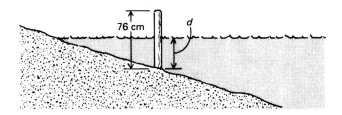

76 cm

d

Figure 4–8d

a. Sketch a graph of the sinusoid.
b. Solve the equation for t in terms of d.
c. What is the earliest time of day at which the water level is just at the top of the post?
d. At the time you calculated in part c, is the post just going under water or just emerging from the water? Explain.
e. When d is negative, the tide is completely out and there is no water at the post. Between what times will the entire post be out of the water?

5. *Tunnel Problem:* Scorpion Gulch & Western Railway is preparing to build a new line through Rolling Mountains. They have hired you to do some calculations for tunnels and bridges needed on the line (Figure 4–8e).

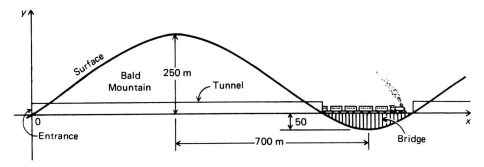

Figure 4–8e

You set up a Cartesian coordinate system with its origin at the entrance to the tunnel through Bald Mountain. Your surveying crew finds that the mountain rises 250 meters above the level of the track and that the next valley goes down 50 meters below the level of the track. The cross section of the mountain and valley is roughly sinusoidal with a horizontal distance of 700 meters from the top of the mountain to the bottom of the valley.

a. Write an equation expressing the vertical distance y from the track to the surface of the mountain or valley in terms of the horizontal distance x from the tunnel entrance. This can be done by finding the constants A, B, and C from the distances given. Finding D requires that you substitute the other constants and the ordered pair $(0, 0)$ into the equation and solve for D.

b. Solve the equation from part a for x in terms of y.

c. How long will the tunnel be?

d. How long will the bridge be?

e. The company thinks it might be cheaper to build the line if the entire project is raised to $y = 20$, thus making the tunnel shorter and the bridge longer. Find the new values of x at the ends of the tunnel and bridge. Then find the new lengths of each.

6. *Roller Coaster Problem:*
In Problem 7 of Section 2–8, a sinusoidal roller coaster track is to be built with a high point $h = 27$ meters at a horizontal distance $d = 0$ meters. It has a low point $h = -3$ meters at $d = 50$ meters (Figure 4–8f).

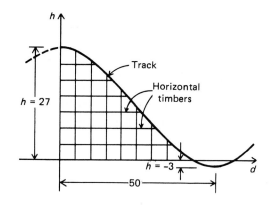

Figure 4–8f

a. Write an equation expressing h in terms of d.

b. Solve the equation of part a for d in terms of h.

c. The lengths of the horizontal timbers used to build the roller-coaster supporting structure are values of d. Calculate the length of the horizontal timber that is 4 meters above the ground.

d. Write a computer program to print the lengths of each of the horizontal timbers. The first one is 2 meters above the ground, and they are spaced 2 meters apart. The program should also find the *sum* of the lengths of the timbers, so that the builders will know how much material to order. If your computer has only the Arctangent function available, you can use the properties in Section 4–7 to express Arccosine as an Arctangent.

7. Sketch the graph of $y = $ Arcsin x.

8. Sketch the graph of $y = $ Arccot x.

9. Show that Arccos $0.7 = 90° - $ Arcsin 0.7 by finding decimal approximations of each.

10. *Triangle Problem:* A right triangle has a longer leg of 5 inches and a larger acute angle Arctan 2. Quick! How long is the shorter leg?

11. *Identity Problem:* Transform $6 \sin 11x \cos 13x$ to a sum of sines or cosines.

12. *Equation Problem:* Solve for $x \in (0, 3)$:

$$\frac{\sin \pi x}{1 + \cos \pi x} = \sqrt{3}$$

13. *Computer Graphics Problem:* How many values of x satisfy the equation $5 \cos x = \sqrt{x}$? Approximately what is the largest such value of x?

14. *Rotary Motion Problem:* A pulley of diameter 10 inches rotates with an angular velocity of 200 rpm. How many inches per second does the pulley belt go?

15. An angle in standard position has the point $(-145, 408)$ on its terminal side. Find the exact value of the secant of the angle.

16. A sinusoid of period 20 units has an amplitude of 7 and a high point at $(3, 11)$. Write a particular equation of the sinusoid.

4–9 CHAPTER REVIEW AND TEST

At the beginning of the chapter are listed six specific objectives. These are summarized as follows:

1. Draw graphs by composition of ordinates.
2. Confirm properties by graphing.
3. Find angular and linear velocities.
4. Graph inverse circular functions.
5. Evaluate and transform expressions containing inverse circular functions.
6. Find values of x for a given value of y in a circular function.

By working the review problems below, you will see how well you can accomplish these objectives when you *know* which one is being tested. The chapter test will measure your ability to accomplish the objectives *without* being told which one is being tested.

Review Problems

The following problems are numbered according to the six objectives above.

1. Sketch one complete cycle of the graph of

    $y = \cos x + \sin 3x$.

2. a. Draw the graph of $y = \cos x + \sin x$ by composition of ordinates.
   b. The resulting graph is a sinusoid. Tell its amplitude, period, and phase displacement from the graph, correct to one decimal place or exactly.
   c. Transform the equation $y = \cos x + \sin x$ into a cosine with a phase displacement, using the linear combination of sinusoids property of Section 3–7, and thus show that your equation in part (b) is correct.

3. A wheel rotates at 20 revolutions per minute.

   a. What is its angular velocity in radians per second?
   b. What is the linear velocity in centimeters per second of a point 30 centimeters from the axis? Right on the axis?

4. Sketch the graph.

   a. $y = \operatorname{arccot} \frac{1}{2}x$
   b. $y = \pi + \operatorname{Cos}^{-1} \frac{1}{2}x$
   c. $y = 2 \operatorname{Arccsc} x$

5. a. Find the *exact* value.
      (i) $\operatorname{Sin}^{-1} (-0.5)$
      (ii) $\operatorname{Arcsec} (-2)$
      (iii) $\operatorname{Tan}^{-1} (-1)$
      (iv) $\sin (90° - \operatorname{Arccos} \frac{1}{3})$

   b. Simplify the expression.

      (i) $\operatorname{Arcsin} (\frac{1}{x})$

(ii) $\text{Tan}^{-1}\left(\frac{y}{x}\right) + \text{Tan}^{-1}\left(\frac{x}{y}\right)$

(iii) $\left(\frac{\pi}{2}\right) - \text{Cos}^{-1} x$

(iv) $\sin(2\,\text{Arccos}\,x), x \geq 0$

6. Given the equation

$$y = 6 + 2\tan\frac{\pi}{5}(x - 3):$$

a. Solve for x in terms of y.
b. Find the first three positive values of x for which $y = 1$.

Chapter Test

Work each of the following problems. Then tell which of the preceding objectives you used in working that problem.

You apply for a job with Y. O. Ming Mining Company. Since your work will involve using inverse circular functions, Mr. Ming poses some problems for you to solve during your interview to see how useful you would be to his company.

1. Find the *exact* value.

a. $\text{Cos}^{-1}\left(-\frac{\sqrt{2}}{2}\right)$

b. $\text{Arccot}\,(-\sqrt{3})$

c. arcsec 2

d. arcsin 2 (Your résumé is *shredded* if you miss *this* one!)

e. $\tan\left(\text{Arccot}\,\frac{2}{5}\right)$

2. Sketch the graph.

a. $y = \arcsin\frac{1}{2}x$

b. $y = 2\,\text{Arctan}\,x$

c. $y = \text{Sec}^{-1}(x - 3)$

3. Prove that $\text{Arcsin}\,x = \text{Arctan}\left(\dfrac{x}{\sqrt{1 - x^2}}\right)$.

Mr. Ming is satisfied with your performance and assigns you to the Uranium Mining Project (UMP). A layer of ore beneath the ground has surfaces that are sinusoidal in cross section, as shown in Figure 4-9a. UMP plans to drill a vertical mine shaft through the ore layer and then dig a horizontal tunnel, again going through the ore layer. Your job is to find out how far this horizontal tunnel goes through the ore.

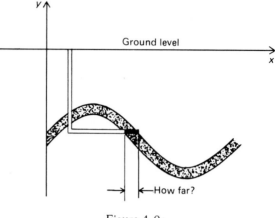

Figure 4-9a

You set up a Cartesian coordinate system with the x-axis at ground level and x and y in meters. You find that the top and bottom surfaces have the following equations:

Top: $y = -100 + 60 \cos \dfrac{\pi}{250}(x - 80)$

Bottom: $y = -120 + 60 \cos \dfrac{\pi}{250}(x - 80)$

4. Solve each equation for x in terms of y.

5. How far will the horizontal shaft go through the formation if it is dug at a depth of

   a. y = -90?
   b. y = -170?

6. As you ride home from work on your bike, you turn the pedals at a steady 120 revolutions per minute. The dimensions of the bike are shown in Figure 4-9b.

   a. What is the angular velocity of the pedals in radians per second?
   b. What is the linear velocity of the chain in centimeters per second?
   c. What is the angular velocity of the back wheel?
   d. How fast is the bike going, in kilometers per hour?

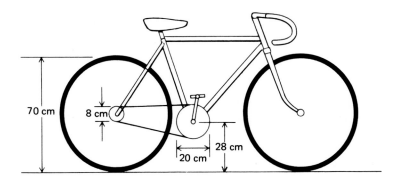

Figure 4-9b

7. You ride your bike up a steep hill. As you do, the vertical distance between your foot and the ground is given by an equation similar to

$y = \frac{1}{2}x + \cos \pi x$.

Sketch the graph of this function from $x = 0$ through $x = 6$.

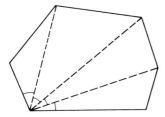

Surveyors measure irregularly shaped land tracts by dividing them into triangles. In this chapter you will learn how to calculate unknown side and angle measures of a triangle, as well as the area.

CHAPTER 5

In Chapter 1 you worked problems on finding unknown sides and angles of right triangles. After a brief review of these techniques, you will extend them in this chapter so that you can analyze a triangle that does *not* have a right angle. The first six sections of the chapter are devoted exclusively to developing the techniques. Learn them well. The last section contains real-world problems in which you must not only be able to use the techniques, but also select the one that is appropriate.

Specific objectives are:

1. Find unknown measures of sides and angles of a right triangle given the measures of
   a. two sides,
   b. one side and one acute angle.

2. Find unknown measures of sides and angles of any triangle given the measures of
   a. two sides and the included angle,
   b. three sides,
   c. one side, the opposite angle, and one other side or angle.

3. Find the area of a triangle given the measures of two sides and the included angle.

4. Use directed line segments ("vectors") as mathematical models of quantities that have both size and direction.

5. Solve real-world problems involving the measurement of triangles.

5-1 RIGHT TRIANGLE REVIEW

In Section 1–6 you solved right triangle problems by placing a known or desired angle in standard position. In this section you will learn a short-cut that will by-pass the coordinate system.

Objective:

Given the measures of two sides or a side and an angle in a right triangle, find the measures of the other side(s) and angle(s).

Figure 5–1a shows $\triangle HDJ$ (triangle HDJ) with acute angle H placed in standard position and right angle D on the u-axis. By the definitions of the six trigonometric functions:

$$\sin H = \frac{v}{r} \qquad \sec H = \frac{r}{u} \qquad \cot H = \frac{u}{v}$$

$$\tan H = \frac{v}{u} \qquad \cos H = \frac{u}{r} \qquad \csc H = \frac{r}{v}$$

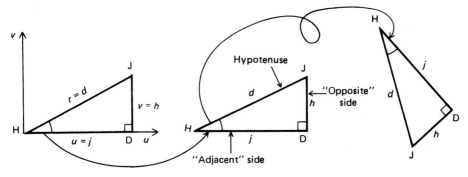

Figure 5–1a

It is customary to name the length of the side *opposite* an angle with the same *lower* case letter as the name of the angle. So the side opposite Angle *H* has measure *h*, and so forth. Using this lettering scheme, sin $H = h/d$, since $h = v$ and $d = r$. But *d* and *h* are properties of the triangle itself, not the coordinate system. So it is possible to write the trigonometric functions of the angles of a right triangle *without* reference to the coordinates *u*, *v*, and *r*. The *hypotenuse* is one of the sides that includes Angle *H*. The other side is called the *adjacent* side, the word "adjacent" meaning "next to." Using these words, the definitions of the six trigonometric functions for Angle *H* of a right triangle become:

$$\sin H = \frac{\text{opposite}}{\text{hypotenuse}} \qquad \cos H = \frac{\text{adjacent}}{\text{hypotenuse}}$$

$$\tan H = \frac{\text{opposite}}{\text{adjacent}} \qquad \cot H = \frac{\text{adjacent}}{\text{opposite}}$$

$$\sec H = \frac{\text{hypotenuse}}{\text{adjacent}} \qquad \csc H = \frac{\text{hypotenuse}}{\text{opposite}}$$

These definitions allow you to write the trigonometric functions of *H* even if the triangle is flipped over and rotated, as in the last sketch of Figure 5–1a.

Example 1: In $\triangle ABC$, *C* is the right angle, m $\angle A$ (Angle *A*) = 27°, and *a* = 31.4. Find:

    (i) *b*,
    (ii) *c*,
    (iii) m $\angle$ *B*, the measure of angle *B*.

    The first thing to do is sketch a right triangle, as in Figure 5–1b. It makes no difference *where* you put the right angle, but the lettering of the sides and angles must be consistent with those given in the problem.

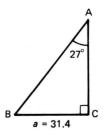

Figure 5–1b

(i) To find b, you need a trigonometric function of the *known* angle A that has the *desired* side measure b in its numerator and the *known* side measure $a = 31.4$ in its denominator. So you write:

$$\frac{b}{a} = \cot A \qquad\qquad\qquad \text{Definition of cotangent}$$

$$\therefore b = a \cot A \qquad\qquad\quad \text{Multiplying by } a$$

$$= 31.4 \cot 27° \qquad\qquad \text{Substitution}$$

$$= 61.6259 \ldots \qquad\qquad \text{By calculator}$$

$$\approx \underline{61.6} \qquad\qquad\qquad\quad \text{Rounding off to three significant digits}$$

Notes:
1. It would have been possible to start with $a/b = \tan A$. However, the algebra will be easier if you start with the side to be calculated in the *numerator* of the trigonometric ratio, rather than in the denominator. You should do all of the algebra *before* you start pressing calculator keys.
2. The 31.4 is assumed to be a *measured* length known to only three significant digits. The value of cot 27° by calculator is a decimal approximation with 5 to 10 significant digits. Whenever two decimal approximations are *multiplied* together, the answer should be rounded off to the number of significant digits in the *least* accurately known factor.

(ii) $\dfrac{c}{a} = \csc A \qquad\qquad\qquad \text{Definition of secant}$

$$\therefore c = a \csc A \qquad\qquad\quad \text{Multiplication by } a$$

$$= 31.4 \csc 27° \qquad\qquad \text{Substitution}$$

$$= 69.1644 \ldots \qquad\qquad \text{By calculator}$$

$$\approx \underline{69.2} \qquad\qquad\qquad\quad \text{Rounding off to three significant digits}$$

(iii) Since the sum of the measures of the angles is $180°$,

$$90° + 27° + m \angle B = 180°,$$

from which

$$m \angle B = 180° - 90° - 27° = \underline{63°}.$$

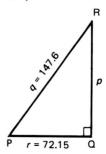

Example 2: In $\triangle PQR$, Q is the right angle, $q = 147.6$, and $r = 72.15$. Find:
  (i) $m \angle P$
  (ii) $m \angle R$
  (iii) p

Figure 5-1c

(i) Using the definition of cosine

$$\cos P = \frac{r}{q} \qquad \text{Definition of cosine}$$

$$= \frac{72.15}{147.6} \qquad \text{Substitution}$$

$$= 0.4888 \dots \qquad \text{By calculator}$$

$$\therefore\ m\angle P = 60.7368 \dots^{\circ} \qquad \text{By calculator}$$

$$\approx \underline{60.74^{\circ}} \qquad \text{Rounding off}$$

Notes:
1. The $60.7368 \dots^{\circ}$ should be saved in memory without round-off, for use later in the problem.
2. The answer $60^{\circ}44'$ can be obtained, if desired, by multiplying the $.7368 \dots$ by 60.

(ii) $m\angle R = 180^{\circ} - 90^{\circ} - 60^{\circ}44' = \underline{29^{\circ}16'}$

(iii) $\dfrac{p}{r} = \tan P \qquad\qquad$ Definition of tangent

$\qquad p = r \tan P \qquad\qquad$ Multiplication by r

$\qquad\quad = 72.15 \tan P \qquad$ Substitution

$\qquad\quad = 128.763 \dots \qquad$ Recalling P from memory

$\qquad\quad \approx \underline{128.8} \qquad\qquad$ Rounding off to four significant digits

The exercise that follows is designed to give you practice finding unknown side and angle measures of right triangles. You should try using the adjacent-opposite-hypotenuse definitions of the trigonometric functions.

Exercise 5–1

Find the other side and angle measures for the following right triangles:

	Name	Right angle	Given data
1.	ABC	A	$m\angle B = 34^{\circ},\ c = 14.7$
2.	ABC	B	$m\angle C = 71^{\circ},\ b = 36.8$
3.	LMN	M	$m\angle N = 47^{\circ}32',\ m = 3.465$
4.	HPJ	H	$m\angle J = 29^{\circ}51',\ j = 4651$
5.	XYZ	X	$x = 35,\ y = 27$
6.	KLM	L	$k = 5.2,\ m = 3.3$
7.	RST	T	$s = 9.85,\ t = 47.3$
8.	UVW	W	$u = 439.8,\ v = 641.2$

9. Sketch the graph of $y = \sec x$.

10. Sketch the graph of $y = \text{Arcsin } x$.

11. *Identity Problem:* Prove that this is an identity:

$$\frac{\sin x + \sec^2 x \sin x}{\cos x} = \tan^3 x.$$

12. *Equation Problem:* Solve for $x \in (1, 2)$: $\sin \pi x \cos \pi x = 1$

5–2 OBLIQUE TRIANGLES—LAW OF COSINES

You have learned to find unknown measures in right triangles. Now you must learn how to do the same things for *oblique* triangles, which do *not* have a right angle.

Objectives:

1. Given two sides and the included angle, find the length of the third side of the triangle.
2. Given three sides of a triangle, find the measure of a specified angle.

Suppose that the lengths of two sides, b and c, of $\triangle ABC$ are known, and also the measure of the included angle A (Figure 5–2a). The length of the third side a is to be found.

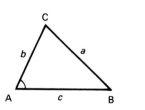 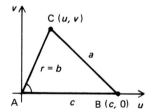

Figure 5–2a

If you construct a *uv*-coordinate system with Angle A in standard position, as in the second sketch of Figure 5–2a, then a becomes a distance between two points in a Cartesian coordinate system. These are the points $B(c, 0)$ and $C(u, v)$. By the Distance Formula,

$$a^2 = (u - c)^2 + (v - 0)^2.$$

In order to get a^2 in terms of b, c, and $m\angle A$, all you need to do is observe that A is the *angle* and b is the *radius* to point $C(u, v)$. By the definitions of cosine and sine,

$$\frac{u}{b} = \cos A \quad \text{and} \quad \frac{v}{b} = \sin A.$$

Multiplying each member of both equations by b gives

$$u = b \cos A \quad \text{and} \quad v = b \sin A.$$

Substituting these values for u and v into the distance formula above gives

$$a^2 = (b \cos A - c)^2 + (b \sin A - 0)^2.$$

Upon expanding the squares on the right, you get

$$a^2 = b^2 \cos^2 A - 2bc \cos A + c^2 + b^2 \sin^2 A.$$

Associating the $\sin^2 A$ and $\cos^2 A$ terms and then factoring out b^2 gives

$$a^2 = b^2(\cos^2 A + \sin^2 A) - 2bc \cos A + c^2.$$

The Pythagorean properties may now be applied to give

$$a^2 = b^2 - 2bc \cos A + c^2,$$

which is usually written:

$$\boxed{a^2 = b^2 + c^2 - 2bc \cos A} \quad \longleftarrow \text{Law of cosines}$$

This equation is called the Law of Cosines because the *cosine* of an angle appears in it. Note that if $m\angle A = 90°$, then $\cos A = 0$. The Law of Cosines thus reduces to

$$a^2 = b^2 + c^2,$$

which is, of course, the Pythagorean theorem! In fact, the Law of Cosines simply says that $2bc \cos A$ is what you must *subtract* from the Pythagorean $b^2 + c^2$ in order to get the proper value for a^2 when A is not a right angle. If A is obtuse, then $\cos A$ is negative. So subtracting $2bc \cos A$ actually *adds* a number to $b^2 + c^2$. The situation is illustrated in Figure 5–2b.

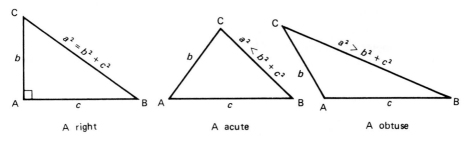

Law of Cosines and the Pythagorean Theorem

Figure 5–2b

You should not jump to the conclusion that the Law of Cosines gives an easy way to *prove* the Pythagorean theorem. Doing so would involve circular reasoning, because Pythagoras was used to *derive* the Law of Cosines!

Accomplishing the first objective, finding the third side from two sides and the included angle, is illustrated in Examples 1 and 2. Accomplishing the second objective, finding an angle from three given sides, is illustrated in Examples 3 and 4.

Example 1: In $\triangle ABC$, if $b = 5$, $c = 7$, and $m\angle A = 39°$, find a.

By direct substitution into the Law of Cosines:

$a^2 = 5^2 + 7^2 - 2(5)(7) \cos 39°$

    $= 19.5997 \ldots$ By calculator

$\therefore a = 4.42716 \ldots$ Taking the square root

    $\approx \underline{4.427}$ Rounding off

The sequence of keystrokes is long, but straightforward.

$$5 \boxed{x^2} \boxed{+} 7 \boxed{x^2} \boxed{-} 2 \boxed{\times} 5 \boxed{\times} 7 \boxed{\times} 39 \boxed{\cos} \boxed{=} \boxed{\sqrt{x}}$$

$$\underbrace{5^2} \quad + \quad \underbrace{7^2} \quad - \quad \underbrace{2(5)(7)} \quad \times \quad \underbrace{\cos 39°}$$

A different sequence is needed if your calculator works in reverse Polish notation.

Example 2:   In $\triangle KSD$, $m\angle S = 127°42'$, $k = 15.78$, and $d = 2.654$. Find s.

You should recognize that the Law of Cosines is *independent* of the letters you use to express it. All that matters is that you know two sides and the *included* angle. A picture such as Figure 5–2c will help. Applying the Law of Cosines gives:

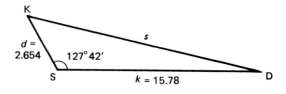

Figure 5–2c

$s^2 = k^2 + d^2 - 2kd \cos S$

    $= 15.78^2 + 2.654^2 - 2(15.78)(2.654) \cos 127°42'$ Substitution

$\therefore s = 17.5292 \ldots$

$\approx \underline{17.53}$

Example 3: In $\triangle XYZ$, $x = 3$, $y = 7$, and $z = 9$. Find $m\angle Z$.

Again, drawing a picture will help you figure out how to set up the Law of Cosines (Figure 5–2d). Since Angle Z is to be measured, and Sides x and y *include* angle Z, you use the Law of Cosines in the form

$$z^2 = x^2 + y^2 - 2xy \cos Z.$$

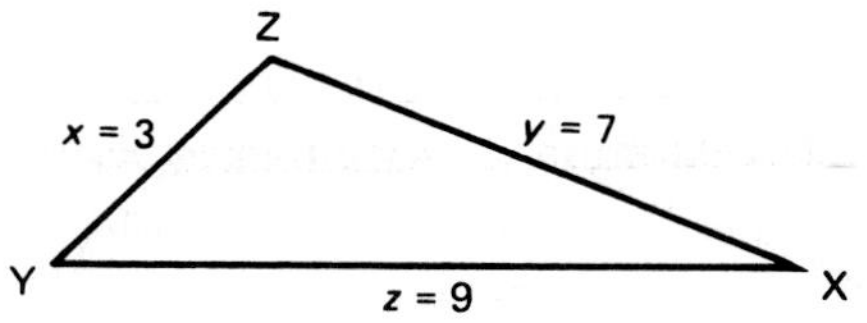

Since x, y, and z are known and $m\angle Z$ is to be found, the equation can be solved for $\cos Z$, giving

Figure 5–2d

$$\cos Z = \frac{x^2 + y^2 - z^2}{2xy}.$$

Substituting the given information yields

$$\cos Z = \frac{3^2 + 7^2 - 9^2}{2(3)(7)}$$

$$= \frac{-23}{42} \qquad\qquad \text{Arithmetic}$$

$$= -0.54761 \ldots \qquad\qquad \text{By calculator}$$

$$\therefore\ m\angle Z = 123.203 \ldots^\circ \qquad\qquad \text{By calculator}$$

$$\approx \underline{123.20^\circ} \qquad\qquad \text{Rounding off}$$

In degrees and minutes, this would be $123^\circ 12'$.

Example 4: In $\triangle XYZ$, $x = 3$, $y = 7$, and $z = 11$. Find $m\angle Z$.

At first glance, this problem seems equivalent to Example 3. Using the Law of Cosines as before gives:

$$\cos Z = \frac{3^2 + 7^2 - 11^2}{2(3)(7)}$$

$$= \frac{-63}{42} \qquad\qquad \text{Arithmetic}$$

$$= -1.5 \qquad\qquad \text{Arithmetic}$$

But there can be *no* such angle Z, because cosines must be between −1 and 1, inclusive. The reason is clear when you compare the lengths of the three sides (Figure 5–2e). Sides x and y add up to 10, which is *less* than the length 11 of

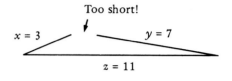

Figure 5–2e

the third side z, so there can be no such triangle! The Law of Cosines automatically detects this situation, if you have overlooked it at first, by giving a cosine *outside* the range $-1 \leq \cos \theta \leq 1$. This fact will be useful when you write a computer program later on for solving triangles.

The exercise that follows is designed to give you practice using the Law of Cosines to find the third side given two sides and the included angle, or to find an angle given three sides.

Exercise 5–2

For Problems 1 through 6, find the length of the side *opposite* the given angle.

1. In $\triangle ABC$, $b = 4$, $c = 5$, and $m\angle A = 51°$.
2. In $\triangle ABC$, $a = 7$, $c = 9$, and $m\angle B = 34°$.
3. In $\triangle PQR$, $p = 3$, $q = 2$, and $m\angle R = 138°$.
4. In $\triangle HJK$, $h = 8$, $j = 6$, and $m\angle K = 172°$.
5. In $\triangle DEF$, $d = 36.2$, $f = 49.8$, and $m\angle E = 67°40'$.
6. In $\triangle BAD$, $a = 2.897$, $d = 5.921$, and $m\angle B = 119°23'$

For Problems 7 through 12, find the measure of the specified angle.

7. $m\angle A$ in $\triangle ABC$, if $a = 2$, $b = 3$, and $c = 4$.
8. $m\angle C$ in $\triangle ABC$, if $a = 5$, $b = 6$, and $c = 8$.
9. $m\angle T$ in $\triangle BAT$, if $b = 6$, $a = 7$, and $t = 12$.
10. $m\angle E$ in $\triangle PEG$, if $p = 12$, $e = 20$, and $g = 16$.
11. $m\angle Y$ in $\triangle GYP$, if $g = 7$, $y = 5$, and $p = 13$.
12. $m\angle N$ in $\triangle GON$, if $g = 8$, $o = 3$, and $n = 12$.
13. $m\angle O$ in $\triangle NOD$, if $n = 1475$, $o = 2053$, and $d = 1428$.
14. $m\angle Q$ in $\triangle SQR$, if $s = 1504$, $q = 2465$, and $r = 1953$.

15. *Accurate Drawing Problem No. 1:* Construct accurately Triangle ABC from Problem 1. Measure $b = 4$ centimeters and $c = 5$ centimeters with a ruler, and use a protractor to construct angle A of measure 51°. Then

measure side *a.* Your answer should agree with the calculated value to within ±0.1 centimeter.

16. *Accurate Drawing Problem No. 2:* Construct accurately Triangle *ABC* from Problem 8. Draw side *c* 8 centimeters long as the base. Use a compass to mark off arcs of 5 centimeters and 6 centimeters from the two ends of side *c.* Where the arcs intersect will be point *C.* Then measure angle *C* with a protractor. The measured value should agree with the calculated value to within 1 degree.

17. Write the exact value of csc 60°.

18. *Graphing Problem:* Sketch the graph of $y = \text{Tan}^{-1} x$.

19. *Equation Problem:* Solve for $\theta \in (-180°, 180°)$:

$$\sec (\theta - 74°) = -2.$$

20. *Identity Problem:* Prove that this is an identity:

$$\cos (\theta + 60°) + \cos (\theta - 60°) = -\sin (\theta - 90°).$$

21. *Rotary Motion Problem:* The rotor blades on a helicopter are 30 feet long. For proper operation, the tips of the blades should move no faster than the speed of sound in air, about 1160 feet per second under average conditions. What is the fastest the rotor should turn in radians per second? In revolutions per minute?

22. *Area Problem:* One leg of a right triangle is 50 feet long. The angle opposite this side is 26°. How long is the other leg? What is the area of the triangle?

5–3   AREA OF A TRIANGLE

Objective:

Given the measures of two sides and the included angle, find the area of the triangle.

From geometry you recall that the area of a triangle is half the product of the base and the altitude. For $\triangle ABC$ in Figure 5–3a,

Area $= \frac{1}{2}bh.$

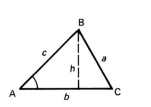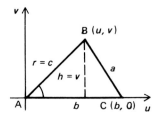

Figure 5–3a

If you know the lengths of b and c and the measure of Angle A, you can calculate the altitude h in terms of these numbers. Constructing a uv-coordinate system as in the second sketch of Figure 5–3a, $B(u, v)$ becomes a point in a Cartesian coordinate system. By the definition of sine,

$$\frac{v}{r} = \sin A.$$

Multiplying each member of this equation by r gives

$$v = r \sin A.$$

Since $h = v$ and $c = r$, you can substitute these and get

$$h = c \sin A.$$

Substituting this value of h into the area equation gives:

$$\boxed{\text{Area} = \frac{1}{2}bc \sin A}$$

Example 1: Find the area of $\triangle ABC$ if $b = 13$, $c = 15$, and $m\angle A = 71°$.
Using the above area equation,

Area $= \frac{1}{2}(13)(15) \sin 71°$

$= 92.1880 \ldots$ By calculator

$\approx \underline{92.19}$ Assuming 13 and 15 are *exact* and rounding off to four significant digits

Example 2: Find the area of $\triangle HPJ$ if $h = 5$, $p = 7$, and $j = 11$.

In order to use the area equation, you must first know one of
the angles. Suppose you decide
to calculate $m\angle J$. Drawing a picture as in Figure 5–3b and applying the Law of Cosines as you
did in Section 5–2,

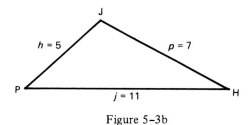

Figure 5–3b

$$j^2 \;=\; h^2 \;+\; p^2 \;-\; 2hp \,\cos J.$$

Solving for $\cos J$ gives:

$$\cos J = \frac{h^2 + p^2 - j^2}{2hp}$$

$$= \frac{25 + 49 - 121}{2(5)(7)} \qquad \text{Substitution}$$

$$= -0.671428 \ldots \qquad \text{By calculator}$$

$$\therefore\; m\angle J \;=\; 132.177 \ldots^{\circ} \qquad \text{By calculator}$$

This value should be saved in memory for use next.

Applying the area equation gives:

Area $= \tfrac{1}{2}hp \sin J$

$= \tfrac{1}{2}(5)(7) \sin J \qquad$ Substitution

$= 12.9687 \ldots \qquad$ Recalling $132.177 \ldots^{\circ}$ from memory

$\approx \underline{12.97} \qquad$ Rounding off to four significant digits

The following exercise is designed to give you practice finding areas of
specified triangles.

Exercise 5–3

Find the area of each triangle.

1. $\triangle ABC$, if $a = 5, b = 9$, and $m\angle C = 14°$.
2. $\triangle ABC$, if $b = 8, c = 4$, and $m\angle A = 67°$.
3. $\triangle RST$, if $r = 4.8, t = 3.7$, and $m\angle S = 43°10'$.
4. $\triangle XYZ$, if $y = 34.19, z = 28.65$, and $m\angle X = 138°27'$.

5. $\triangle MAP$, if $m = 6$, $a = 9$, and $p = 13$.
6. $\triangle ABX$, if $a = 5$, $b = 12$, and $x = 13$.
7. You may recall from geometry that Hero's Formula can be used to find the area in *one* computation. This formula is

$$\text{Area} = \sqrt{s(s-a)(s-b)(s-c)} \, ,$$

where s (for "semiperimeter") equals half the perimeter of the triangle. Use Hero's Formula to find the area of $\triangle MAP$ in Problem 5.
8. Use Hero's Formula to find the area of $\triangle ABX$ in Problem 6.

9. *Identity Problem:* Wanda Ngo wants to know if $\sin x = \tan x$ is an identity. So she substitutes 0, π, and 2π.

    a. Show that the two expressions are equal for all three of these values of x.

    b. Explain to Wanda why these substitutions do not *prove* that the equation is an identity.

10. *Equation Problem:* Find the general solution of $\sin x = \tan x$.

11. Find the exact value of $\tan (\text{Sin}^{-1} \dfrac{231}{569})$.

12. *Graphing Problem:* Sketch the graph of $y = 3 + 5 \cos \pi (x - 0.3)$.

13. Find 30% of 524. (It's not trig, but you should be able to *do* it!)

14. *Triangle Problem:* A triangle has sides 376 inches, 421 inches, and 593 inches. Is the largest angle acute or obtuse? Justify your answer. See how *little* work you can do to get your answer!

5–4 OBLIQUE TRIANGLES—LAW OF SINES

The Law of Cosines may be used directly when you know two sides and the included angle, or if you know all three sides. If you know only *one* side length, the Law of Cosines cannot be used. In this section you will find out what can be done in this case to calculate other side measures.

Objective:

Given the measure of an angle, its opposite side, and one other angle measure, find the length of another side.

In the previous section you learned that the area of a triangle such as $\triangle ABC$ in Figure 5–4a is

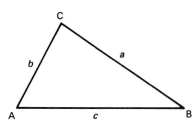

Figure 5–4a

Area = $\frac{1}{2}bc \sin A$.

The area is also equal to $\frac{1}{2}ac \sin B$ and to $\frac{1}{2}ab \sin C$, since the area is *constant* no matter which sides and angle you use to measure it. Setting these expressions equal to each other gives

$\frac{1}{2}bc \sin A = \frac{1}{2}ac \sin B = \frac{1}{2}ab \sin C.$

Multiplying all three members by 2 eliminates the fraction $\frac{1}{2}$ each time it occurs. Dividing all three members by abc produces a rather startling simplification.

$$\frac{bc \sin A}{abc} = \frac{ac \sin B}{abc} = \frac{ab \sin C}{abc}$$

In each member, the coefficients of the sine cancel, giving:

$$\boxed{\frac{\sin A}{a} = \frac{\sin B}{b} = \frac{\sin C}{c}}$$ ◀——Law of sines, first form

This relationship is called the Law of Sines for reasons that should be obvious! Since a is opposite Angle A, and so forth, the law actually says,

"Within any given triangle, the ratio of the sine of an angle to the length of its opposite side is *constant*."

Since you know that if two nonzero numbers are equal, then their reciprocals are equal, you can "flip over" the Law of Sines, getting:

$$\boxed{\frac{a}{\sin A} = \frac{b}{\sin B} = \frac{c}{\sin C}}$$ ◀—— Law of sines, second form

The following examples show you how the Law of Sines may be used to accomplish the objective of this section. Watch out for surprises!

Because of the different combinations of sides and angles that might be given in a triangle, it is convenient to revive some terminology that you may recall from geometry. The abbreviation "SAS" stands for "side, angle, side."

This means that as you go around the perimeter of the triangle, you are given the length of a side, the measure of the next angle, and the length of the next side. Thus, "SAS" is equivalent to knowing two sides and the included angle. Similar meanings are attached to ASA, AAS, SSA, and SSS.

Example 1: Given AAS, find the other sides.
In $\triangle ABC$, $m\angle B = 64°$, $m\angle C = 38°$ and $b = 9$. Find c and a.

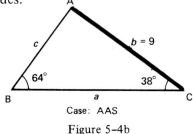

The first thing to do is draw a picture, as in Figure 5–4b. Using part of the Law of Sines,

$$\frac{c}{\sin C} = \frac{b}{\sin B}.$$

Case: AAS

Figure 5–4b

You pick two of the three members of the Law of Sines equation in such a way that the quantity you are looking for is in the *numerator* of the left member and the *known* side and opposite angle are in the *right* member. Multiplying each member by sin C isolates the quantity you seek on the left side, giving

$$c = \frac{b \sin C}{\sin B}$$

$$= \frac{9 \sin 38°}{\sin 64°} \qquad \text{Substitution}$$

$$= 6.16487 \ldots \qquad \text{By calculator}$$

$$\approx \underline{6.165} \qquad \text{Rounding off to four significant digits}$$

To find a, you must first find the measure of its opposite angle A. Since the sum of the three angle measures is $180°$,

$$m\angle A = 180° - 38° - 64° = 78°.$$

Using the appropriate form of the Law of Sines:

$$\frac{a}{\sin A} = \frac{b}{\sin B}$$

$$\therefore a = \frac{b \sin A}{\sin B} \qquad \text{Multiplication by sin } A$$

$$= \frac{9 \sin 78°}{\sin 64°} \qquad \text{Substitution}$$

$$= 9.79460 \ldots \qquad \text{By calculator}$$

$$\approx \underline{9.795} \qquad \text{Correct to four significant digits}$$

Example 2: Given ASA, find another side.
In $\triangle ABC$, $a = 8$, $m\angle B = 64°$, and $m\angle C = 38°$. Find c.

Drawing a picture as in Figure 5-4c, you immediately notice that you do *not* know the measure of Angle A, opposite the given side. To use the Law of Sines, you must know a side and the opposite angle. Again using the fact that the sum of the angle measures is $180°$,

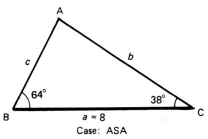

Case: ASA

Figure 5-4c

$$m\angle A = 180° - 64° - 38° = 78°.$$

Using the appropriate part of the Law of Sines:

$$\frac{c}{\sin C} = \frac{a}{\sin A}$$

$$\therefore c = \frac{a \sin C}{\sin A} \qquad \text{Multiplication by } \sin C$$

$$= \frac{8 \sin 38°}{\sin 78°} \qquad \text{Substitution of known information}$$

$$= 5.03532 \ldots \qquad \text{By calculator}$$

$$\approx \underline{5.035} \qquad \text{Correct to four significant digits}$$

The exercise that follows is designed to give you practice using the Law of Sines to find unknown side lengths when you know one side and its opposite angle.

Exercise 5-4

1. In $\triangle ABC$, $m\angle A = 52°$, $m\angle B = 31°$, and $a = 8$. Find:

    a. b b. c

2. In $\triangle PQR$, $m\angle P = 13°$, $m\angle Q = 133°$, and $q = 9$. Find:

   a. p b. r

3. In $\triangle AHS$, $m\angle A = 27°$, $m\angle H = 109°$, and $a = 120$. Find:

   a. h b. s

4. In $\triangle BIG$, $m\angle B = 2°$, $m\angle I = 79°$, and $b = 20$. Find:

   a. i b. g

5. In $\triangle PAF$ $m\angle P = 28°$, $f = 6$, and $m\angle A = 117°$. Find:

   a. a b. p

6. In $\triangle JAW$, $m\angle J = 48°$, $a = 5$, and $m\angle W = 73°$. Find:

   a. j b. w

7. In $\triangle ALP$, $m\angle A = 85°$, $p = 30$, and $m\angle L = 87°$. Find:

   a. a b. ℓ

8. In $\triangle LOW$, $m\angle L = 2°$, $o = 500$, and $m\angle W = 3°$. Find:

   a. ℓ b. w

9. *Law of Sines for Angles Problem:*   The Law of Sines can be used to find an unknown *angle* measure. However, the technique is risky! In this problem you will find out *why*.

   Triangle ABC has sides of 4, 7, and 10 units, as shown in Figure 5-4d.

   a. Use the Law of Cosines to find $m\angle A$, as you did in Section 5-2.

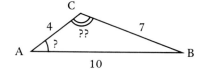

Figure 5-4d

   b. Use the answer to part (a) in the Law of *Sines* to find $m\angle C$.

   c. Find $m\angle C$ again, directly from the side lengths, using the Law of Cosines.

   d. Your answers to parts (b) and (c) probably do not agree! If not, and if you have made no computation errors, your error is in interpreting the results of the Law of Sines in part (b). Use the fact that there is also an *obtuse* angle whose sine is the same as in part (b) to correct your answer to part (b).

e.   Explain why it is dangerous to use the Law of Sines to find an angle measure, but is *not* dangerous to use the Law of Cosines.

10. *Accurate Drawing Problem:* Using ruler, protractor, and a sharp pencil, draw a triangle with base 10.0 centimeters, and angles of 40° and 30° at the ends of the base. Measure the side opposite the 30° angle. Then calculate its length by the Law of Sines. Your measured value should be within ±0.1 centimeter of the calculated value.

11. *Equation Problem:* Solve for $\theta \in (0°, 360°)$: $\dfrac{\cos \theta}{\sin \theta} = 1$.

12. *Identity Problem:* Prove that $\sin x \tan x = \sec x - \cos x$.

13. *Rotary Motion Problem:* How fast does the hour hand of a clock travel in radians per minute?

14. *Triangle Problem:* A triangle has sides 5 chains and 7 chains long. The angle included between these sides is 67°. How long is the third side? What is the area of the triangle? How long is a "chain"?

15. *Graphing Problem:* Sketch the graph of $y = \text{Arccsc } x$.

16. *Ambiguous Triangle Problem:* Draw a ray starting near the left side of your paper. At the end point of the ray, draw a line about 5 inches long, making an angle of about 30° with the ray. The line and the ray are to form two sides of a triangle. The third side is to start at the other end of the 5-inch line and is to be 4 inches long. Draw *two* possible triangles that meet this description. What does the word "ambiguous" mean?

5–5   THE AMBIGUOUS CASE

You may recall from geometry that a triangle is not necessarily determined by the measures of two sides and a non-included angle. This case is called *SSA* (side, side, angle), and is illustrated in Figure 5–5a.

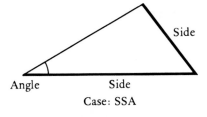

Case: SSA

Figure 5–5a

There are *four* ways a triangle *ABC* would come out if you knew the lengths of *a* and *b* and the measure of Angle *B*. To see why, it is helpful to start *constructing* the triangle. Figure 5–5b shows *a* and Angle *B* constructed.

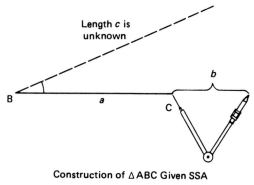

Length *c* is unknown

Construction of △ABC Given SSA

Figure 5–5b

Since *c* is not given, you simply draw a long line in the correct direction, making an angle of m∠*B* with *a*. To complete the triangle, you place the point of a compass at Point *C*, open it to length *b*, which *is* given, and draw an arc. Wherever the compass arc cuts the dotted line in Figure 5–5b is the correct position for Point *A*. Figure 5–5c shows the four possible ways Point *A* might come out. There are either *two, one,* or *no* possible triangles when you are given SSA. For this reason, SSA is sometimes called the "ambiguous case." *Ambiguous* means "two or more possible meanings."

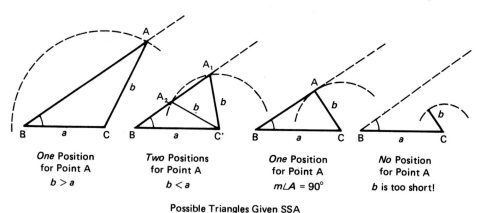

One Position for Point A	*Two* Positions for Point A	*One* Position for Point A	*No* Position for Point A
b > a	*b < a*	m∠A = 90°	*b* is too short!

Possible Triangles Given SSA

Figure 5–5c

Objective:

Given SSA, determine whether or not there are possible triangles, and if so, find the other side length and angle measures.

Example 1:   In $\triangle XYZ$, $x = 4$, $y = 5$, and $m\angle X = 27°$. Find the possible values of z.

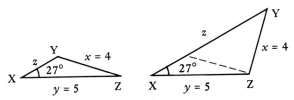

Figure 5-5d

Since $x < y$, there can be two possible triangles, as shown in Figure 5-5d. The Law of Sines cannot be used directly to find z, since $m\angle Z$ is unknown. The Law of Cosines can be used, however, because there are two side lengths known. The process is complicated by the fact that z is not opposite the known angle. You write:

$$4^2 = z^2 + 5^2 - 2(z)(5) \cos 27°$$

This is a quadratic equation in the variable z. Making the left member equal 0, and using the Quadratic Formula gives

$$0 = z^2 - (10 \cos 27°)z + 25 - 16$$

$$0 = z^2 - (8.91\ldots)z + 9$$

$$z = \frac{8.91\ldots \pm \sqrt{(8.91\ldots)^2 - 4(1)(9)}}{2(1)}$$

$$z = \frac{8.91\ldots \pm 6.58\ldots}{2}$$

$$z \approx \underline{7.75 \text{ or } 1.16}$$

When you evaluate the Quadratic Formula, it helps to evaluate the radical first. Then save its value in memory for use when you calculate the second value of z.

Example 2:   In $\triangle XYZ$, $x = 6$, $y = 5$, and $m\angle X = 27°$. Find the possible values of z.

Since $x > y$, there will be only *one* possible triangle, as shown in the left sketch of Figure 5-5c. This triangle is shown in Figure 5-5e. By the Law of Cosines,

$6^2 = z^2 + 5^2 - 2(z)(5) \cos 27°$

$0 = z^2 - (8.91 \ldots)z - 11$

$z = \dfrac{8.91 \ldots \pm \sqrt{(8.91 \ldots)^2 - 4(1)(-11)}}{2}$

$z = 10.009 \ldots$ or $-1.099 \ldots$

$\underline{z \approx 10.01}$

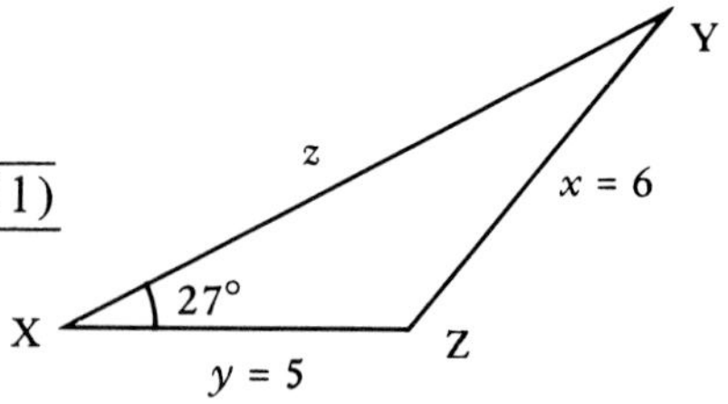

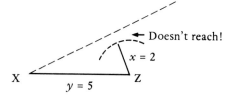

Figure 5-5e

The negative value of z confirms that there is only *one* possible triangle.

Example 3:   In $\triangle XYZ$, $x = 2$, $y = 5$, and $m\angle X = 27°$. Find the possible values of z.

This example is the same as Examples 1 and 2 except for the value of x. By the Law of Cosines,

$2^2 = z^2 + 5^2 - 2(z)(5) \cos 27°$

$0 = z^2 - (8.91 \ldots)z + 21$

$z = \dfrac{8.91 \ldots \pm \sqrt{(8.91 \ldots)^2 - 4(1)(21)}}{2(1)}$

$z = \dfrac{8.91 \ldots \pm \sqrt{-4.61 \ldots}}{2}$

No solutions because of the negative radicand.

∴ There is <u>no triangle</u>.

The radicand will be negative whenever the side opposite the given angle is too short to reach the other side, as shown in Figure 5-5f.

In the following exercise you will analyze more triangles of the case SSA.

Figure 5-5f

Exercise 5-5

For Problems 1 through 8, find the possible lengths of the indicated side.

1. In $\triangle ABC$, $m\angle B = 34°$, $a = 4$, and $b = 3$. Find c.

2. In $\triangle XYZ$, $m\angle X = 13°$, $x = 12$, and $y = 5$. Find z.
3. In $\triangle ABC$, $m\angle B = 34°$, $a = 4$, and $b = 5$. Find c.
4. In $\triangle XYZ$, $m\angle X = 13°$, $x = 12$, and $y = 15$. Find z.
5. In $\triangle ABC$, $m\angle B = 34°$, $a = 4$, and $b = 2$. Find c.
6. In $\triangle XYZ$, $m\angle X = 13°$, $x = 12$, and $y = 60$. Find z.
7. In $\triangle RST$, $m\angle R = 130°$, $r = 20$, and $t = 16$. Find s.
8. In $\triangle OBT$, $m\angle O = 170°$, $o = 19$, and $t = 11$. Find b.

The Law of Sines can be used to find an angle in the SSA case. But you must be careful because there can be two different angles, one acute and the other obtuse, which have the same sine. For Problems 9 through 12, determine beforehand whether there can be two triangles or just one. Then find the possible values of the indicated angle measure.

9. In $\triangle ABC$, $m\angle A = 19°$, $a = 25$, and $c = 30$. Find $m\angle C$.
10. In $\triangle HDJ$, $m\angle H = 28°$, $h = 50$, and $d = 20$. Find $m\angle D$.
11. In $\triangle XYZ$, $m\angle X = 58°$, $x = 9.3$, and $z = 7.5$. Find $m\angle Z$.
12. In $\triangle BIG$, $m\angle B = 110°$, $b = 1000$, and $g = 900$. Find $m\angle G$.

13. *Accurate Drawing Problem No. 1:* Triangles ABC in Problems 1, 3, and 5 differ only in the length of side b. Draw side a 4 centimeters long as the base. Then construct Angle B of measure 34° at one end of the base.

    a. Use a compass to mark off the two possible triangles if $b = 3$ centimeters, as in Problem 1. Measure the two possible values of c. Your answers should be within ±0.1 centimeter of the calculated values.
    b. Use a compass to mark off $b = 5$ centimeters, as in Problem 3. Measure the value of c, and confirm that it agrees with the calculated value. Then extend segment $\overline{AB}$ beyond angle B. Find the point on this segment where the 5 centimeter arc cuts it. Show that the distance between this point and B equals the *negative* value of c that is discarded in working Problem 3.
    c. Use a compass to draw an arc of radius $b = 2$ centimeters, as in Problem 5. Show that this arc *misses* the other side of Angle B, and thus that there is *no* possible triangle.

14. *Accurate Drawing Problem No. 2:* Repeat Problem 13 for Triangles XYZ in Problems 2, 4, and 6.

15. *Property of Ambiguous Case Triangles:* Figure 5–5g shows two possible cases of triangle ABC for which a, b, and $m\angle A$ are given.

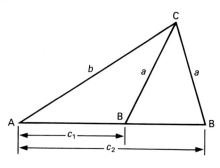

Figure 5-5g

a. Find c_1 and c_2 if $a = 7$, $b = 10$, and $m\angle A = 28°$.

b. Find c_1 and c_2 if $a = 8$, $b = 10$, and $m\angle A = 28°$.

c. Multiply the values of c_1 and c_2 in part (a). Multiply the values of c_1 and c_2 in part (b). What do you notice?

16. *Proof of Property:* Prove that if a, b, and $m\angle A$ are given, then the product of the two side lengths, $c_1 c_2$, is a constant, dependent only on the measures of side b and angle A.

17. *Graphing Problem:* Sketch the graph of

$$y = -7 + 3 \cos \frac{\pi}{8}(x + 4).$$

18. Write the exact value of $\cos \frac{4\pi}{3}$.

19. Write the exact value of $x = \text{Arccot}(-1)$.

20. *Triangle Problem:* Find the length of the third side of a triangle if two sides are 15 furlongs and 23 furlongs, and the included angle is 2 radians. How long is a furlong?

21. *Triangle Problem:* A triangle is constructed with base 7 cm and base angles 34° and 49°. Find the length of the shortest side of the triangle.

22. *Area Problem:* Find the area of a triangle if two sides are 4.7 m and 3.8 m, and the included angle is 87°.

23. *Identity Problem:* The function $f(0) = 7 \cos 20 + 3 \sin 20$ can be expressed as a single cosine function with a phase displacement. What is the phase displacement to the nearest tenth of a degree?

24. *Equation Problem:* Solve for $\theta \in (30°, 70°)$:

$$\sin 2\theta + \sin 9\theta = 0.$$

5–6   GENERAL SOLUTION OF TRIANGLES

You have learned the techniques necessary for analyzing oblique triangles when you are told which to use, the Law of Sines or the Law of Cosines. Before you tackle the real-world problems in Section 5–7, you must be sure that you can select the appropriate technique when you are *not* told which one to use.

Objective:

Given SSS, SAS, ASA, AAS, or SSA, be able to select the appropriate technique and to calculate the other side and angle measures and the area of the triangle.

Sometimes you can use either the Law of Cosines or the Law of Sines. You should recognize situations where a given technique does *not* work. Some guidelines are presented below.

Triangle Techniques

1. The Law of Cosines involves *three* sides. Therefore, it will *not* work for ASA or AAS, where there are *two unknown sides.*
2. The Law of Sines involves the ratio of the sine of an angle to the length of its *opposite* side. Therefore, it will *not* work where *no* angle is known (SSS) or where only *one* angle is known, but *not* its opposite side (SAS).
3. The Law of Sines should *not* be used to find *angle* measures unless you know in advance whether the angle is obtuse or acute.
4. The area formula requires you to know SAS. If you do not know two sides and the included angle, you must first find them. Heron's Formula (Exercise 5–3, Problem 7) will work if you know SSS.

The following exercise requires you to select the appropriate technique and then work the problem. Your instructor may assign you only certain parts of each problem. Since working all parts of the problems requires much computation, you may wish to write and use a computer program as outlined in Problems 29 and 30.

Exercise 5-6

Unless your instructor tells you otherwise, find the measures of all three unspecified sides and angles as well as the area. If you are going to write a
computer program to do this, go immediately to Problem 29 and then come
back to Problems 1 through 28.

	Case	a	b	c	A	B	C
1.	SAS	3	4				71°40'
2.	SAS	8	5				32°10'
3.	SAS	30	60				23°50'
4.	SAS	18	40				82°30'
5.	SAS	100	210				113°20'
6.	SAS	2000	1700				142°00'
7.	SSS	8	9	7			
8.	SSS	4	3	2			
9.	SSS	3	6	4			
10.	SSS	18	10	9			
11.	SSS	3	9	4			
12.	SSS	18	8	9			
13.	ASA			400	143°10'	8°20'	
14.	ASA			30	122°50'	15°00'	
15.	ASA			50	11°30'	27°40'	
16.	ASA			17	84°20'	87°30'	
17.	AAS	6			56°20'	64°30'	
18.	AAS	10			139°10'	38°40'	
19.	SSA	7	5		25°50'		
20.	SSA	10	6		31°10'		
21.	SSA	5	7		25°50'		
22.	SSA	6	10		31°10'		
23.	SSA	5	7		126°40'		
24.	SSA	10	6		144°50'		
25.	SSA	7	5		126°40'		
26.	SSA	3	10		31°10'		
27.	SSA	3	5		36°52.19385'		
28.	SSA	5	13		22°37.19189'		

29. *Computer Solution of Triangles:* In this problem you will write a
computer program to find unspecified sides, angles, and area of a given
triangle. Since there are five different ways the data might be given and

a different sequence of computations for each case, the program is divided into blocks. Your class may wish to divide into seven groups, each group responsible for one of the tasks outlined below. By writing the program in this manner, you will get experience in the way really big programs are written, such as those used to get spacecraft to the Moon. The length of such programs makes it impossible for one person to write the program above in a reasonable length of time.

Specific tasks are given below. (If you are using a language other than BASIC, you may need to modify some of the instructions.)

Task 1: Write a "menu." This part of the program directs the activities of all other parts. It should first print on the screen a way for you to select the case, such as

    ENTER CASE
    1 FOR SSS
    2 FOR SAS
    3 FOR SSA
    4 FOR AAS
    5 FOR ASA
    WHICH?

Depending on what the person using the program enters, the menu should direct the computer to the proper subroutine described below. Upon returning from the subroutine, this portion of the program should direct the computer to find the area, convert angles in radians (as the computer calculates them) to angles in degrees and minutes, and print the results in a form such as

    CASE: SAS
    S1 = 3
    S2 = 4
    S3 = 4.177
    A1 = 42D, 59M
    A2 = 65D, 21M
    A3 = 71D, 40M
    AREA = 5.695

Task 2: Write a subroutine for the case SSS. It should begin with a statement letting the user input the three lengths. The screen should display a message such as

    TYPE S1,S2,S3

The computer should then calculate the three angles, and return to the menu. The subroutine should also be able to detect when the three given sides are impossible for a triangle.

Task 3: Write a subroutine for the case SAS. It should first print a message such as

TYPE S1,D3,M3,S2

where S1 and S2 are two side lengths, and D3 and M3 are the degrees and minutes in Angle 3, included between sides 1 and 2. The subroutine should calculate the third side length and the measures of the other two angles, then return to the menu.

Task 4: Write a subroutine for the case SSA. Since this is the ambiguous case, the subroutine should allow the computer to detect when there are two possible triangles, or no triangle, and return an appropriate message to the menu so that it will know what to do.

Task 5: Write a subroutine for the case AAS, as above.

Task 6: Write a subroutine for the case ASA, as above.

Task 7: Write any special functions needed. If you use ordinary BASIC, you will have COS (X), SIN(X), and ATN(X) available. These are the *circular* cosine, sine, and Arctangent, respectively, where the argument or Arctangent is in *radians.* So you will need to define

a.   FNR(X) for converting X degrees to radians.
b.   FND(X) and FNM(X) for converting X radians to degrees and minutes, respectively.
c.   FNC(X) and FNS(X) for finding acrcos X and arcsin X, respectively, from ATN(X). The properties of Section 4–7 should be helpful.

30. Debug the program from Problem 29 by using it to work the *odd-*numbered problems above. If your program can solve each triangle correctly, you may consider it to be completely debugged.

31. *Equation Problem:*   Find the general solution for

$$\frac{1 - \cos x}{\sin x} = \sin 2x.$$

32. *Identity Problem:*   Prove that this is an identity and confirm the result by computer graphics.

$$\sin x + \sin 2x + \sin 3x = \sin 2x (2 \cos x + 1)$$

33. *Graphing Problem:*   Sketch the graph of $y = 3 + \csc 2\theta$.

34. *Graphing Problem:*   Sketch the graph of $y = \arcsin x$.

35. Write the exact value of $\sec 150°$.

36. Arc x in standard position makes two complete counterclockwise revolutions before terminating in the second quadrant. The value of $\cos x$ is -0.7. Find, approximately, the value of $\tan\left(\dfrac{x}{3}\right)$.

5–7   VECTORS

A *vector quantity* is something that has *direction* as well as magnitude (size). Velocity is an example. When you are traveling, it is important to know in what direction as well as how fast! A quantity that has *no* direction, such as volume, is called a *scalar* quantity. The *scalar* quantity "speed" and a direction combine to form the *vector* quantity "velocity."

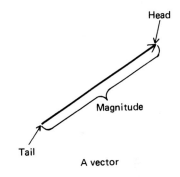

A vector

Figure 5–7a

In this section you will use directed line segments to represent vector quantities. The *length* of the line segment represents the *magnitude* (size) of the vector quantity, and the direction of the line segment represents the direction of the vector quantity. An arrowhead is used to distinguish the head of a vector from its tail (Figure 5–7a).

If a variable is used to represent a vector, you put a small arrow over the top of it, such as $\vec{x}$, to distinguish it from a scalar. The three vectors in Figure 5–7b are considered to be *equal* since they have the same length and the same direction.

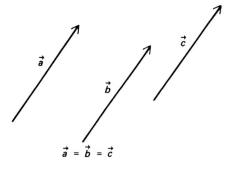

$\vec{a} = \vec{b} = \vec{c}$

Figure 5–7b

The above discussion leads to the following definitions.

DEFINITIONS

1. A *vector* is a directed line segment.

2. Two vectors are *equal* if and only if they have the same magnitude and the same direction.

3. The *absolute value* of a vector is its length or magnitude.

Having invented a new kind of mathematical quantity, you must now find out how to operate with it.

Objective:

Given two vectors, be able to *add* them or *subtract* them.

Vector Addition: Vectors are added by placing the tail of one vector at the head of the other, as shown in Figure 5-7c. The *sum* of the vectors is defined to be the vector that goes from the tail of the first vector to the head of the last one. This definition arises from vectors in the real world. If you walk 20 meters in a certain direction, then turn and walk 13 meters more in a new direction, these "displacements" could be represented by Vectors $\vec{a}$ and $\vec{b}$ in Figure 5-7c. The sum $\vec{a} + \vec{b}$ would be a vector representing your net displacement from the starting point. A displacement of $\vec{a} + \vec{b}$ would produce the same result as a displacement of $\vec{a}$ followed by another displacement of $\vec{b}$. For this reason, the sum of two vectors is often called the *resultant* vector.

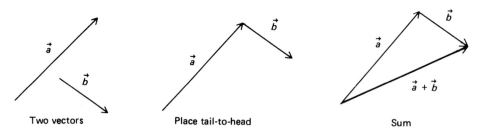

Two vectors   Place tail-to-head   Sum

Figure 5-7c

Vector Subtraction: You recall that −1 · x equals −x, the opposite of x. It is natural, therefore, to define the opposite of a vector $\vec{v}$ to be −1 · $\vec{v}$. So −$\vec{v}$ is a vector having the *same magnitude* as $\vec{v}$ but pointing in the *opposite direction* (Figure 5-7d). The definition of vector subtraction follows directly from the definition of subtraction for real numbers.

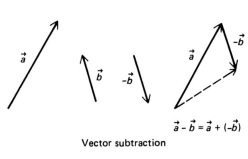

$$\vec{a} - \vec{b} = \vec{a} + (-\vec{b})$$

Vector subtraction

Figure 5-7d

DEFINITION

$$\vec{a} - \vec{b} = \vec{a} + (-\vec{b})$$

Since vector addition and subtraction involve forming triangles, the triangle techniques you have just learned will be useful.

Example 1:   Two vectors, $\vec{a}$ and $\vec{b}$, have magnitudes of 5 and 9, respectively. The angle between the vectors is 53°, as shown in the first sketch of Figure 5-7e. Find |$\vec{a}$ + $\vec{b}$|, |$\vec{a}$ − $\vec{b}$|, and the angles these sum and difference vectors make with $\vec{a}$.

A vector can be moved *parallel* to itself without changing its magnitude or direction. Moving $\vec{b}$ parallel to itself until its tail is at the head of $\vec{a}$ forms a triangle (Figure 5-7e). Since θ and the 53° angle are supplementary,

θ = 180° − 53° = 127°.

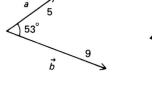 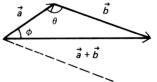 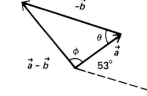

Figure 5-7e

Vectors $\vec{a}$ and $\vec{b}$ are two sides of a triangle with included angle θ and third side $\vec{a} + \vec{b}$. By the Law of Cosines,

$$|\vec{a} + \vec{b}|^2 = 5^2 + 9^2 - 2(5)(9)\cos 127°$$

$= 160.163 \ldots$	By calculator
$\therefore \ |\vec{a} + \vec{b}| = 12.655 \ldots$	Taking the square root
$\approx \underline{12.66}$	Rounding off

The 12.655 ... should be stored, without roundoff, in the calculator's memory for use in the next part of the problem.

To find the angle θ that $\vec{a} + \vec{b}$ makes with $\vec{a}$, you may use the Law of Cosines as in Section 5-2.

$$\cos\theta = \frac{5^2 + (12.655 \ldots)^2 - 9^2}{2(5)(12.655 \ldots)}$$

$= 0.8230 \ldots$	By calculator
$\therefore \ \theta = 34.607 \ldots °$	Taking inverse cosine
$\approx \underline{34°36'}$	Transforming to degrees and minutes

To find $\vec{a} - \vec{b}$, you simply turn $\vec{b}$ around in the opposite direction and slide its tail to the head of $\vec{a}$, as shown in the third sketch of Figure 5-7e. Angle θ between $\vec{a}$ and $-\vec{b}$ is now an alternate interior angle of the 53° angle. So θ is also 53°. Applying the Law of Cosines:

$$|\vec{a} - \vec{b}|^2 = 5^2 + 9^2 - 2(5)(9)\cos 53°$$

$= 51.836 \ldots$	By calculator
$\therefore |\vec{a} - \vec{b}| = 7.199$	Taking the square root.
$\approx \underline{7.200}$	Rounding off.

Using the Law of Cosines to find θ:

$$\cos\theta = \frac{5^2 + (7.199 \ldots)^2 - 9^2}{2(5)(7.199 \ldots)}$$

$= -0.0578 \ldots$	By calculator.
$\therefore \ \theta = 93.315 \ldots °$	Taking inverse cosine.
$\approx \underline{93°19'}$	Transforming to degrees and minutes.

Note: The Law of Sines could have been used to find θ.

$$\sin \theta = \frac{9 \sin 53°}{7.199 \ldots}$$

$$= 0.9983 \ldots$$

Taking the inverse sine would give 86.684 . . .°, which is the *reference* angle for 93.315 . . .°. Since there is no easy way to tell whether θ is obtuse or acute, it is preferable to use the Law of Cosines technique. The sign of $\cos \theta$ tells that θ is obtuse.

Vectors can be used to find displacements of objects that move on the earth's surface. Navigators commonly measure angles clockwise from north as shown in Figure 5–7f, rather than counterclockwise from the positive x-axis. The direction thus determined is called a *bearing*. The figure shows a vector with a bearing of 250 degrees.

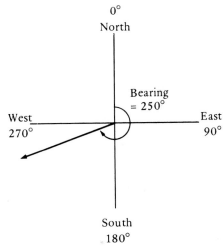

Figure 5–7f

Example 2:   An object moves 90 meters due south (bearing 180 degrees), then turns and moves 40 more meters along a bearing of 250 degrees (Figure 5–7g).

a.   Find the resultant of these two displacement vectors.
b.   What is the bearing from the end point back to the starting point?

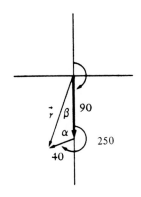

Figure 5–7g

a.   The resultant, $\vec{r}$, goes from the tail of the first vector to the head of the last.

Angle $\alpha = 360° - 250° = 110°$

By the Law of Cosines,

$$|\vec{r}|^2 = 90^2 + 40^2 - 2(90)(40)\cos 110°$$

$$= 12162.54\ldots$$

$$\therefore |\vec{r}| = 110.283\ldots$$

By the Law of Cosines,

$$\cos\beta = \frac{90^2 + (110.283\ldots)^2 - 40^2}{2(90)(110.283\ldots)}$$

$$= 0.9401\ldots$$

$$\therefore \beta = 19.927\ldots°$$

From Figure 5-7g,

$$\text{Bearing} = 180° + 19.927\ldots°$$

$$= 199.927°$$

Vector is 110.3 at 199.9°

b. To find the bearing from the end point to the starting point, all you need realize is that it points the opposite direction.

$$\text{Bearing} = 199.9° + 180°$$

$$= 379.9°$$

Since this is greater than 360°, you subtract 360° (one full revolution) getting

$$\text{Bearing} = 19.9°$$

The following exercise gives you practice adding and subtracting vectors.

Exercise 5-7

For Problems 1 through 4, find $|\vec{a} + \vec{b}|$, $|\vec{a} - \vec{b}|$, and the angle that each of these resultant vectors makes with $\vec{a}$ (Figure 5-7h).

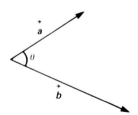

1. $|\vec{a}| = 7$, $|\vec{b}| = 11$, $\theta = 73°$

2. $|\vec{a}| = 8$, $|\vec{b}| = 2$, $\theta = 41°$

Figure 5-7h

3. $|\vec{a}| = 9,$ $|\vec{b}| = 20,$ $\theta = 163°$

4. $|\vec{a}| = 10,$ $|\vec{b}| = 30,$ $\theta = 122°$

For Problems 5 through 8, do the following:

a. Find the resultant of the two given displacements. Express the answer as a distance and a bearing (clockwise from north) from the starting point to the end point.

b. Tell the bearing from the end point back to the starting point.

c. Draw the vectors on graph paper, using ruler and protractor, and thus show that your answers are correct to 0.1 unit of length and 1 degree of angle.

5. 11 units north ($0°$) followed by 5 units along a bearing of $70°$.

6. 8 units east ($90°$) followed by 6 units along a bearing of $210°$.

7. 6 units west ($270°$) followed by 14 units along a bearing of $110°$.

8. 4 units south ($180°$) followed by 9 units along a bearing of $320°$.

9. *Identity Problem:*   Write $\cos^2 x$ in terms of:

   a. $\sin x$ b. $\cos 2x$ c. $\sec x$

10. *Equation Problem:*   Solve for $x \in (0, \pi)$:

$$\frac{\sin^2 x - 1}{\cos^2 x} = 1.$$

11. *Area Problem:*   Find the area of the triangle with sides 420 cm, 421 cm, and 29 cm.

12. *Triangle Problem:*   Find the longest side of the triangle with angles $35°$, $71°$, and $74°$ if the shortest side is 15 cm.

13. *Rotary Motion Problem:*   A hiki pulls a ricksha at a speed of 230 meters per minute. The wheels have a diameter of 1.2 meters. What is the angular velocity of the wheels, in radians per minute? What is a ricksha? What is a hiki?

14. Write the exact value of $\tan 210°$.

5–8 VECTORS—RESOLUTION INTO COMPONENTS

Sometimes it is important to reverse the addition process and express a single vector as the sum of two other vectors. For example, if a pilot knows the plane's air speed and angle of climb, the rate of climb and the ground velocity can be calculated (Figure 5–8a). For this purpose you must be able to resolve, or break up, a vector into components whose sum is the original vector. Two pieces of background information are helpful.

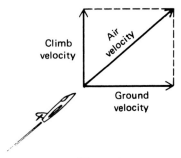

Figure 5–8a

Vector times scalar: When you add a real number x to itself, you get

$$x + x = 2x.$$

It is reasonable to say that when you add a *vector* to itself, you get twice that vector. That is,

$$\vec{a} + \vec{a} = 2\vec{a}.$$

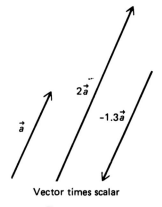

Vector times scalar

Figure 5–8b

The answer $2\vec{a}$ is a vector in the *same* direction, but with 2 times the magnitude. The reasoning leads you to define what you mean by a scalar (i.e., a real number) times a vector.

DEFINITION

The *product* $x\vec{a}$ is a vector in the *same* direction as $\vec{a}$ but with a magnitude equal to x times the magnitude of $\vec{a}$.

Note: Multiplying a vector by -1 gives a vector of the *same* magnitude, but *opposite* direction. Thus, $-1 \cdot \vec{a} = -\vec{a}$, as was mentioned in the last section.

Unit vectors and components: A vector of magnitude 1 is called a *unit* vector. The letters $\vec{i}$ and $\vec{j}$ are used for unit vectors in the x- and y-directions, respectively. Any vector in the x-direction can be written as a scalar multiple of $\vec{i}$ and any vector in the y-direction can be written as a scalar multiple of $\vec{j}$. Figure 5–8c shows vector $\vec{v}$ which is the sum of $4\vec{i}$ and $3\vec{j}$. These two perpendicular vectors are called *components* of $\vec{v}$.

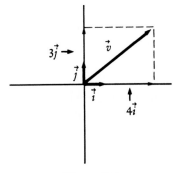

Figure 5–8c

Objective:

Given a vector in a Cartesian coordinate system, express it as the sum of two component vectors, one in the x-direction, the other in the y-direction.

Example 1: Vector $\vec{a}$ has magnitude 3 and direction 143°, as shown in Figure 5–8d. Resolve $\vec{a}$ into horizontal and vertical components.

By the definitions of sine and cosine,

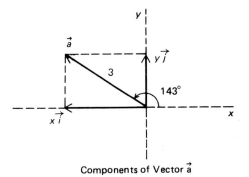

$$\frac{x}{3} = \cos 143° \text{ and } \frac{y}{3} = \sin 143°$$

$$\therefore x = 3 \cos 143° = -2.3959 \ldots$$

$$y = 3 \sin 143° = 1.8054 \ldots$$

$$\therefore \vec{a} \approx -2.396\,\vec{i} + 1.805\,\vec{j}$$

Components of Vector $\vec{a}$

Figure 5–8d

From Example 1 you can conclude that if θ is the angle in standard position for vector $\vec{v}$, then

$$\vec{v} = (|\vec{v}|\cos\theta)\vec{i} + (|\vec{v}|\sin\theta)\vec{j}$$

Components give an easy way to add two vectors. As shown in Figure 5–8e, if $\vec{r}$ is the resultant of $\vec{a}$ and $\vec{b}$, then the components of $\vec{r}$ are the sums of the components of $\vec{a}$ and $\vec{b}$. Since

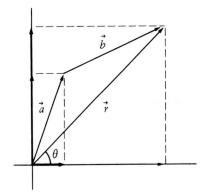

Figure 5–8e

the two horizontal components have the same direction, they can be added simply by adding their magnitudes. The same is true for the vertical components.

Example 2: If $\vec{a}$ has magnitude 5 and direction 70°, and $\vec{b}$ has magnitude 6 and direction 25° (Figure 5–8e), find the resultant, $\vec{r}$,

  a.   as the sum of two components,
  b.   as a magnitude and direction.

a. $\vec{r} = \vec{a} + \vec{b}$

$\qquad = (5 \cos 70°)\vec{i} + (5 \sin 70°)\vec{j}$
$\qquad\quad + (6 \cos 25°)\vec{i} + (6 \sin 25°)\vec{j}$ Resolving $\vec{a}$ and $\vec{b}$ into components

$\qquad = (5 \cos 70° + 6 \cos 25°)\vec{i}$
$\qquad\quad + (5 \sin 70° + 6 \sin 25°)\vec{j}$ Collecting like terms

$\qquad = 7.1479 \ldots \vec{i} + 7.2341 \ldots \vec{j}$ By calculator

$\qquad \approx 7.15\,\vec{i} + 7.23\,\vec{j}$ Rounding off

b. The more precise values of x and y should be stored in the calculator's memory or written down for use in this part of the problem.

$\qquad |\vec{r}| = \sqrt{(7.147 \ldots)^2 + (7.234 \ldots)^2}$ By the Pythagorean Theorem

$\qquad\quad = 10.169 \ldots$ By calculator

$\qquad \tan \theta = \dfrac{7.234 \ldots}{7.147 \ldots} = 1.012 \ldots$ Definition of tangent

$\qquad \therefore\ \theta = 45.343 \ldots°$ θ is in Quadrant I since sin θ
and cos θ are both positive

$\qquad \therefore\ \vec{r} \approx 10.17$ at $45°21'$

The component technique is useful for navigation problems. When neither vector is along a coordinate axis, the triangle technique of the last section can be difficult. You can first transform the bearing, β, into an angle in standard position. As shown in Figure 5–8f, the bearing β and the angle θ are complementary. Thus,

$\boxed{\beta = 90° - \theta \ \text{ and } \ \theta = 90° - \beta}$

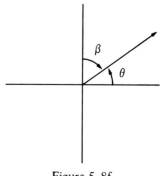

Figure 5–8f

If this relationship produces a negative value of θ or β, a positive coterminal angle can be found by adding 360°.

Example 3: A ship sails for 20 miles on a bearing of 325°, then turns and sails on a bearing of 250° for 7 more miles. Find its displacement vector, $\vec{d}$, from the starting point (Figure 5–8g).

The two angles are

$$\theta_1 = 90° - 325° = -235°$$

$$\theta_2 = 90° - 250° = -160°$$

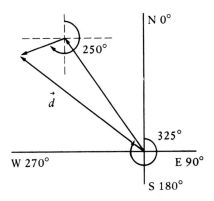

Figure 5-8g

Adding 360° to each gives coterminal angles of positive measure.

$$\theta_1 = 125°$$

$$\theta_2 = 200°$$

$$\therefore \vec{d} = (20 \cos 125° + 7 \cos 200°)\vec{i}$$
$$+ (20 \sin 125° + 7 \sin 200°)\vec{j} \qquad \text{Adding the components}$$

$$\underline{\vec{d} = -18.049 \ldots \vec{i} + 13.988 \ldots \vec{j}}$$

This vector can be transformed to a distance and bearing.

$$|\vec{d}| = \sqrt{(-18.049 \ldots)^2 + (13.988 \ldots)^2}$$

$$= 22.835 \ldots$$

$$\tan \theta = \frac{13.988 \ldots}{-18.049 \ldots}$$

$$= -0.7750 \ldots$$

$$\therefore \quad \theta = 142.223 \ldots °$$

$$\therefore \quad \beta = 90° - 142.223 \ldots °$$

$$= -52.223 \ldots °$$

Adding 360° gives

$$\beta = 307.776\ldots°$$

$$\therefore \vec{d} \approx 22.84 \text{ miles at } 307°47'$$

Note: This problem can also be worked using the bearings themselves, without first finding θ. The main thing to remember is that the quadrants will be numbered *clockwise*, starting from northeast.

Example 4: A ship sails at a speed of 20 knots (nautical miles per hour) on a bearing of 325°. The water has a current of 7 knots along a bearing of 250°. Find the ship's resultant velocity vector, $\vec{v}$.

$$\vec{v} \approx 22.84 \text{ knots at } 307°47'$$

Note: This problem is the same, mathematically, as Example 3. The mathematics is independent of what physical quantity the vectors represent.

The following exercise gives you practice resolving vectors into components, and adding vectors by adding their components.

Exercise 5–8

For Problems 1 through 4, resolve the vector into horizontal and vertical components.

1.

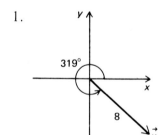

2.

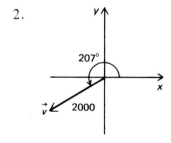

3.

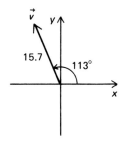

4.

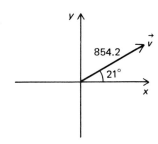

5. If $\vec{r}$ = 21 units at θ = 70° and $\vec{s}$ = 40 units at θ = 120°, find $\vec{r} + \vec{s}$

    a. as a sum of two components,
    b. as a magnitude and a direction.

6. If $\vec{u}$ = 12 units at θ = 160° and $\vec{v}$ = 8 units at 310°, find $\vec{u} + \vec{v}$

    a. as a sum of two components,
    b. as a magnitude and direction.

7. A ship sails 50 miles on a bearing of β = 20°, then 30 miles further on a bearing of β = 80°. Find the resultant displacement vector as a distance and bearing.

8. A plane flies 30 miles on a bearing of β = 200°, then turns and flies 40 miles on a bearing of β = 10°. Find the resultant displacement vector as a distance and bearing.

9. A plane flies 200 miles per hour (mph) along a bearing of 320°. The air is moving with a wind speed of 60 mph along a bearing of 190°. Find the plane's resultant velocity (speed and bearing) by adding these two velocity vectors.

10. A scuba diver swims 100 feet per minute along a bearing of 170°. The water is moving with a current of 30 feet per minute along a bearing of 115°. Find the diver's resultant velocity (speed and bearing) by adding these two velocity vectors.

Problems 11 through 15 refer to $\vec{a}$, $\vec{b}$, and $\vec{c}$, shown in Figure 5–8h.

11. a. On a piece of graph
       paper, draw $\vec{a} + \vec{b}$
       by placing the tail of $\vec{b}$
       at the head of $\vec{a}$.
    b. On the same Cartesian
       coordinate system, draw
       $\vec{b} + \vec{a}$ by placing the tail
       of $\vec{a}$ at the head of $\vec{b}$.
    c. How does your picture
       illustrate the fact that
       vector addition is
       commutative?

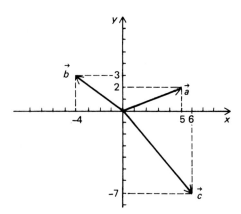

Figure 5-8h

12. Illustrate that vector addi-
    tion is *associative* by draw-
    ing $(\vec{a} + \vec{b}) + \vec{c}$ and $\vec{a} + (\vec{b} + \vec{c})$.

13. Draw $\vec{a} + (-\vec{a})$ on a Cartesian coordinate system. What is the *magnitude*
    of $\vec{a} + (-\vec{a})$? Does it make sense to assign a *direction* to this vector?
    Why do you suppose this vector is called the "zero vector"?

14. How can you conclude that {vectors} is *closed* under addition? Why is
    the zero vector necessary to insure closure?

15. How can you conclude that {vectors} is closed under multiplication
    by a scalar? Is the zero vector necessary to insure closure in this case?
    Explain.

16. *Identity Problem:* Write sin 7x sin 3x as a sum of sines or cosines.

17. *Equation Problem:* Solve for $x \in (0, 2\pi)$:

    sin x cos π = 0.5.

18. *Rotary Motion Problem:* Suppose that you tie a weight on a string
    and then twirl it so that the string wraps around your finger. The linear
    velocity of the weight remains about the same as the string winds.
    Describe what happens to the angular velocity of the weight.

19. *Triangle Problem:* The area of a triangle is 300 cm². Two sides of the
    triangle are 19 cm and 37 cm. Find the *two* possible values of the angle
    included between these two sides.

20. *Triangle Problem:* An isosceles triangle has two angles of 1 radian each.
    What is the degree measure of the third angle?

5–9   REAL-WORLD TRIANGLE PROBLEMS

Throughout this chapter you have been developing the computational skills
you need to work real-world problems involving measurement of triangles.
Each problem in the following exercise requires you to identify one or more
triangles, right or oblique, and then apply the appropriate technique to find
the side, angle, or area you seek. The computer program of Section 5–6 or
a pocket calculator will help with the arithmetic and leave you more time to
concentrate on identifying the proper triangle and interpreting the results.

Exercise 5–9

1. *Flagpole Problem:*
    Calvin Butterball is wait-
    ing outside the school
    building for his trigono-
    metry test to begin. He
    observes that the flag-
    pole is casting a shadow
    on the ground and de-
    cides to calculate how
    high the pole is. He steps
    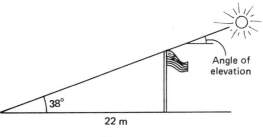
    Figure 5-9a

    off the shadow, finding it to be 22 meters long. From an almanac, he
    finds that the Sun's angle of elevation is 38° (Figure 5–9a). How tall
    is the pole?

2. *Airplane Problem:* Aloha
    Airlines Flight 007 is
    approaching Kahului Air-
    port at an altitude of
    5 kilometers. The angle
    of depression (Figure 5–9b)
    from the plane to the air-
    port is 9° 32′.
    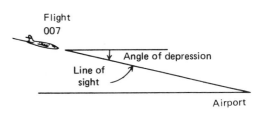
    Figure 5-9b

    a. What is the plane's ground
        distance from the airport?
    b. If the plane descends directly along the line of sight, how far will
        it travel along this line in reaching the airport?

3. *Raindrop Vector Problem:* Raindrops are falling vertically at a speed of 120 kph through air that is moving horizontally at a speed of 40 kph (i.e., the wind speed is 40 kph).

    a. At what angle do the drops strike the ground?
    b. How fast are the drops actually going?

4. *Displacement Vector Problem:* Portia Udell walks on a bearing of 90° (due east) for 100 meters and then on a bearing of 180° (due south) for 182 meters.

    a. What is her bearing from the starting point?
    b. What is the starting point's bearing from her?
    c. How far and along what bearing must Portia walk to go directly back to the starting point?

5. *Swimming Problem 1:* You swim at 3 kph with your body perpendicular to a stream with a current of 5 kph. Your actual velocity is the vector sum of the stream's velocity and your swimming velocity. Find your actual velocity.

6. *Swimming Problem 2:* You swim at 4 kph with your body perpendicular to a stream. But because the water is moving, your actual velocity vector makes an angle of 34° with the direction you are heading.

    a. How fast is the current?
    b. What is the magnitude of your *actual* velocity vector?

7. *Mountain Height Problem:* A surveying crew is given the job of measuring the height of a mountain (Figure 5–9c). From a point on level ground, they measure an angle of elevation to the top of 21°34'. They move 507 meters closer and find the angle is now 35°41'. How high is the mountain? (You may need to calculate some other numbers first!)

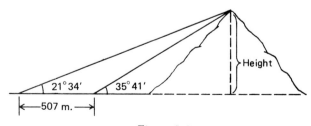

Figure 5-9c

8. *Harbor Problem:* As a ship sails into harbor, the navigator sights a buoy at an angle of 15° to the path of the ship (Figure 5-9d). The ship sails 1300 meters further and finds that the buoy now makes an angle of 29°.

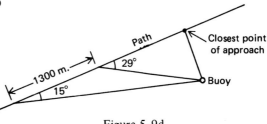

Figure 5-9d

   a. How far is the ship from the buoy at the second sighting?
   b. What is the closest the ship will come to the buoy?
   c. How far must the ship go from the second sighting point to this closest point of approach?
   d. When the ship has gone 7000 meters beyond the second sighting point, what will be the angle from the bow of the ship to the line-of-sight with the buoy?

9. *Missile Problem:* An observer 2 kilometers from the launching pad observes a vertically ascending missile at an angle of elevation of 21°. Five seconds later, the angle has increased to 35°.

   a. How far did the missile travel during the 5-second interval?
   b. What was its average speed during this interval?
   c. If it keeps going vertically at the same average speed, what will its angle of elevation be 15 seconds after the *first* sighting?

10. *Cloud Ceiling Problem:* Ground controllers at airports need to know the "ceiling." That is, they must know how close the bottoms of the clouds come to the ground. One method used is shining a light on the cloud bottoms and observing the angle of elevation to the spot of light, as shown in Figure 5-9e.

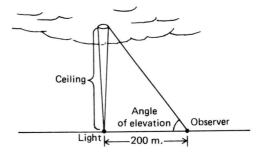

Figure 5-9e

   a. If the observer is 200 meters from the spotlight, write an equation expressing ceiling in terms of angle of elevation.

b. Make a table that an observer could use to find the ceiling when he or she knows the angle of elevation. Use 10° intervals from 10° through 80°.

c. What would the angle of elevation be if the ceiling were 300 meters?

11. *Oil Well Problem 1:* A geologist prospecting for oil finds a likely rock formation outcropping from the ground. The dip angle is 27° (Figure 5-9f).

a. If the oil well is located 5971 feet from the nearest edge of the outcropping, how deep will the driller have to go to reach the formation?

b. If the formation is 54 feet wide where it outcrops, how much further must the driller go to get completely through it?

c. If the geologist's measurements were off by 1° and the dip angle was really 28°, how much deeper would the driller have to go to reach the top of the formation?

12. *Oil Well Problem 2:* Another oil well is to be located on a hillside that slopes at 10° (Figure 5-9g). The desired rock formation has a dip of 27° to the horizontal in the same direction as the hill slope. The well is located 3200 feet downhill from the nearest edge of the outcropping rock formation.

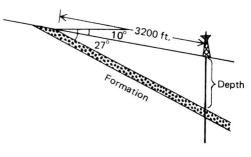

Figure 5-9g

How deep will the driller have to go to reach the top of the formation?

13. *Oil Well Problem 3:* Oil is most likely to be found at a "fault," where the rock formation has cracked and slipped (Figure 5-9h). Suppose that the rock formation is 85 feet higher on one side of the fault. The fault dips at 74° and the formation dips at 27° in the same direction. The fault is 2100 feet from the closest edge of the outcropping formation.

a. How far from the fault should the oil well be located to strike the formation at the point shown?
b. How deep must the well be drilled to reach the formation at this point?

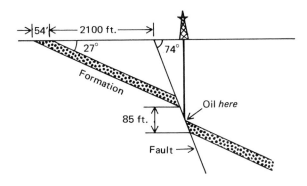

Figure 5-9h

14. *Visibility Problem:* Suppose you are aboard a jet destined for Hawaii. The pilot announces that your altitude is 10 kilometers. Since you have nothing to do but stare at the Pacific Ocean, you decide to calculate how far away the horizon is. You draw a sketch as in **Figure 5-9i** and realize that you must calculate an *arc length*. You recall that the radius of the Earth is about 6400 kilometers. How far away is the horizon along the Earth's curved surface? Surprising?

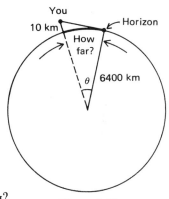

Figure 5-9i

15. *Stump Force Problem:* Joe Jamoke and Ivan Hoe are pulling up a tree stump. Joe can pull with a force of 200 pounds and Ivan with a force of 250 pounds. A total force of 400 pounds is sufficient to pull up the stump.

a. If they pull at an angle of 25° to each other, will the sum of their force vectors be enough to pull up the stump?
b. At what angle must they pull in order to exert *exactly* the 400 pounds needed to pull up the stump?

16. *Airplane Velocity Problem:* An airplane is flying through the air at a speed of 500 km/h. At the same time, the air is moving with respect to the ground at an angle of 23° to the plane's path through the air with a speed of 40 km/h (i.e., the wind speed is 40 km/h). The plane's ground speed is the magnitude of the *vector sum* of the plane's air speed and the air's speed with respect to the ground. Find the plane's ground speed if it is flying

    a. against the wind,
    b. with the wind.

17. *Velocity Components Problem:* As you drive north on Interstate 94 through Chicago, your actual bearing is 311° (N is 0°, E is 90°, S is 180°, and W is 270°). If you are driving at 50 km/h, what is your velocity

    a. in the east-west direction,
    b. in the north-south direction?

18. *Airplane Lift Problem:* When an airplane is in flight, the air pressure creates a force vector, called the "lift," perpendicular to the wings. When the plane banks for a turn, this lift vector may be resolved into horizontal and vertical components. The vertical component has magnitude equal to the plane's weight (this is what holds the plane up), and the horizontal component "pushes" the plane into its curved path. Suppose that a jet plane weighing 500,000 pounds banks at an angle θ (Figure 5–9j).

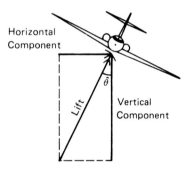

Figure 5-9j

    a. Find the magnitude of the lift and the horizontal component if

        (i) $\theta = 10°$,   (ii) $\theta = 20°$,   (iii) $\theta = 30°$,   (iv) $\theta = 0°$.

    b. Based on your answers to part a, why do you suppose a plane can turn in a *smaller* circle when it banks at a *greater* angle?
    c. Why do you suppose a plane flies *straight* when it is *not* banking?
    d. If the maximum lift the wings can sustain is 600,000 pounds, what is the maximum angle at which the plane can bank?
    e. What *two* things might happen if the plane tried to bank at an angle *steeper* than this maximum?

19. *Canal Barge Problem:* Freda
    Pulliam and Yank Hardy are
    on opposite sides of a canal,
    pulling a barge with tow
    ropes (Figure 5-9k). Freda
    exerts a force of 50 pounds
    at 20° to the canal, and
    Yank pulls at an angle of
    15° with just enough force
    so that the resultant force
    vector is directly along the

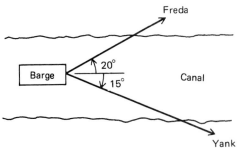

Figure 5-9k

    canal. Find the number of pounds with which Yank must pull and the
    magnitude of the resultant vector.

20. *Cold Front Problem:* The Weather Bureau reports that a cold front
    has just passed Austin and is heading toward San Antonio at 42 kph.
    Since you know that San Antonio is 126 kilometers from Austin, you
    first think you have 126/42 = 3 hours before the front arrives there.
    However, you realize that triangles and vectors are involved. You find
    out the following information:

    > San Antonio's bearing from Austin is 217°, measured clockwise
    > from north. The cold front lies along a line whose bearing is 63°,
    > measured clockwise from north, and its movement is perpendicu-
    > lar to that line.

    How long will it *really* be until the front reaches San Antonio?

21. *Ship's Velocity Problem:*
    A ship is sailing through the
    water in the English Chan-
    nel with a velocity of 22
    knots along a bearing of
    157°, as shown in Figure
    5-9ℓ. (A knot is a nautical
    mile per hour, or slightly
    faster than a regular mile
    per hour.) The current has
    a velocity of 5 knots along
    a bearing of 213°. (Navi-
    gators measure bearings
    clockwise from north.)

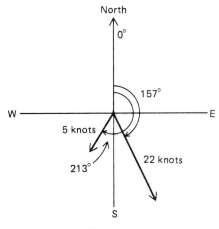

Figure 5-9ℓ

The *actual* velocity of the ship is the vector sum of the ship's velocity and the water's velocity (i.e., the current). Find the actual velocity.

22. *Wind Velocity Problem:* A navigator on an airplane knows that the plane's velocity through the air is 250 kph on a bearing of 237° measured clockwise from north. By observing the motion of the plane's shadow across the ground, she finds to her surprise that the plane's ground speed is only 52 kph, and its direction is along a bearing of 15°. She realizes that ground velocity is the vector sum of the plane's air velocity and the velocity of the wind. What wind velocity would account for the observed ground velocity?

23. *Detour Problem:* Suppose that you are pilot of a commercial airliner. You find it necessary to detour around a group of thunder-showers (Figure 5–9m). You turn at an angle of 21° to your original path, fly for a while, turn, and intercept your original path at an angle of 35°, 70 kilometers from where you left it.

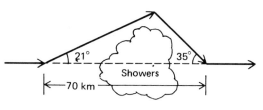

Figure 5-9m

a. How much further did you have to go because of the detour?
b. What area is enclosed by this triangle?

24. *Surveying Problem 1 :* A surveyor measures the three sides of a triangular field and gets 114, 165, and 257 meters.

a. What is the measure of the largest angle of the triangle?
b. What is the area of the field?

25. *Surveying Problem 2 :* A field has the shape of a quadrilateral that is *not* a rectangle. Three sides measure 50, 60, and 70 meters, and two angles measure 127° and 132° (Figure 5–9n).

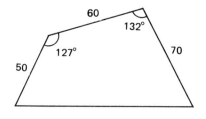

Figure 5-9n

a. By dividing the quadrilateral into two triangles, find its area.

You may have to find some intermediate sides and angles first.
b.   Find the length of the fourth side.
c.   Find the measures of the other two angles.

26. *Surveying Problem 3:*
Surveyors can find the area
of an irregularly shaped tract
of land by taking "field
notes." These notes con-
sist of the length of each
side and information for
finding each angle measure.
Then, starting at one vertex, the tract is divided into
triangles. For the first triangle, two sides and the included angle are known
(Figure 5–9o), so its area
can be calculated. To calcu-

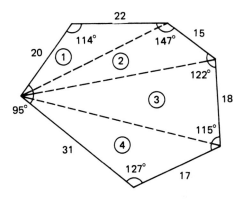

Figure 5-9o

late the area of the second triangle, you must recognize that one of its
sides is also the *third* side of the *first* triangle, and one of its angles is
an angle of the polygon (147° Figure 5–9o) *minus* an angle of the first
triangle. By calculating this side and angle and using the next side of
the polygon (15 in Figure 5–9o), you can calculate the area of the
second triangle. The areas of the remaining triangles are calculated in
the same manner. The area of the tract is the *sum* of the areas of the
triangles.

a. Write a computer program for calculating the area of a tract, using
the technique described above. The input should be the sides and
angles of the polygon, and the output should be the area of the
tract. As a check on your program, you can have it print out the
intermediate sides and angles.
b. Use your program to show that the area of the tract in Figure 5–9o
is 1029.69 square units.
c. Show that the last side of the polygon is calculated to be
30.6817 units, which is close to the measured value of 31.
d. The polygon in Figure 5–9o is called a *convex polygon,* because
none of its angles measure more than 180°. Explain why your
program might give *wrong* answers if the polygon were *not* convex.

For Problems 27 through 30, suppose that the country of Parah has just launched two satellites. The government of Noya sends aloft its most self-reliant astronaut, Ivan Advantage, to observe the satellites.

27. *Ivan Problem 1:* As Ivan approaches the two satellites, he finds that one of them is 8 kilometers from him and the other is 11 kilometers, and the angle between the two (with Ivan at the vertex) is 120°. How far apart are the satellites?

28. *Ivan Problem 2:* Several orbits later as he is about to re-enter, only Satellite No. 1 is visible to Ivan, the other one being near the opposite side of the Earth (Figure 5–9p). He determines that Angle A measures 37°43′, Angle B measures 113°00′, and the distance between him and Satellite No. 1 is 4362 kilometers. Correct to the nearest kilometer, how far apart are Ivan and Satellite 2?

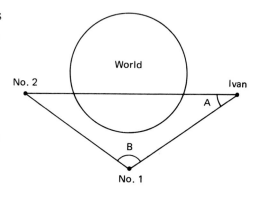

Figure 5-9p

29. *Ivan Problem 3:* Three ships are assigned to rescue Ivan as his spacecraft plunges into the ocean. The ships are at the vertices of a triangle with sides of 5, 7, and 10 kilometers.

a. Find the measure of the largest angle of this triangle.
b. Find the area of ocean in the triangular region bounded by the three ships.

30. *Ivan Problem 4:* To welcome their returning hero, the Noyacs give Ivan a parade. The parade goes between the cities of Om, Mann, and Tra. These cities are at the vertices of an equilateral triangle. The roads connecting them are straight, level, and direct, and the parade goes at a constant speed with no stops. From Om to Mann takes 80 minutes, from Mann to Tra takes 80 minutes, but from Tra back to Om takes 1 hour and 20 minutes. How do you explain the discrepancy in times?

31. *CB Radio Problem:* A CB radio operator has a base station on Farm Road 1984, 8 miles from where it intersects Highway 87

(Figure 5–9q). The farm road makes an angle of 32° with the highway. If the radio has a range of 5 miles, between what two distances from the intersection can cars on the highway hear the base station radio?

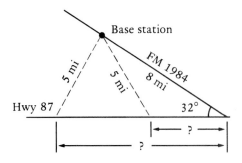

Figure 5-9q

32. *Grand Piano Problem:*   The lid on a grand piano is held open by a prop 28 inches long. The base of the prop is 55 inches from the lid's hinges (Figure 5-9r). At what possible distances along the lid could you place the end of the prop so that the lid makes an angle of 26° with the piano?

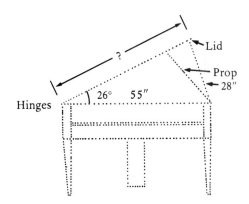

Figure 5-9r

33. *Torpedo Problem:* Suppose that you are Torpedo Officer aboard the U.S.S. Skipjack. Your submarine is conducting torpedo practice off the Florida coast. The target is 7200 meters from you on a bearing of 276° and is steaming on a course of 68° (Figure 5-9s).   You have long-range torpedoes that will go 6400 meters, and short-range torpe-

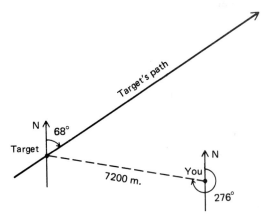

Figure 5-9s

does that will go 3200 meters. Between what two bearings can you fire torpedoes that will reach the target's path if you use

a. long-range torpedoes,
b. short-range torpedoes?

34. *Alligator Problem:* Calvin Butterball is swimming in Lake Rancid when he spots two alligators. He tells you that his distance to Alligator 1 is 30 meters, the distance between the alligators is 20 meters, and the angle at Calvin is 58° (Figure 5–9t).

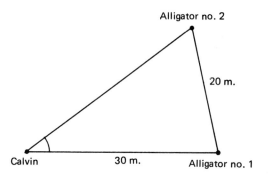

Figure 5-9t

a. Show Calvin that he must have made a mistake in measurement, since there is no such triangle.
b. Find the *two* possible distances between Calvin and Alligator 2 using the *correct* angle, 28°.

35. *Equation Problem:* Find the general solution for

$$\cos 50 = \cos 30.$$

36. *Identity Problem:* Prove that the following is an identity:

$$\frac{2 \tan A}{2 - \sec^2 A} = \tan 2A.$$

37. *Graphing Problem:* Sketch the graph of $y = \text{Arcsec } x$.

38. Write the exact value of $\cos \pi$.

39. In $\tan x = 0.8$, find the exact value of $\tan 2x$.

40. *Rational Tangent Problem:* Prove that if $\tan x$ is a rational number, then $\tan 2x$ is also a rational number.

5–10   CHAPTER REVIEW AND TEST

At the beginning of this chapter are listed five specific objectives. These are summarized below.

1. Solve right triangle problems, given

   a. two sides,
   b. one side and one acute angle.

2. Solve oblique triangle problems, given

   a. two sides and the included angle,
   b. three sides,
   c. one side, the opposite angle, and one other side or angle.

3. Find the area of a triangle, given two sides and the included angle measure.

4. Add and resolve vectors.

5. Solve real-world problems involving triangles.

The review problems below are designed to measure your ability to accomplish these objectives when you are *told* which one is being tested. The chapter test is designed to measure how well you can apply all of these techniques to the analysis of a single real-world problem, selecting whichever technique is appropriate for the part you are working on.

Review Problems

The following problems are numbered according to the five objectives listed above.

1. a. Right triangle XYZ has hypotenuse of length $y = 14.7$ centimeters and one leg of length $z = 8.3$ centimeters. Find x and the measures of the acute angles.

   b. Right triangle BJF has $m \angle B = 39°54'$ and hypotenuse $f = 19$ kilometers. Find $b, j,$ and $m \angle J$.

2. a. Triangle FUN has $u = 14, n = 13,$ and $m \angle F = 145°20'$. Find f, $m \angle U$, and $m \angle N$.

   b. Triangle GYM has $g = 7, y = 8,$ and $m = 13$. Find the measures of the three angles.

c. i. Triangle BAS has m∠B = 123°, m∠S = 56°, and a = 10 millimeters. Find the lengths of the other two sides. Surprising?

ii. Triangle TWO has o = 20 meters, t = 12 meters, and m∠T = 31°.
Find the *two* possible values of w.

3. Find the area of △FUN in Problem 2a.

4. Vectors $\vec{a}$ and $\vec{b}$, which have magnitudes 6 and 10, respectively, make an angle of 174° with each other, as shown in Figure 5–10a. Find the magnitude of $\vec{a} - \vec{b}$ and the angle that this difference vector makes with $\vec{a}$ when placed tail-to-tail.

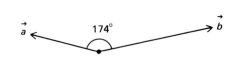

Figure 5–10a

5. The rotor on a helicopter creates an upward force vector. To move forward, the pilot tilts the helicopter forward. The vertical component of the force vector (the "lift") holds the helicopter up, and the horizontal component (the "thrust") makes it move forward.

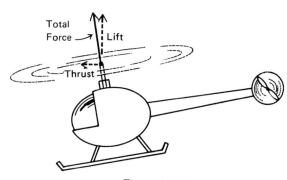

Figure 5–10b

Suppose that a helicopter tilts forward at a sufficient angle to generate a thrust of 400 pounds. The helicopter weighs 3000 pounds, so the lift has a magnitude of 3000 pounds.

a. What angle does the helicopter make with the ground?

b. What total force must the rotor generate?

Chapter Test

Work each part of the following problem. Then tell which one or ones of the five objectives of the chapter you used in working that part of the problem.

As a jet plane takes off, its path makes a fairly steep angle to the ground. The plane itself makes an even steeper angle. Its velocity vector may be resolved into two components, as shown in Figure 5–10c. The axial component (the one directed along the plane's axis) is the

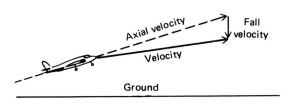

Figure 5–10c

plane's velocity ignoring the action of gravity. The vertical component is the velocity at which the plane is "falling" under the influence of gravity.

1. A plane's velocity vector is 250 kph at an angle of $10°$ to the ground. The plane's axis makes an angle of $15°$ with the ground.

    a. Find the speed in the axial direction.
    b. Find the speed at which the plane is falling.
    c. Find the area of the triangle formed by the three vectors.

2. If the plane maintains an angle of $15°$ with the ground, and the fall vector stays the same as in Problem 1:

    a. What is the minimum speed the plane can go without going downward? (That is, the velocity vector must be *horizontal.*)
    b. At this minimum speed, what will the axial velocity vector equal?

3. The plane increases its speed to 700 kph. The navigator determines the axial speed to be 702 kph and the fall speed to be the same as in Problem 1. What angle does the plane's path make with the ground?

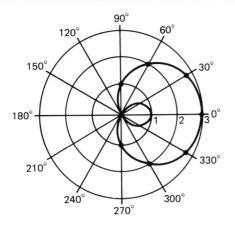

In this chapter you will see how square roots of negative numbers unify algebra and trigonometry. The resulting mathematical techniques allow you to calculate circular function values to an accuracy needed for space flight.

CHAPTER 6

In this chapter you will apply the concepts of trigonometry to topics in mathematics. First you will see how angles in standard position lead to a new coordinate system, *polar coordinates*. Periodic functions plotted in polar coordinates have shapes that apply in topics ranging from figure skating to orbitals of atoms. Then you will see how polar coordinates make sense out of complex numbers, which involve square roots of negative numbers. These "imaginary" numbers have very real applications in vectors and electricity. Finally, you will see how complex numbers, cleverly applied to polynomials, lead to infinite series with which trigonometric function values can be calculated using only arithmetic, to the accuracy needed to get spaceships to remote destinations.

Specific objectives for this chapter are:

1. Given a polar equation, draw the graph in polar coordinates, either by hand or by computer graphics.
2. Given a polar equation, transform it to Cartesian coordinates, and vice versa.
3. Given two polar equations, find the intersection points of their graphs.
4. Given complex numbers, transform to polar form and operate with them in that form.
5. Given vectors, write them as complex numbers, and add or subtract them in that form.
6. Given a value of x, calculate $\sin x$ or $\cos x$ to as many decimal places as desired using infinite series.

6-1 POLAR COORDINATES

You have been plotting graphs such as $f(\theta) = \cos\theta$ by letting θ be a distance along the horizontal axis. A more natural way to plot such graphs is for θ to be an angle in standard position. Then $f(\theta)$ is represented by a distance from the origin along the terminal side of the angle. A graph drawn this way is said to be in a *polar* coordinate system. Figure 6-1a shows the same point located by Cartesian coordinates x and y on the right, and by polar coordinates, θ and r (for radius) on the right.

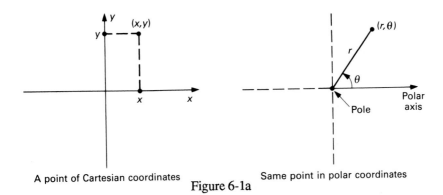

A point of Cartesian coordinates   Same point in polar coordinates
Figure 6-1a

Polar coordinates are written (r, θ). This is a reversal of the usual agreement that the independent variable comes first.

DEFINITION

The *pole* is the point corresponding to the origin.

The *polar axis* is a ray starting at the pole and going horizontally to the right.

θ is the measure of an angle in standard position.

r is the directed distance from the pole to the point (r, θ).

There are two surprises with polar coordinates. First, one point has many different ordered pairs. For (r, θ), any angle coterminal with θ gives a different representation of the same point. Figure 6-1b shows three ways to represent $(5, 60°)$.

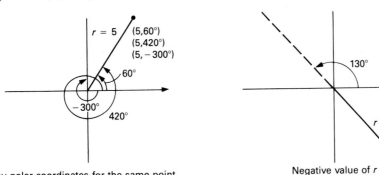

Many polar coordinates for the same point   Negative value of r $(-7, 130°)$

Figure 6-1b   Figure 6-1c

Objective:

Be able to plot points in a Polar Co-ordinate System.

Example 1:   Plot the points
(4, 30°), (3, –120°), (–6, 45°), and
(–2, –90).

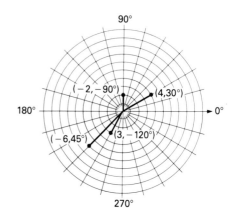

Figure 6-1d shows these points.
You should be careful not to fall into
the trap of thinking $r = 0$ at the inner
circle. Actually, $r = 0$ at the pole,
and $r = 1$ at the inner circle.

Figure 6-1d

Example 2: Write two other ordered pairs for the point (4, 30°), one with a
positive value of r, and the other with a negative value of r.

For a positive value of r, the angle needs to be coterminal with 30°. So all
you need to do is add a multiple of 360°. Some possible values are
(4, 390°), (4, 720°), (4, –330°).

For a negative vaue of r, the angle must terminate half a revolution from
30°, at 210°. Any angle coterminal with 210° will do. Some possible values
are (–4, 210°), (–4, 570°), (–4, –150°).

Once you have learned to plot points, you can draw graphs of functions in
polar coordinates. In this section you will plot graphs pointwise. When
you are sure you know what is happening, you will draw more complicated polar graphs in the next section by computer graphics.

Example 3: Plot the graph of $r = 3 + 7 \cos \theta$.

You can use a programmable calculator or computer to get plotting data
quickly. Otherwise, you can calculate points one by one with a regular
calculator. It is not necessary for you to write down the data unless your
instructor calls for it.

θ	r
0	10
15	9.76
30	9.06
45	7.95
60	6.5
75	4.81
90	3
105	1.19
120	−0.5
135	−1.95
150	−3.06
180	−4

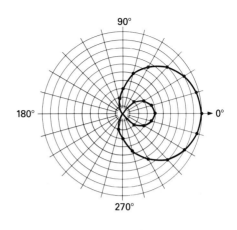

Figure 6-1e

Beyond 180° the values repeat themselves. Once the points are plotted, you connect them with a smooth curve, as shown in Figure 6-1e. Where r is negative, the graph has a "loop."

The figure in Example 2 is called a *limaçon*. from a French word for "snail." Limaçons are polar graphs of sinusoids with period of one revolution, and thus have the general equation below.

> *General Equation of a Limaçon:*
> $r = c + a \cos (\theta - d)$

If a is greater than c as in Example 2, then r will take on negative values. These negative values are what cause the loop in the limaçon. As you will see in the following exercise, limaçons also come without loops.

Limaçons are of particular interest since their reciprocals turn out to be conic sections (circles, parabolas, ellipses, and hyperbolas).

Exercise 6-1

For Problems 1 through 8, draw a graph of the given point in polar coordinates. Then give *two* other pairs of polar coordinates for the point, one with a positive value of r and the other with a negative value of r.

1. (6, 40°)   2. (8, 70°)   3. (3, 150°)   4. (2, 120°)
5. (−7, 30°)   6. (−4, 50°)   7. (−5, 250°)   8. (−6, 210°)

For Problems 9 through 14, plot the graph in polar coordinates. Pick a large enough domain for θ to generate the entire graph.

9. $r = 1 + 2 \sin \theta$
10. $r = 4 + 6 \cos \theta$
11. $r = 5 + 4 \cos \theta$
12. $r = 3 + 2 \sin \theta$
13. $r = 1 + \sin \theta$
14. $r = 2 + 2 \cos \theta$

15. *Limaçon Conclusions Problem*: Each graph in Problems 9 through 14 is a limaçon. How can you tell just by looking at the equation whether or not the graph will have a loop?

16. *Cardioid Conclusions Problem*: The graphs for Problems 13 and 14 are special cases of limaçons in which the graph just touches the pole, but does not go through it. These graphs are called *cardioids*. What must be true about the coefficients in the limaçon equation for the graph to be a cardioid? What does the name "cardioid" mean?

In Problems 17 through 22 you will learn what the graph of each trigonometric function looks like in polar coordinates. Use a scale that is large enough for you to be able to see the shape of the graph. For instance, in Problems 17 and 18 you might use 10 spaces in the r-direction for each unit.

17. $r = \cos \theta$ 18. $r = \sin \theta$
19. $r = \tan \theta$ 20. $r = \cot \theta$
21. $r = \csc \theta$ 22. $r = \sec \theta$

23. *Sine and Cosine Polar Graphs Problem:* From the graphs in Problems 17 and 18, make a conjecture about the shape of the graph of $r = \cos \theta$ and $r = \sin \theta$.

24. *Secant and Cosecant Polar Graphs Problem:* From the graphs in Problems 17 and 18, make a conjecture about the shape of the graph of $r = \sec \theta$ and $r = \csc \theta$.

25. Quick! Sketch the graph of $r = 5$. Describe the graph.

26. Quick!! Sketch the graph of $\theta = 60°$. Describe the graph.

27. *Triangle Problem:* Figure 6-1f
    shows a vertical line at a distance of
    7 units from the pole in a polar co-
    ordinate system. Let (r, θ) be the
    polar coordinates of a point on this
    line.

    a. Use the properties of right trian-
        gles to get an equation express-
        ing r in terms of θ.
    b. State the relationship between
        part (a) of this problem and your
        conjecture in Problem 24.

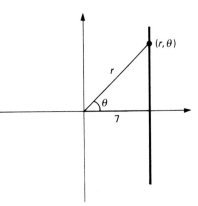

Figure 6-1f

28. *Triangle Problem:* Figure 6-1g
    shows a circle of diameter 10 units
    centered on the polar axis, passing
    through the pole. Let (r, θ) be the
    polar coordinates of a point on the
    circle.

    a. How do you know that the tri-
        angle shown in the figure is a
        right triangle?
    b. Use the properties of right
        triangles to write an equation
        expressing r in terms of θ.
    c. State the relationship between
        part (b) of this problem and
        your conjecture in Problem 23.

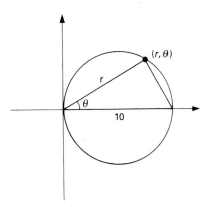

Figure 6-1g

29. *Identity Problem:* Prove that this equation is an identity.

$$\sec x \cos x \tan^2 x = \sec^2 x - 1$$

30. *Equation Problem:* If $r = 4 + 6 \cos \theta$, find the first positive value of
    x for which the graph touches the pole.

6-2 POLAR GRAPHS BY COMPUTER

Once you understand how to plot polar graphs, you can learn their properties more quickly by having a computer draw the graphs for you. The program PLOT POLAR on the accompanying disk, or similar plotting program, can be used.

Objective:

Discover properties of polar graphs, using computer graphics to do the
plotting.

Example: For the function $r = 8 \cos \theta$, do the following.

a. Plot the graph by computer, using the domain $0° \le \theta \le 360°$.
b. Explain what is happening on the screen when θ is between 90° and
180°.
c. Explain what is happening on the screen when θ is between 180° and
360°.

The following description is for the program PLOT CONIC. Other instructions will apply if your are using different software.

a. Load the program into the computer. Then type

LIST 1

On line 1 the function to be plotted is defined. To enter $r = 8 \cos \theta$,
type

1 DEF FNR(T) = 8 · COS(T)

Then type RUN. You may use the scale shown. Use 1 revolution.
Using 180 points per revolution gives a reasonably smooth graph
reasonably fast. You may instruct the computer to show the whole
screen.

The completed graph is shown in Figure 6-2a. It should be a circle. If
not, either adjust the vertical size on your monitor or use the variable
WF (for "width factor") as described in the Instructor's Guide.

b. The moving dot shows the location of θ as the graph is being plotted. When θ is between 90° and 180°, the dot is in the second quadrant, but the graph is being plotted in the fourth quadrant. This happens because $\cos \theta$ is *negative* when θ is in Quadrant II.

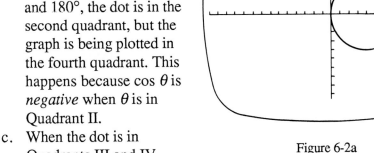

Figure 6-2a

c. When the dot is in Quadrants III and IV, nothing seems to be happening to the graph! This is because the graph is being *retraced* for these values of θ.

In the following exercise you will plot more polar graphs, and try to reach some conclusions about them.

Exercise 6-2

For problems 1 through 6, plot the graphs of the six trigonometric functions to confirm, the plotting you did in Problems 17 through 22 of Exercise 6-1. You will have to be clever for Problems 4 through 6 because the cotangent, cosecant, and secant functions are not available in BASIC. Change scales to make the graph fill the screen.

1. $r = \cos \theta$ 2. $r = \sin \theta$
3. $r = \tan \theta$ 4. $r = \cot \theta$
5. $r = \csc \theta$ 6. $r = \sec \theta$

7. *Polar Equations of Lines Problem:*

   a. Plot the polar graphs of the following.
      i. $r = 3 \sec \theta$
      ii. $r = 3 \sec (\theta - 60°)$ You must convert 60° to radians since PLOT POLAR uses radian measure of angles.
   b. Each graph is a *line*. How far is the line from the pole in each case?
   c. What is the effect on the graph of subtracting 60° in part (ii)?
   d. What would be the equation of a *horizontal* line, passing 3 units above the pole? Transform the equation, if necessary, so that it is in as simple a form as possible.

8. *Polar Equations of Circles Problem*:

    a.   Plot the polar graphs of the following.
        i. $r = 5 \sin \theta$
        ii. $r = 2 \cos \theta$
        iii. $r = -4 \cos \theta$
        iv. $r = -6 \sin \theta$

    b.   Each of the graphs in part (a) is a circle. What special point do all these graphs go through? How does the equation tell you where the center will be and what the diameter is?

    c.   Predict what the graph of $r = 8 \cos (\theta - 60°)$ will look like. Then confirm your prediction by computer graphics. You must convert the 60° to radians since PLOT POLAR uses radian measure of angles.

9. *Rose Problem*: The graph of $r = k \cos n\theta$, where k and n are constants, and n is an integer, is called a *rose*. Figure 6-2b shows the graph of $r = 8 \cos 3\theta$, which is a *three-leaved* rose.

    a. Plot the graph of $r = 8 \cos 3\theta$ on your computer. Does it look like Figure 6-2b?

    b. Plot the graph of $r = 8 \cos 5\theta$. Make a conjecture about how you can tell from the equation how many leaves the rose will have.

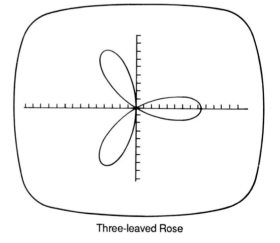

Three-leaved Rose

Figure 6-2b

    c. Plot the graph of $r = 8 \cos 2\theta$. How many leaves does it have? Was your conjecture in part (b) correct? If not, make another conjecture.

    d. Test your conjecture on other roses.

10. *Limaçon Problem*: The graph of $r = c + a \cos \theta$ is a limaçon.

    a. Plot $r = 5 + 3 \cos \theta$.

b. Plot $r = 3 + 5 \cos \theta$.
c. Plot $r = 4 + 4 \cos \theta$.
d. Plot $r = 0 + 8 \cos \theta$.
e. How can you tell just by looking at the particular equation whether or not the limaçon will have a loop?
f. What special name is given to the limaçon $r = 4 + 4 \cos \theta$?
g. What special graph is the limaçon in part (d)?

11. *Conic Section Problem:* If $r = f(\theta)$ is a limaçon, then the reciprocal, $r = \dfrac{1}{f(\theta)}$, turns out to be a circle, ellipse, hyperbola, or parabola (a "conic section"). The following are the reciprocals of the limaçons in Problem 9, multiplied by 10 so that the graph fills the computer screen.

a. Plot $r = 10(5 + 3 \cos \theta)$.
b. Plot $r = 10(3 + 5 \cos \theta)$.
c. Plot $r = 10(4 + 4 \cos \theta)$.
d. Tell which conic section each graph in parts (a) through (c) is.
e. What seems to be the relationship between the kind of limaçon and the kind of conic section?

12. *Spiral Problem:* If r increases in some regular manner as θ increases, the graph will be a spiral.

a. Plot three revolutions of the spiral $r = \dfrac{2\theta}{\pi}$, where θ is in radians.

    At what points does the graph cross the horizontal and vertical axes? How would you describe this spiral? Think of something in the real world shaped like this kind of spiral.
b. Plot four revolutions of the spiral $r = 1.1^{\theta}$, where θ is in radians. This is called an *equiangular* or *logarithmic* spiral. The spiral nautilus has a shell that grows in the shape of this kind of spiral. How does an equiangular spiral differ from the spiral in part (a)?
c. Plot two revolutions of the spiral $r = 0.2\ \theta^{1.5}$, where θ is in radians. This is called an *Archimedean* spiral, after Archimedes. Rotary pumps, lawnmowers, etc., have bases made in the shape of this kind of spiral. How does an Archimedean spiral differ from a logarithmic spiral?

For problems 13 through 16, plot the polar graph.

13. Plot $r = 9 \cos\frac{\theta}{2}$. Use two revolutions.

14. Plot the *bifolium* $r = 20 \sin\theta \cos^2\theta$. Why do you suppose the graph is called a "bifolium?"

15. Plot the *conchoic of Nichomedes*, $r = 3 \csc\theta + 5$.

16. Plot the *lemniscate of Bernoulli*, $r^2 = 9 \cos 2\theta$. What happens to the graph when $\cos 2\theta$ is negative?

For Problems 17 through 20, the graph of a polar equation is shown. Figure out what the equation is. Then try it on the computer to make sure the graph is correct.

17.

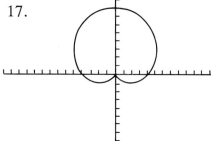

18.

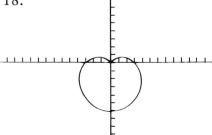

19.

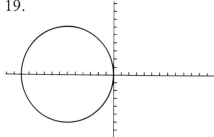

20.

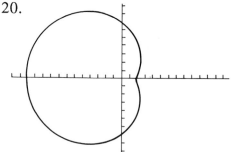

21. *Identity Problem*: Prove that this is an identity.

$$\cos 4x = \cos^2 x - 6 \cos^2 x \sin^2 x + \sin^4 x$$

22. *Equation Problem*: Find all values of θ from $0°$ through $360°$ for which

$$\sin\theta \cos\theta = 0.25$$

23. *Triangle Problem*: Find the third side and the area of a triangle with
    two sides 17 cm and 23 cm, and the included angle Arccos (-0.3).

24. *Graphing Problem*: Sketch the graph of the inverse circular function
    $y = 0.5 \text{ Sin}^{-1} x$.

6-3 POLAR-CARTESIAN TRANSFORMATIONS

For any given polar curve, it is possible to find a Cartesian equation with
the same curve for its graph. The polar equation can be transformed by
substituting for r and θ in terms of x and y. Figure 6-3a shows that

$$\frac{x}{r} = \cos \theta \text{ and } \frac{y}{r} = \sin \theta.$$

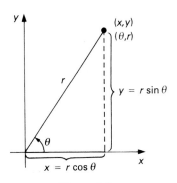

Multiplying each member of both equations by r
gives equations for x and y. The radius, r, can be
expressed in terms of x and y by the Pythagorean
theorem.

Figure 6-3a

Polar-Cartesian Transformations

$x = r \cos \theta$ and $y = r \sin \theta$

$r = \pm \sqrt{x^2 + y^2}$

Objective:

Given a polar equation, transform it to Cartesian coordinates, and vice
versa. If possible, identify the shape of the graph from its Cartesian equation.

Example 1: Transform $r = 6 \cos \theta$ to Cartesian coordinates. Identify the
graph from its Cartesian equation.

Multiplying each member of the equation by r gives r^2 on the left, and $r \cos$
θ on the right. Each expression is easy to represent in terms of x and y.

$r^2 = 6r \cos \theta$

$x^2 + y^2 = 6x$

$x^2 + y^2 - 6x = 0$

This is the equation of a *circle* since it is a quadratic relation in which the two squared terms have equal coefficients.

In case you need a review, the following table tells you how to recognize the graph of a quadratic relation from its equation.

Recognition of Conic Sections from Their Equations

If $Ax^2 + Cy^2 + Dx + Ey + F = 0$, the following features allow you to tell which conic section the graph will be:

Circle	x^2 and y^2 have *equal* coefficients.
Ellipse:	x^2 and y^2 have *unequal* coefficients, but the *same* sign.
Hyperbola:	x^2 and y^2 coefficients have *opposite* signs.
Parabola:	Only *one* squared term.

Note: If the equation has a term Bxy, the discriminant $B^2 - 4AC$ must be used. $B^2 - 4AC$ positive implies hyperbola, $B^2 - 4AC$ negative implies ellipse, $B2 - 4AC = 0$ implies parabola.

Example 2: Transform the ellipse $3x^2 + 4y^2 - 6x - 9 = 0$ to polar coordinates. Transform the resulting equation so that r is expressed explicitly in terms of θ.

The first part of the transformation is a simple substitution.

$$3r^2 \cos^2 \theta + 4r^2 \sin^2 \theta - 6r \cos\theta - 9 = 0$$

The second part requires some clever algebra and trigonometry. The secret is to make the $\cos^2 \theta$ and $\sin^2 \theta$ have equal coefficients. Adding and subtracting $r^2 \cos^2 \theta$ gives

$$4r^2 \cos^2 \theta + 4r^2 \sin^2 \theta - r^2 \cos^2 \theta - 6r \cos \theta - 9 = 0.$$

Associating terms and factoring gives

$$4r^2(\cos^2 \theta + \sin^2 \theta) - (r \cos \theta + 3)^2 = 0.$$

Making use of the Pythagorean properties and doing appropriate algebra enables you to isolate the r.

$$4r^2 = (r \cos \theta + 3)^2$$

$$2r = r \cos \theta + 3$$

$$2r - r \cos \theta = 3$$

$$r(2 - \cos \theta) = 3$$

$$r = \frac{3}{2 - \cos \theta}$$

Note that the answer involves the reciprocal of the equation of a limaçon. In the following exercise you will prove that the reciprocal of a limaçon equation is *always* a conic section.

Exercise 6-3

For problems 1 through 8,

  a. Transform the equation to Cartesian coordinates and simplify.
  b. Tell which of the conic sections the graph will be.

1. $r = 8 \cos \theta$

2. $r = 8 \sin \theta$

3. $r = \dfrac{3}{1 + 2 \cos \theta}$

4. $r = \dfrac{3}{2 - \cos \theta}$

5. $r = \dfrac{11}{6 - 5 \cos \theta}$

6. $r = \dfrac{5}{2 + 3 \cos \theta}$

7. $r = \dfrac{2}{1 + \cos \theta}$

8. $r = \dfrac{2}{1 - \sin \theta}$

For Problems 9 through 14, transform the equation to Cartesian coordinates and simplify, eliminating any radicals.

9. $r = 1 + \sin \theta$

10. $r = 1 + \cos \theta$

11. $r = \sin \theta \tan \theta$

11. $r = 2 \cos \theta + 3 \sin \theta$

12. $r = \tan^2 \theta \sec \theta$

14. $r = \cos 2\theta$

For Problems 15 through 20, transform the given equation to polar coordinates. If possible, solve for r in terms of θ.

15. $y = x^2$

16. $y^2 = x$

17. $x^2 + y^2 = 25$

18. $x^2 - y^2 = 25$

19. $x^2 + y^2 + 2x = 0$

20. $x^2 + y^2 - 4y = 0$

21. *Limaçons and Conic Sections Problem:* The general equation of a limaçon is $r = c + a \cos \theta$.

 a. Prove that the graph of the reciprocal equation,

$$r = \frac{1}{c + a \cos \theta}$$

 is a conic section by showing that its Cartesian equation is a quadratic relation.

 b. Prove that when the limaçon has a loop, the graph of the reciprocal equation is a hyperbola.

 c. Prove that when the limaçon is a cardiod, the graph of the reciprocal equation is a parabola.

 d. Prove that when the licaçon has no loop and does not touch the pole, the graph of the reciprocal equation is an ellipse.

 e. Prove that when $c = 0$, the graph of the reciprocal equation is a straight line.

22. *Polar Equations of Lines Problem:* Figure 6-3b shows a line in a polar coordinate system. Its perpendicular distance from the pole is k units and an angle α to the polar axis. (r, θ) is a variable point on the line.

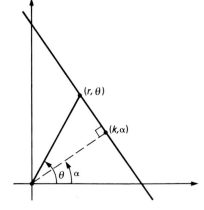

 a. Prove that the polar equation of the line is

 $r = k \sec (\theta - \alpha)$

 b. Sketch the graph of:

Figure 6-3b

 i. $r = 2 \sec \theta$

 ii. $r = -0.5 \sec \theta$

 iii. $r = 2 \sec (\theta - 45°)$

 iv. $r = 5 \sec (\theta - 150°)$

 c. Write the particular equation for the line described.

 i. perpendicular to the polar axis, passing 5 units from the pole

 ii. perpendicular to the line $0 = -70°$, passing 3 units from the pole

23. *General Polar Equation of a Circle:* Figure 6-3c shows a circle in a polar coordinate system. Its center is at the fixed point (k, α). Its radius is the fixed distance a. (r, θ) is a variable point on the circle.

    a. Use the Law of Cosines to show that the general equation of the circle is

$$a^2 = r^2 + k^2 - 2rk \cos(\theta - \alpha).$$

    b. For the circle

$$r^2 - 10r \cos(\theta - 60°) + 16 = 0$$

    do the following.

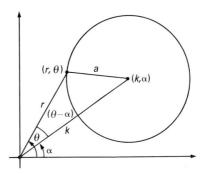

Figure 6-3c

    i.   Find the polar coordinates of the center.
    ii. Find the radius of the circle. (You will need the answer to part (i) above and some clever algebra.
    iii. Find the *two* values of r for which $\theta = 90°$.
    iv. Show that there are *no* values of r for which $\theta = 0°$.

24. *Polar Equation of Circle from Graph Problem:*

    a. Using graph paper, compass, and protractor, draw a circle of radius 8 units, centered at $(5, 60°)$.
    b. Write the polar equation of this circle.
    c. Substitute $120°$ for θ. Solve the resulting quadratic equation to find the two possible values of r.
    d. Show that these two calculated values are consistent with your graph in part (a).

25. *Vector Problem:* Two sharks pull on the Orca. Jaws I pulls with a force of 2000 pounds and Jaws II pulls with 3000 pounds. The angle between the two sharks is $33°$. What is the magnitude of the resultant force vector?

26. *Rotary Motion Problem:* A wheel is turning with an angular velocity of 5 revolutions per second. To the nearest foot per second, what is the linear velocity of a point 3 feet from the axle of the wheel?

27. *Equation Problem:* Solve for $\theta \, \varepsilon \, [-180°, 180°]$:

$$\cos \theta \cos 73° - \sin \theta \sin 73° = -0.5 \sqrt{3}$$

28. *Identity Problem:* Prove that this is an identity.

$$2 \sin^2 x \cot x = \sin 2x$$

29. *Figure Skating Problem:* Figure 6-3d shows a roller skating loop as it appears in a manual of the Roller Skating Rink Operations Association of America. The figure is composed of arcs of circles that represent as closely as possible a limaçon. Assuming that the figure is a limaçon, write an equation for it. Confirm that your equation is correct by plotting the graph on the computer. You may need to adust the constants in the equation so that the graph will fit on the screen.

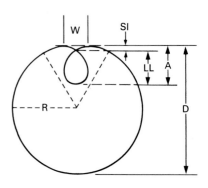

Figure 6-3d

30. Prove that the graph of $r = \dfrac{1}{(a + b \cos \theta)}$ is always a conic section. Tell what the relationship between a and b must be for the graph to be the following.

   a. an ellipse
   b. a hyperbola
   c. a parabola
   d. a circle

6-4   SYSTEMS OF POLAR EQUATIONS

Figure 6-4a shows two circles plotted on the same polar coordinate system using the program PLOT POLAR TWO on the accompanying disk. Their equations are

$$r = 12 \cos \theta,$$
$$r = 6 \sin \theta.$$

The graphs intersect at two points, the pole and a point in the first quadrant.

To calculate the exact locations of these points, it seems reasonable to do what you did to find intersections of graphs in Cartesian coordinates — solve the two equations as a system.

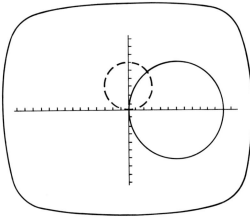

With polar coordinates, however, there turn out to be surprises! The variable r can be eliminated by substitution, giving

Figure 6-4a

$$6 \sin \theta = 12 \cos \theta.$$

Dividing by $\cos \theta$ gives $\tan \theta$ on the left. Dividing by 6 gives

$$\tan \theta = 2.$$

Taking the inverse tangent of each member gives

$$\theta = 63.434 \ldots° + 180n°.$$

So values of 0 in the first revolution are

$$\theta = 63.434 \ldots° \text{ or } \theta = 243.434 \ldots°.$$

Substituting each value in either equation gives

$$r = 6 \sin 63.434 \ldots° \text{ or } r = 6 \sin 243.434 \ldots°$$

$$= 5.366 \ldots \qquad\qquad = -5.366 \ldots$$

So the intersections appear to be about

$$(5.37, 63.43°) \text{ and } (-5.37, 243.43°).$$

The first surprise is that both ordered pairs represent the same point! This happens because 243.43° is half a revolution around from 63.43°, and the r-values are opposites of each other.

The second surprise is that although the graphs intersect at the pole, solving the system of equations did *not* find this point. This happens because the two curves passed through the pole for different values of θ. Setting $r = 0$ in each equation gives the following.

$0 = 12 \cos \theta$ $0 = 6 \sin \theta$

$\cos \theta = 0$ $\sin \theta = 0$

$\theta = 90° + 180n°$ $\theta = 0° + 180n°$

If you run the program PLOT PLOAR TWO or a similar graphing program using these equations, you will see that $r = 6 \sin \theta$ starts at the pole when $\theta = 0°$, but $r = 12 \cos \theta$ doesn't reach the pole until $\theta = 90°$.

The third surprise is that polar graphs may intersect at different values of θ for points *other* than the pole. Figure 6-4b shows the two limaçons

$r = 2 + 8 \cos \theta \ldots$ (1)

$r = 5 + 3 \sin \theta \ldots$ (2)

as plotted by the program PLOT POLAR TWO. Graphs (1) and (2) intersect at four points. But as you will see in Example 1,

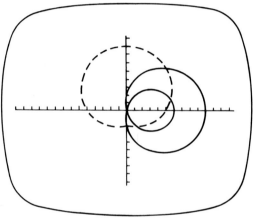

Figure 6-4b

solving the system of equations finds only the points where both graphs have positive values of r, or where both have negative values. The graphs also cross at points where the r s are opposites of each other and the θ s are half a revolution apart. If you run PLOT POLAR TWO, you will see immediately what is happening.

Fortunately, there is a way to calculate coordinates of these other intersection points. Figure 6-4c shows that the point (r, θ) is the same as the point $(-r, \theta + 180°)$. Replacing the r and θ in one of the equations gives a new system with the same two graphs. You could write

$-r = 2 + 8 \cos (\theta + 180°)$
$r = 5 + 3 \sin \theta$

or

$r = 2 + 8 \cos \theta$
$-r = 5 + 3 \sin (\theta + 180°).$

Solving either of these sysems finds the other two solutions. In general, you will get the same polar curve each time you increase θ by a multiple of $180°$ and change the sign of r.

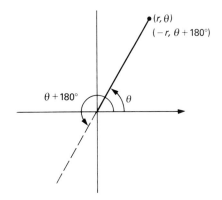

Figure 6-4c

Equivalent Polar Curves

If $r = f(\theta)$ is the equation of a polar curve and n is an integer, then

$$r = (-1)^n \, f(\theta + 180n°)$$

is another equation of the same curve.

Objective:

Given equations of two polar curves, find all intersection points by graphing, and calculate polar coordinates of these points.

Example 1: Find all intersection points of the graphs of the following.

$$r = 2 + 8 \cos \theta$$
$$r = 5 + 3 \sin \theta$$

(These are the equations written above.)

First you should draw a graph, either sketched by hand or plotted by computer, to find out roughly where the intersections are. Figure 6-4b shows the graph. You can use a protractor and a marked piece of paper to measure the points directly on the computer screen. The coordinates are about

$(6, 10°)$, $(7.5, 50°)$, $(3, -55°)$, and $(2, -90°)$.

Next, you observe that the pole is *not* an intersection point. Although the pole is on graph (1), it is not on graph (2).

Solving the system of equations by substitution gives

$$2 + 8 \cos \theta = 5 + 3 \sin \theta$$

$$8 \cos \theta - 3 \sin \theta = 3$$

The left number is a linear combination of sinusoids with equal periods. It can be expressed as a cosine with a phase displacement. See Section 3-7 if you need a refresher.

$$\sqrt{73} \cos (\theta + 20.556 \ldots°) = 3$$

$$\cos (\theta + 20.556 \ldots°) = 0.351123 \ldots$$

$$\theta + 20.556 \ldots° = \pm 69.443 \ldots° + 360n°$$

$$\theta = 48.877 \ldots° + 360n° \text{ or } -90° + 360n°$$

Substituting $48.877 \ldots°$ and $-90°$ into Equation (1) gives this.

$$r = 2 + 8 \cos 48.877° = 7.260 \ldots$$

$$r = 2 + 8 \cos (-90°) = 2$$

So two ordered pairs are about (7.26, 48.88°) and (2, –90°).

To calculate the other two ordered pairs, replace r with $-r$ and θ with $\theta + 180°$ in Equation (1). (You could use Equation (2).)

$$-r = 2 + 8 \cos (\theta + 180°)$$
$$-r = 2 - 8 \cos \theta$$
$$r = -2 + 8 \cos \theta \ldots . (3)$$

Solving the system formed by Equations (2) and (3) gives this.

$$-2 + 8 \cos \theta = 5 + 3 \sin \theta$$

$$8 \cos \theta - 3 \sin \theta = 7$$

$$\sqrt{73} \cos (\theta + 20.556 \ldots°) = 7$$

$$\cos (\theta + 20.556 \ldots°) = 0.81928 \ldots$$

$$\theta + 20.556 \ldots° = \pm 34.986 \ldots° + 360n°$$

$$\theta = 14.430 \ldots° + 360n° \text{ or } -55.542 \ldots° + 360n°.$$

Substituting $14.430\ldots°$ and $-55.542\ldots°$ into Equation (3) gives this.

$$r = -2 + 8 \cos 14.430\ldots° = 5.747\ldots$$
$$r = -2 + 8 \cos (-55.542\ldots°) = 2.526\ldots$$

Combining this result with the ordered pairs above, the four intersection points are approximately

$$(7.26, 48.88°), (2, -90°), (9.75, 14.43°) \text{ and } (6.53, -55.54°).$$

These values are confirmed by the approximate values found on the graph, $(6, 10°), (7.5, 50°), (3, -55°),$ and $(2, -90°).$

In the following exercise you will find approximate and exact intersections of other pairs of polar curves. You will also see that the concepts of this section are related to determining whether or not satellites orbiting in the same plane will collide with each other.

Exercise 6-4

1. *Polar Coordinates of the Same Point Problem:*
   a. Sketch the point $(5, 60°)$ on a polar coordinate system.
   b. Show on your sketch that $(-5, 240°)$ is the same point as in part (a).
   c. If $r = 5(-1)^n$ and $\theta = 60° + 180n°$, show that the point is the same as in parts (a) and (b) when the following is true.
      i. $n = 4$
      ii. $n = -3$

2. *Equivalent Polar Graphs Problem:* Given the polar equation $r = 2 + 8 \cos \theta$, do the following.

   a. Show that replacing r with $-r$ and θ with $\theta + 180°$ gives the new equation $r = -2 + 8 \cos \theta$.
   b. Demonstrate that the two equations have the same graph by plotting $r = 2 + 8 \cos \theta$ and $r = -2 + 8 \cos \theta$ on the same polar coordinate system using PLOT POLAR TWO or a similar graphing program.

For Problems 3 through 20, complete a and b.

   a. Draw graphs of the two equations, preferably by computer graphics.
   b. Calculate polar coordinates of all intersection points.

3. $r = 8 \cos \theta$
    $r = 8 \sin \theta$

4. $r = 5 \sin \theta$
    $r = 9 \cos \theta$

5. $r = 10 \cos \theta$
    $r = 5$

6. $r = 5 \sin \theta$
    $r = 4$

7. $r = 4 + 4 \cos \theta$
    $r = 4 - 4 \sin \theta$

8. $r = 4 - 4 \sin \theta$
    $r = 4 + 4 \sin \theta$

9. $r = 8 + 6 \cos \theta$
    $r = 5$

10. $r = 7 - 5 \cos \theta$
    $r = 4$

11. $r = \dfrac{20}{8 + 6 \cos \theta}$
    $r = 5$

12. $r = \dfrac{20}{7 - 5 \cos \theta}$
    $r = 4$

13. $r = 1 + 7 \sin \theta$
    $r = 4$

14. $r = 6 + 8 \cos \theta$
    $r = 5$

15. $r = 5 + 3 \cos \theta$
    $r = 4 - 6 \cos \theta$

16. $r = 6 - 5 \cos \theta$
    $r = 4 + 10 \cos \theta$

17. $r = 6 + 4 \cos \theta$
    $r = 2 - 4 \sin \theta$

18. $r = -1 - 3 \cos \theta$
    $r = 4 + 3 \sin \theta$

19. $r = 4 + 6 \cos \theta$
    $r = -2 + 6 \sin \theta$

20. $r = 1 + 7 \sin \theta$
    $r = -3 + 7 \cos \theta$

21. *Limaçon and Rose Problem:* Find all distinct points of intersection of the limaçon and rose.

$r = 5 + 3 \cos \theta$
$r = 8 \cos 2\theta$

You must recall the double-argument properties and not be afraid to use the quadratic formula!

22. *Lemniscate and Circle Problem:* Find all distinct points of intersection of the lemniscate and circle.

$r^2 = 16 \cos 2\theta$
$r = 3 \sin \theta$

You will have to be clever about which form of the double-argument property to use.

23. *Spiral and Line Problem:* One kind of spiral has the equation $r = k\theta$, where k stands for a constant. A line through the pole has polar equation θ = constant. Write all points of intersection of the spiral and line

$$r = \frac{\theta}{\pi}$$

$$\theta = \frac{\pi}{6}$$

Sketch the graph. Assume that θ is the *radian* measure of the angle.

24. *Two Rose Problem:* Find all points of intersection of the two roses.

$$r = 8 \cos 3\theta$$
$$r = 8 \sin (3\theta - 90°)$$

25. *Spaceship Problem and Meteorite Problem:* Figure 6-4d shows the Earth at the pole of a polar coordinate system, and a spaceship in elliptical orbit around the Earth. A meteorite is following a hyperbolic path, with the Earth at the focus. The equations of the two paths are

$$r = \frac{10}{2 + 3 \cos \theta} \quad \text{and}$$

$$r = \frac{9}{5 - 4 \cos \theta},$$

where r is in thousands of miles. Show that the meteorite *will* collide with the spaceship by showing that both will be at the same position for the same value of θ.

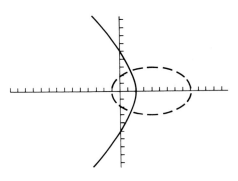

Figure 6-4d

26. *Two Spaceship Problem:* Figure 6-4e shows the paths of two spaceships in elliptical orbit about the Earth. The equations of the two ellipses are

$$r = \frac{10}{-3 + 2 \cos \theta}, \text{ and}$$

$$r = \frac{8}{3 + 2 \sin \theta}.$$

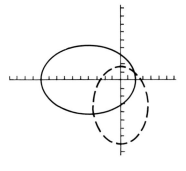

Figure 6-4e

Show that although the two paths cross each other, the spaceships will not collide because they are never at the intersection point for the same value of θ.

6-5   IMAGINARY AND COMPLEX NUMBERS

The radical $\sqrt{-9}$ means "the number that, when squared, gives -9 for the answer." Since squares of real numbers are never negative, $\sqrt{-9}$ does not stand for a real number. But square roots of negative numbers occur in such things as solutions of quadratic equations. For this reason it is convenient to define a new kind of number.

DEFINITION

An *imaginary number* is a square root of a negative real number.

Objective:

Be able to perform operations with expressions containing imaginary numbers.

The name "imaginary" was picked since people found it hard to imagine such a number. It is important for you to realize, however, that *all* numbers are inventions of peoples' imaginations to do such things as measure and count. It was probably hard for you to imagine fractions when you used numbers only for counting!

By careful selection of definitions, imaginary numbers can be made to fit in with real numbers. First, $\sqrt{-1}$ is given the name i. Next, square roots of negative numbers are transformed so that they involve i. For instance,

$$\sqrt{-9} = \sqrt{(9)(-1)} = \sqrt{9}\,\sqrt{-1} = 3i.$$

Similarly, $\sqrt{-25} = 5i$, $\sqrt{-17} = i\sqrt{17}$, $-\sqrt{-100} = -10i$, and so forth.

As you can see by the examples, any imaginary number can be expressed as the *product* of a real number and i. The formal definitions are as follows.

DEFINITIONS

$$i = \sqrt{-1}$$

Note that i is called the *unit* imaginary number, just as 1 (or $\sqrt{+1}$) is the unit *real* number.

If x is a positive real number, then

$$\sqrt{-x} = i \sqrt{x}$$

Handling sums of real and imaginary numbers, such as $4 + 3i$, is trickier. Just as the real number 4 can be plotted on a number line, imaginary numbers can be plotted on their own number line.

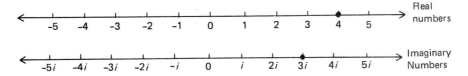

The number $0i$ can be defined to equal 0, thus extending the Multiplication Property of Zero to imaginary numbers. With this definition, it is reasonable to *cross* the two number lines, forming a Cartesian coordinate system (Figure 6-5a). The number $4 + 3i$ is thus represented by the ordered pair $(4, 3)$.

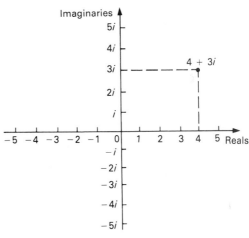

Figure 6-5a

Since numbers like $4 + 3i$ are on neither the real-number line nor the imaginary-number line, they are given the name *complex numbers*. The coordinate system is called the *complex-number plane*. A number such as $3i$ is called a *pure imaginary number*.

DEFINITION

A *complex number* is a number that can be expressed as the sum of a real number and a pure imaginary number. That is, z is an imaginary number if and only if

$z = a + bi,$

where a and b are real numbers, and $i = \sqrt{-1}$.

The real number a is called the *real part* of z.
The real number b is called the *imaginary part* of z.

Note that both real numbers and pure imaginary numbers are also complex numbers. For instance,

$7 = 7 + 0i$ and $5i = 0 + 5i.$

So both {real numbers} and {imaginary numbers} are *subsets* of {complex numbers.}

Two facts enable you to accomplish the objective of operating with expressions containing imaginary numbers.

Conclusions: Operations with Complex Numbers

1. Since $i = \sqrt{-1}$, it follows that $i^2 = -1$.

2. Operations with complex numbers are carried out using the same techniques as operations with linear binomials with real coefficients, observing that $i^2 = -1$.

The fact that $i^2 = -1$ allows you to simplify powers of i. To find i^3, you multiply i^2 by i. To find i^4, multiply i^3 by i, and so forth. An interesting pattern emerges!

$i^3 = i^2 \cdot i = -1 \cdot i = -i$

$i^4 = i^3 \cdot i = -i \cdot i = -(-1) = 1$

$i^5 = i^4 \cdot i = 1 \cdot i = i$

$i^6 = -1$

$i^7 = -i$

$i^8 = i$

-
-
-
-

When the exponent is a multiple of 4, the power equals 1. For instance,

$$i^{76} = 1$$

because 76 is a multiple of 4. To evaluate a power such as i^{39}, you could write

$$i^{39} = i^{36} \cdot i^3 = 1 \cdot i^3 = i^3 = -i.$$

A faster technique is to divide the exponent by 4, getting a quotient of 9 and a remainder of 3. Throw away the quotient and use the remainder as the new exponent. You would write

$$i^{39} = i^3 = -i.$$

Technique: Powers of i

To simplify i^n where n is an integer, divide n by 4. If the remainder is r, then

$$i^n = i^r$$

where $r = 0, 1, 2,$ or 3. Then use the pattern

$$i^0 = 1, \; i^1 = i, \; i^2 = -1, \; i^3 = -i.$$

Example 1: Write $\sqrt{-24}$ in terms of i using the following.

  a. simple radical form
  b. decimal form

     1. $\sqrt{-24} = i\sqrt{24} = i \cdot 2\sqrt{6} = 2i\sqrt{6}$

     2. $\sqrt{-24} = i\sqrt{24} = \underline{4.89897 \ldots i}$

Note that when the coefficient of i contains a radical, it is customary to commute the radical factor to the right. You are less likely to think the i belongs under the radical sign when it is in this form.

Example 2: Simplify:

  a. i^{446}.
  b. i^{-15}.

     1. Dividing 446 by 4 gives a remainder of 2. So

$$i^{446} = i^2 = \underline{-1}.$$

2. Dividing -15 by 4 gives a remainder of -3. So

$$i^{-15} = i^{-3} = \frac{1}{i^3} = \frac{i}{i^4} = \underline{i}.$$

Example 3: If $z_1 = 4 + 3i$ and $z_2 = 5 - 2i$, find

a. $z^1 + z^2$ b. $z^1 - z^2$ c. $z^1 z^2$ d. $\dfrac{z^1}{z^2}$

Adding, subtracting, and multiplying are done the same as for linear binomials, with i^2 being equal to -1.

a. $z^1 + z^2 = (4 + 3i) + (5 - 2i) = (4 + 5) + (3 - 2)i = \underline{9 + i}$

b. $z_1 - z_2 = (4 + 3i) - (5 - 2i) = (4 + 5) + (3 + 2)i = \underline{7 + i}$

c. $z_1 z_2 = (4 + 3i)(5 - 2i) = 20 + 7i - 6i^2 = 20 + 7i - 6i^2 = \underline{26 + 7i}$

d. Dividing z_1 by z_2 takes some preliminary work. The quotient

$$\frac{4 + 3i}{5 - 2i}$$

has a radical, i, in the denominator. Dividing two complex numbers is done by *rationalizing* the denominator. You multiply the fraction by 1 in the form

$$\frac{5 + 2i}{5 + 2i}$$

So to divide z_1 by z_2, you would write

$\dfrac{z_1}{z_2} = \dfrac{4 + 3i}{5 - 2i} \cdot \dfrac{5 + 2i}{5 + 2i}$ Multiplication property of 1

$= \dfrac{20 + 23i + 6i^2}{25 - 4i^2}$ Multiplication property of fractions

$= \dfrac{20 + 23i - 6}{25 + 4}$ $i^2 = -1$

$= \dfrac{14 + 23i}{29}$ Arithmetic

$= \dfrac{14}{29} + \dfrac{23}{29} i$ $\div$ distributes over $+$

The answers to Example 3 show that adding, subtracting, multiplying, and dividing two complex numbers produces a complex number for the answer. In fact, except for division by zero, {complex numbers} is *closed* under each of these operations. As you will learn in the next section, each complex number also has n^{th} roots in the set of complex numbers, a property not possessed by real numbers.

The number $5 + 2i$ used in part (d) of Example 3 is called the *complex conjugate* of $5 - 2i$.

DEFINITION

If $a + bi$ is a complex number, then $a - bi$ is its *complex conjugate* and vice versa.

An interesting thing happens when you multiply a complex number by its conjugate.

Example 4: Multiply: $(7 + 11i)(7 - 11i)$

$$(7 + 11i)(7 - 11i) = 49 - 77i + 77i - 11i^2 = 49 + 11 = \underline{60}$$

Conclusion:

The product of a complex number and its complex conjugate is always a *real* number.

In the following exercise you will practice operating with complex numbers.

Exercise 6-5

For problems 1 through 6, write the number in terms of i using the following.

a. simple radical form
b. decimal form

1. $\sqrt{-16}$ 2. $\sqrt{-25}$ 3. $\sqrt{-18}$ 4. $\sqrt{-48}$

5. $\sqrt{-7}$ 6. $\sqrt{-3}$

For Problems 7 through 20, simplify the power.

7. i^5 8. i^7 9. i^{55} 10. i^{25}

11. i^{62} 12. i^{74} 13. i^{300} 14. i^{180}

15. i^0 16. i^{-2} 17. i^{-7} 18. i^{-25}

19. i^{-38} 20. i^{-54}

21. Simplify: $i + i^2 + i^3 + i^4$

22. Simplify: $i^{-1} + i^{-2} + i^{-3} + i^{-4}$

For problems 23 through 30, plot the graph of the number on the complex plane.

23. $5 + 7i$ 24. $6 + 3i$ 25. $3 - 2i$ 26. $7 - 4i$
27. $-4 + 6i$ 28. $-2 + i$ 29. $-1 - 8i$ 30. $-5 - 2i$

If z is a complex number, then its *absolute value*, $|z|$, is defined to be the distance between the origin and the graph of z on the complex plane. Use the Pythagorean theorem in an appropriate manner to find the absolute value of the numbers in Problems 31 through 34.

31. $4 + 3i$ 32. $2 - 3i$ 33. $-5 + 12i$ 34. $-8 - 15i$

For Problems 35 through 38, find (a) $z_1 + z_2$, (b) $z_1 - z_2$, (c) $z_1 \cdot z_2$, and (d) $\frac{z_1}{z_2}$.

35. $z^1 = 2 + 3i$
     $z_2 = 4 - 5i$
37. $z_1 = -1 + 2i$
     $z_2 = 6 + 7i$

36. $z^1 = 6 + 2i$
     $z_2 = 5 - 7i$
38. $z_1 = -3 - i$
     $z_2 = 4 + 8i$

39. Suppose that $z_1 = 3 + 5i$ and $z_2 = 7 + 2i$.

   a. Plot the points z_1, z_2, and $z_1 + z_2$ on a complex number plane. Then connect each point to the origin. What do the lengths of these lines represent?
   b. Connect z_1 to $z_1 + z_2$. What is the length of this line equal to?
   c. Explain why the inequality $|z_1 + z_2| \le |z_1| + |z_2|$ is true for any two complex numbers z_1 and z_2. (Clue: This is called the "Triangle Inequality.")

40. Suppose that $z_1 = 1 + i$ and $z_2 = 2 + 5i$.

   a. Find the product $z_1 z_2$.
   b. Find $|z_1|$, $|z_2|$, and $|z_1 z_2|$, then try to arrive at some conclusion about how these three absolute values are related to each other.
   c. Plot the points z_1, z_2, and $z_1 z_2$ on a complex number plane. Then connect each point to the origin. How do the *angles* between the positive real axis and these lines seem to be related to one another?

41. Draw graphs of i, i^2, i^3, and i^4 on the same complex number plane. What seems to be happening to the graph each time the power of i is increased by one?

42. Suppose that $z = 3 + 4i$.

   a. What does iz equal?
   b. Plot the points z and iz on a complex number plane, then connect each point to the origin.
   c. Show that multiplying z by i has *not* changed its absolute value.
   d. Show that multiplying z by i has *rotated* its graph through an angle of 90°.

43. Show that

   $$z = \frac{\sqrt{2}}{2}(1 + i)$$

   is a *square root* of i by squaring $\frac{\sqrt{2}}{2}(1 + i)$ and showing that you get i for an answer.

44. a. Show that $|z| = 2$.
   b. Show that z is a *cube root* of 8 by cubing $-1 + i\sqrt{3}$ and showing that you get 8 for an answer.

45. *Triangle Problem:* A triangle has legs 31 inches and 41 inches, with included angle 179°. By how much is the third side shorter than the sum of the other two sides?

46. *Identity Problem:* Prove that cos (Arcsin 0.8 + Arccos 0.6) is equal to 2 cos² (arccos 0.6) −1.

47. *Graphing Problem:* Sketch the polar graph of $r = \cos 2\theta$. What is the name of the curve?

48. *Rotary Motion Problem:* An asteroid is revolving about its axis at approximately 3.7π Earth days. What is the linear velocity of a point on the surface, 111 km from the axis?

49. *Complex Conjugate Problem:* Prove that the product of the complex number $a + bi$ and its conjugate is a *real* number.

50. *Sum of Two Squares Problem:* In algebra you learn how to factor a diffrence of two squares, such as $x^2 - y^2$. If you are willing to pay the price of using complex numbers, it is possible

to factor a *sum* of two squares. Use the results of Problem 49 to factor $x^2 + y^2$.

6-6   COMPLEX NUMBERS IN POLAR FORM

Since you have studied polar coordinates, you can discover some interesting
properties of complex numbers.

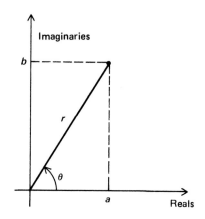

Figure 6-6a

Suppose that $z = a + bi$. A graph of
z is shown in Figure 6-6a. The polar
coordinates of z are (r, θ). Using the
definitions of sine and cosine,

$$a = r \cos \theta \text{ and } b = r \sin \theta$$

Therefore, z can be written

$$z = r \cos \theta + ir \sin \theta,$$

or, more simply,

$$z = r(\cos \theta + i \sin \theta).$$

A complex number written this way is said to be in *polar form*. The expression $\cos \theta + i \sin \theta$ is abbreviated "cis θ." The c comes from *cosine*,
the i from $\sqrt{-1}$, and the s from *sine*. The radius, r, is called the *modulus* of
the complex number, and the angle θ is called the *argument*.

DEFINITION

For a complex number $z = a + bi$, its *polar form* is

$$z = r(\cos \theta + i \sin \theta) = r \text{ cis } \theta,$$

where $r = \sqrt{a^2 + b^2}$ is the *modulus* of z, and θ is the smallest nonnegative
angle in standard position to the radius vector.

The absolute value of a real number is defined to be the distance between
the origin and the number's graph on the number line. The absolute value
of a complex number is defined the same way, except that the graph is in
the complex *plane*.

DEFINITION

For a complex number $z = a + bi = r$ cis θ, its *absolute value* is
$|z| = \sqrt{a^2 + b^2}$, or $|z| = r$.

Objectives:

1. Given a complex number $a + bi$, transform it to polar form, and vice versa.
2. Given complex numbers in polar form, find products, quotients, powers, and roots.

Example 1: Transform $z = \sqrt{3} - i$ to polar form.

First, sketch the number on the complex plane, as in Figure 6-6b.

The definition of r is simply a form of the Pythagorean theorem. So

$$r = \sqrt{(\sqrt{3})^2 + (-1)^2} = 2.$$

To find θ, observe that

$$\cos \theta = \sqrt{\tfrac{3}{2}}, \text{ and}$$

$$\sin \theta = \frac{-1}{2}$$

The smallest nonnegative angle satisfying both conditions is 330°. So

$$z = \underline{2 \text{ cis } 330°}.$$

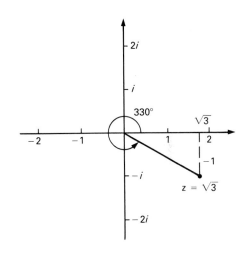

Figure 6-6b

Example 2: Transform $z = 5$ cis 144° to rectangular form, $a + bi$.

$$z = 5 \text{ cis } 144°$$

$$= 5 (\cos 144° + i \sin 144°)$$

$$= \underline{-4.04508 \ldots + 2.93892 \ldots i}$$

Operations with complex numbers in polar form are performed as follows:

Products: Suppose that $z_1 = r_1 \text{ cis } \theta_1$ and $z_2 = r_2 \text{ cis } \theta_2$. Then

$$
\begin{aligned}
z_1 z_2 &= r_1 \text{ cis } \theta_1 \cdot r_2 \text{ cis } \theta_2 \\
&= r_1 r_2 (\cos \theta_1 + i \sin \theta_1)(\cos \theta_2 + i \sin \theta_2) \\
&= r_1 r_2 (\cos \theta_1 \cos \theta_2 - \sin \theta_1 \sin \theta_2 + i \sin \theta_1 \cos \theta_2 \\
&\quad + i \cos \theta_1 \sin \theta_2).
\end{aligned}
$$

The first two terms in parentheses are recognizable as $\cos (\theta_1 + \theta_2)$, and the last two are $i \sin (\theta_1 + \theta_2)$.

Conclusion: *Product of two complex numbers*

$$
\begin{aligned}
z_1 z_2 &= r_1 r_2 (\cos(\theta_1 + \theta_2) + i \sin (\theta_1 + \theta_2)) \\
&= r_1 r_2 \text{ cis } (\theta_1 + \theta_2)
\end{aligned}
$$

Observe that to multiply two complex numbers in polar form, you need only *multiply* their moduli and *add* their arguments. If you have worked Problem 36 in Exercise 6-5, you may already have discovered this property.

Reciprocals: If $z = r \text{ cis } \theta = r(\cos \theta + i \sin \theta)$, then

$$
\frac{1}{z} = \frac{1}{r(\cos\theta + i \sin \theta)}.
$$

Multiplying numerator and denominator by $\cos \theta - i \sin \theta$, the *conjugate* of $\cos \theta + i \sin \theta$, gives

$$
\frac{1}{z} = \frac{\cos \theta \ - i \sin \theta}{r(\cos^2 \theta - i^2 \sin^2 \theta)}.
$$

Since $i^2 = -1$ and $\cos^2 \theta + \sin^2 \theta = 1$,

$$
\frac{1}{z} = \frac{1}{r}(\cos \theta - i \sin \theta).
$$

By the odd-even properties of sine and cosine, $\cos \theta = \cos (-\theta)$ and $-\sin \theta = \sin (-\theta)$.

Conclusion: *Reciprocal of a Complex Number*

$$
\frac{1}{z} = \frac{1}{r}(\cos (-\theta) + i \sin (-\theta)) = \frac{1}{r} \text{ cis } (-\theta)
$$

Quotients: Combining the preceding two conclusions, you find an easy way to divide complex numbers in polar form. If $z_1 = r_1$ cis θ_1 and $z_2 = r_1$ cis θ_2, then

$$\frac{z_1}{z_2} = z_1 \cdot \frac{1}{z_2}$$

$$= r_1 \text{ cis } \theta_1 \cdot \frac{1}{r_2} \text{cis } (-\theta_2)$$

$$= \frac{r_1}{r_2} \text{ cis } (\theta_1 - \theta_2)$$

So to divide two complex numbers, you simply *divide* their moduli and *subtract* their arguments.

Conclusion: *Quotient of Two Complex Numbers*

$$\frac{z_1}{z_2} = \frac{r_1}{r_2} \text{cis } (\theta_1 - \theta_2)$$

Powers: If $z = r$ cis θ, then

$$z^2 = z \cdot z = r \text{ cis } \theta \cdot r \text{ cis } \theta = r^2 \text{ cis } (\theta + \theta) = r^2 \text{ cis } 2\theta.$$

This process can be extended to *any* integer power. The result is known as De Moivre's Theorem.

De Moivre's Theorem: *If $z = r$ cis θ, then*

$$z^n = r^n \text{ cis } n\theta$$

Roots: De Moivre's Theorem also works for fractional exponents. That is,

$$\sqrt[n]{z} = z^{1/n} = r^{1/n} \text{cis} \frac{\theta}{n}.$$

To see if the answer is right, raise the right and left members of the equation to the nth power.

$$(\sqrt[n]{z})^n = (r^{1/n})^n \text{ cis } (n \cdot \frac{\theta}{n})$$

$$z = r \text{ cis } \theta,$$

which is correct. However, $r^{1/n}$ cis θ/n is not the *only* nth root of z. Others can be found by recognizing that angles are coterminal with θ when their measures are $\theta + 360k°$, where k is an integer. For example, suppose you seek the cube roots of $z = 8$ cis $60°$. Then

$$\sqrt[3]{z} = \sqrt[3]{8} \text{ cis } \frac{60°}{3}$$

$$= 2 \text{ cis } 20°.$$

Since $420°$ (i.e., $60° + 360°$) is coterminal with $60°$, z is also equal to 8 cis $420°$. So another cube root of z is

$$\sqrt[3]{z} = \sqrt[3]{8} \text{ cis } \frac{420°}{3}$$

$$= 2 \text{ cis } 140°.$$

This is *different* from the first value obtained. A *third* cube root can be found if you use the coterminal angle $60° + 720°$, which equals $780°$.

$$\sqrt[3]{z} = 2 \text{ cis } 260°.$$

The coterminal angle $60° + 1080° = 1140°$ seems to produce a fourth cube root, 2 cis $380°$. But this is the same as 2 cis $20°$ since $20°$ and $380°$ are coterminal. Consequently, there are *exactly three* distinct cube roots of z. These cube roots are sketched on a complex plane in Figure 6-6c. Note that the three lines connecting these cube roots with the origin are equally spaced, $120°$ apart. In general, there are n distinct nth roots of a complex number. If $z = r$ cis θ, then

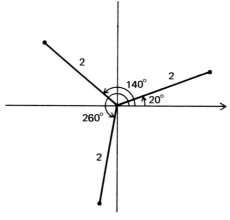

Figure 6-6c

Conclusion: Roots of a Complex Number

If $z = r$ cis θ, then

$$\sqrt[n]{z} = \sqrt[n]{r} \text{ cis } \left(\frac{\theta + 360k°}{n} \right)$$

where k is an integer ranging from 0 through n^{-1}.

Example 3: Find all distinct fifth roots of $z = 243$ cis $140°$. Graph them in the complex plane.

It is easier to use the "equal spacing" property of Figure 6-6c than it is to remember the formula. There will be *five* fifth roots, each equally spaced. So the angle between each will be

$$\frac{360°}{5} = 72°.$$

The first of the angles will be

$$\frac{140°}{5} = 28°.$$

The modulus is

$$\sqrt[5]{243} = 3.$$

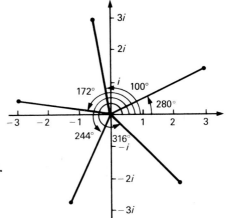

All you need to write are the answers.

3 cis 28°,
3 cis 100°,
3 cis 172°,
3 cis 244°,
3 cis 316°.

Figure 6–6d

The other arguments are obtained by adding 72° to the one before. The graphs are shown in Figure 6-6d.

Note that the formula shows that an nth root of a complex number is another complex number. However, since there are n discinct n^{th} roots of each complex number, the answer is not unique. Thus, {complex numbers} is *not* closed under the operation $\sqrt[n]{}$.

Exercise 6-6

For Problems 1 through 16, write the given complex number in polar form.

1. $1 + i$
2. $1 - i$
3. $-1 + i$
4. $-1 - i$
5. $1 + i\sqrt{3}$
6. $\sqrt{3} + i$
7. $\sqrt{3} - i$
8. $1 - i\sqrt{3}$
9. $3 - 4i$
10. $4 - 3i$
11. $-4 - 3i$
12. $-3 + 4i$
13. 1
14. i
15. $-i$
16. -8

For Problems 17 through 26, write the given complex number in the form $a + bi$.

17. 6 cis 120°   18. 8 cis 150°
19. 10 cis 225°   20. 4 cis 45°
21. 5 cis 180°   22. 9 cis 90°
23. 3 cis 270°   24. 2 cis 0°
25. 8 cis 34°   26. 11 cis 247°

For Problems 27 through 30, find (a) $z_1 z_2$, (b) $\dfrac{z_1}{z_2}$ (c) $z_1{}^2$, and (d) $z_2{}^3$.

27. $z_1 = 3$ cis 47°, $z_2 = 5$ cis 36°
28. $z_1 = 2$ cis 154°, $z_2 = 3$ cis 27°
29. $z_1 = 4$ cis 238°, $z_2 = 2$ cis 51°
30. $z_1 = 6$ cis 19°, $z_2 = 4$ cis 96°

For Problems 31 through 40, find the indicated roots, and sketch the answers on a complex number plane.

31. Cube roots of 27 cis 120°
32. Cube roots of 8 cis 15°
33. Fourth roots of 16 cis 80°
34. Fourth roots of 81 cis 64°
35. Square roots of i
36. Square roots of $-i$
37. Cube roots of 8
38. Cube roots of -27
39. Sixth roots of -1
40. Tenth roots of 1

41. By De Moivre's Theorem, $(\cos \theta + i \sin \theta)^3 = \cos 3\theta + i \sin 3\theta$. By expanding the binomial on the left and equating the real parts and the imaginary parts, derive *triple* argument properties expressing $\cos 3\theta$ and $\sin 3\theta$ in terms of $\cos \theta$ and $\sin \theta$.

42. By De Moivre's Theorem, $(\cos \theta + i \sin \theta)^4 = \cos 4\theta + i \sin 4\theta$. By expanding the binomial on the left and equating the real parts and the imaginary parts, derive *quadruple* argument properties expressing $\cos 4\theta$ and $\sin 4\theta$ in terms of $\cos \theta$ and $\sin \theta$.

43. Although $\dfrac{2}{6} = \dfrac{1}{3}$,

$$(-8)^{2/6} \neq (-8)^{1/3} .$$

This awkward situation arises because $(-8)^{1/3} = -2$, but

$$(-8)^{2/6} = ((-8)^2)^{1/6} = 64^{1/6} = 2.$$

With De Moivre's Theorem you can make some sense out of this seeming paradox.

 a. Write –8 as a complex number in polar form. Then write the three distinct cube roots of –8 in polar form.

 b. Show that one of the cube roots, above, equals –2.

 c. Write 64 as a complex number in polar form. Then write the six distinct sixth roots of 64 in polar form.

 d. Show that one of the sixth roots of 64 in part c equals 2, and that another one equals –2.

 e. Show that every cube root of –8 is also a sixth root of 64, but *not* vice versa.

44. Explain why a negative number raised to an *irrational* power, such as $(-8)\sqrt{3}$, has an *infinite* number of values, *none* of which is a real number.

45. *Vector Problem:* Two force vectors act on the same object, but at an angle of 37° to each other. One is 120 pounds and the other is 180 pounds. What is the magnitude of the resultant force? How much more would the resultant force be if both vectors acted in the same line with each other?

46. *Vector Components Problem:* Two vectors act on the origin of a Cartesian coordinate system. One is magnitude 7 at 58° and the other is magnitude 10 at 143°.

 a. Find the horizontal and vertical components of each vector.

 b. Find the horizontal and vertical components of the resultant vector.

 c. Find the magnitude and angle of the resultant vector.

47. *Identity Problem:* Write the composite argument property for $\cos (A + B)$, then use it in an appropriate manner to derive the double argument property for $\cos 2x$ in terms of $\sin x$.

48. *Rotary Motion Problem:* Find the linear velocity of the Earth in its orbit about the Sun. Write the answer in miles per second.

49. *Polar Graph Problem:* Sketch the limaçon $r = 3 + 5 \sin \theta$.

50. *Sinusoid Problem:* Write a particular equation of the sinusoid with amplitude 7 and period 40°, if a high point occurs at $\theta = 19°$ and $y = 10$.

6-7   COMPLEX NUMBERS FOR VECTORS

In Section 5-8 you added vectors by adding their horizontal components and adding their vertical components. You have just been adding complex numbers by adding their real parts and adding their imaginary parts. You should be able to tell that the two processes are exactly alike, mathematically.

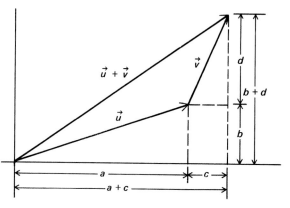

Figure 6-7a shows two vectors, $\vec{u}$ and $\vec{v}$, represented as complex numbers. Letting

$$\vec{u} = a + bi$$

and

$$\vec{v} = c + di,$$

you can see that

$$\vec{u} + \vec{v} = (a + c) + (b + d)i.$$

This is the sum of the complex numbers $a + bi$ and $c + di$.

Figure 6-7a

From the above discussion you should be able to reach the following conclusions.

Conclusions:

1. If $\vec{v}$ is a vector, then it can be represented as a complex number,

   $\vec{v} = r \text{ cis } \theta = a + bi.$

2. Vector addition may be accomplished by adding the respective complex numbers.

Note: The unit imaginary number i should not be confused with the unit vector $\vec{i}$ of Section 5-8.

Mathemeticians use the word *isomorphism* to indicate this relationship between {vectors} and {complex numbers}. *Iso* means *same,* and *morph* means *form.* So {vectors} is said to be *isomorphic* to {complex numbers} under the operation of addition.

It is not hard to show that sums or differences of *more* than two vectors may be found by adding the complex numbers which represent them.

Example: Evaluate the vector represented by

$$\vec{v} = 3 \text{ cis } 71° - 2 \text{ cis } 27° + 5 \text{ cis } 158°.$$

If you have a calculator that operates with complex numbers, you can enter three vectors, transform to complex form using the polar-to-rectangular conversion key, and add. Then use the rectangular-to-polar key to get $v = 6.63770 \ldots$ cis $145.0592 \ldots°$.

Otherwise, transform the vectors to rectangular form, using the definition cis $\theta = \cos \theta + i \sin \theta$.

$$\vec{v} = 3 \text{ cis } 71° - 2 \text{ cis } 27° + 5 \text{ cis } 158°$$

$$= 3(\cos 71° + i \sin 71°) - 2 (\cos 27° + i \sin 27°) + 5(\cos 158° + i \sin 158°)$$

$$= (3 \cos 71° - 2 \cos 27° + 5 \cos 158°) + i(3 \sin 71° - 2 \sin 27° + 5 \sin 158°)$$

$$= -5.44122 \ldots + 3.80160 \ldots i$$

$$\approx \underline{-5.44 + 3.81i}$$

This number can be transformed back to polar form by first finding its absolute value.

$$|\vec{v}| = \sqrt{(-5.44122 \ldots)^2 + (3.80160 \ldots)^2}$$

$$= 6.63770 \ldots$$

The argument, θ, is given by

$$\tan \theta = \frac{3.80160 \ldots}{-5.44122 \ldots}$$

$$= -0.69866 \ldots$$

Since $\cos \theta$ is negative and $\sin \theta$ is positive, θ terminates in Quadrant II. Therefore,

$$\theta = 145.0592 \ldots°$$

So the answer is

$$\vec{v} \approx \underline{6.64 \text{ cis } 145°04'}$$

The following exercise lets you add vectors as complex numbers. You might want to skip to Problem 16 at the end of the exercise and write a computer program to add the vectors before working the earlier problems.

Exercise 6-7

For Problems 1 through 6, find the sum (or difference) of the indicated vectors as complex numbers in *rectangular* form, $a + bi$.

1. 3 cis 27° + 5 cis 152°
2. 7 cis 255° + 4 cis 56°
3. 5 cis 130° + 9 cis 20° + 15 cis 220°
4. 2 cis 320° + 6 cis 205° + 5 cis 80°
5. 8 cis 42° − 11 cis 80° + 5 cis 100°
6. 9 cis 18 + 2 cis 73° − 4 cis 41°

7. through 12. Transform the answers to Problems 1 through 6 to vectors expressed as complex numbers in polar form.

13. *Pirate Problem:* A pirate's treasure map says, "Start at the elm tree. Go 150 paces at an angle of 35° (Figure 6-7b). Then go 30 paces at 228. Then go 100 paces at 110°. Then go 40 paces at 306°." Since you have studied vectors, you set up a Cartesian coordinate system with its origin at the elm tree and represent the displacements as vectors.

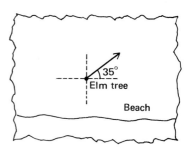

Figure 6-7b

a.   To the nearest pace, what are the coordinates of the treasure?
b.   Write in polar form the vector from the elm tree to the treasure.

14. *Spaceship Force Problem:*
Suppose that the gravity of the sun, the moon, and the earth are pulling on a spaceship, as shown in Figure 6-7c. The force vectors are

Earth: 120 lb at 27°

Sun: 50 lb at 142°

Moon: 20 lb at 243°.

To the nearest pound and the nearest degree, what is the resultant of these three forces?

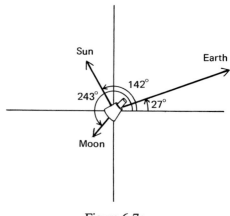

Figure 6-7c

15. *Neutron Problem:* A neutron escaping from a nuclear reactor enters the surrounding shielding at an angle of 27° (Figure 6-7d). It goes 20 centimeters along this path before colliding with an atom in the shielding. Then it goes 31 centimeters at an angle of −118° before colliding with another shielding atom. If the neutron goes 53 centimeters further in the direction 54°,

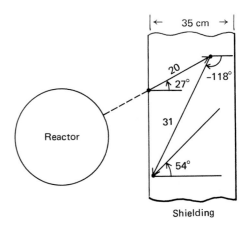

Figure 6-7d

a. What is its displacement vector from the point at which it entered the shielding?

b. Has it gone all the way through the shielding? Explain.

16. *Complex Vector Sums by Computer:* Write a computer program to add vectors as complex numbers. The program should begin by letting you input the number of vectors to be added. Then the program should enter a loop in which the vectors are input one at a time, by magnitude and direction (modulus and argument). At each pass through the loop the computer should calculate the real part and the imaginary part of the complex number, and add these to the respective sums of the previous real and imaginary parts. When all vectors have been input, the computer should calculate the magnitude and direction of the resultant vector. The arctangent function, ATN(X), can be used, but you must realize that the answer must first be transformed from radians to degrees, then perhaps have 180° or 360° added to it to put the angle in the correct quadrant. The output of the program should be a complex both in $a + bi$ form and in r cis θ form.

17. *Identity Problem:* Write the following.

a. the Pythagorean Property for tangents and secants

b. the Quotient Property for tangent in terms of sine and cosine

c. the Reciprocal Property for cosecant

d. the Composite Argument Property for cos $(A + B)$

e. the Composite Argument Property for sin $2A$

f. the Half-Argument Property for tan $2A$ without radicals

g. the Sum and Product Property for sin A + sin B

    h.   the Cofunction Property for secant
    i.   the Odd-Even Property for cotangent
    j.   the Linear Combination Property for $A \cos \theta + B \sin \theta$

18. *Equation Problem:* Solve if $x \, \varepsilon \{ \frac{-\pi}{2}, \frac{3\pi}{2} \}$.

    $\tan x \cos x + \cos x = 1$

19. *Polar Coordinate Problem:* Transform to rectangular coordinates and identify the graph.

$$r = \frac{1}{(2 + \cos \theta)}$$

20. Multiply: $(3 \text{ cis } 29°)(5 \cos 213°)(2 \text{ cis } 194°)$

6-8 INTRODUCTION TO POWER SERIES

So far in your study of trigonometry you have found values of functions by calculator or by tables. But how does the calculator figure out the values when the only operations it can do are addition, subtraction, multiplication, and division? And how were the values calculated for the tables?

    In the next two sections you will find answers to these questions. This section will introduce you to the concept of "infinite series." In the next section you will use infinite series to calculate decimal approximations for values of the circular functions.

    You recall that a *polynomial* is an expression such as

$$2 + 5x - 3x^2 - 4x^3 + x^4,$$

which is a *sum* of various *powers* of x, with *coefficients* for each term. Suppose that a polynomial "went on forever." That is, suppose an expression had an *infinite* number of monomial terms such as those in a polynomial. Such an expression is called a power series.

DEFINITION

A *power series* is an expression of the form

$$c_0 + c_1 x + c_2 x^2 + c_3 x^3 + c_4 x^4 + c_5 x^5 + \ldots,$$

where the c's stand for constant coefficients, and the ellipsis indicates that the terms go on forever.

The name "power series" is used since polynomials have only a *finite* number of terms. In this section you will investigate a particular power series.

Objective:

Given the power series

$$f(x) = 1 + x + \frac{x^2}{1 \cdot 2} + \frac{x^3}{1 \cdot 2 \cdot 3} + \frac{x^4}{1 \cdot 2 \cdot 3 \cdot 4} + \frac{x^5}{1 \cdot 2 \cdot 3 \cdot 4 \cdot 5} + \cdots,$$

find out what the series equals for various values of x and for various numbers of terms.

Before you proceed you should be able to see the pattern which the terms in the series follow. The exponent of x increases by one each term. The denominator is the product of consecutive positive integers, starting at 1 and ending at the exponent of x. There is a shorthand way of writing such products. For example, $1 \cdot 2 \cdot 3 \cdot 4 \cdot 5$ is written "5!" and pronounced "five factorial."

DEFINITION

If n is a positive integer, then

$$n! = 1 \cdot 2 \cdot 3 \cdot 4 \cdot \ldots \cdot n.$$

Using factorials, you can write the preceding power series as

$$f(x) = 1 + x + \frac{x^2}{2!} + \frac{x^3}{3!} + \frac{x^4}{4!} + \frac{x^5}{5!} + \cdots.$$

The next terms would be $\frac{x^6}{6!}, \frac{x^7}{7!}$, and so forth.

Example: Calculate an approximate value of $f(0.3)$ using only the first five terms of the series.

$$f(0.3) \approx 1 + 0.3 + \frac{0.3^2}{2!} + \frac{0.3^3}{3!} + \frac{0.3^4}{4!}$$

$$= 1 + 0.3 + \frac{0.09}{2} + \frac{0.027}{6} + \frac{0.0081}{24}$$

$$= 1 + 0.3 + 0.045 + 0.0045 + 0.0003375$$

$$= \underline{1.3498375}$$

As you can see, the values of the higher degree terms get smaller. There are two reasons. First, the denominator gets large very rapidly. For example; $10! = 3{,}628{,}800$. Second, the proper fraction 0.3 raised to a large power is very small. For example, $0.3^{10} = 0.0000059049$. So the eleventh term of the series is only

$$\frac{0.3^{10}}{10!} \approx 0.000000000001627.$$

This term would contribute nothing to the first 11 decimal places of $f(0.3)$.

In the following exercise you will perform similar calculations with different values of x and different parts of this power series. A calculator will help with the arithmetic. You will be led to some rather startling conclusions about just what function f really is. The last problem calls on you to write a computer program to evaluate the power series of this section.

Exercise 6-8

1. Let $f(x)$ be the power series

$$f(x) = 1 + x + \frac{x^2}{2!} + \frac{x^3}{3!} + \frac{x^4}{4!} \cdots .$$

Find 7-decimal place approximations for $f(0.2)$, using

   a. the first 5 terms of the series,
   b. the first 6 terms of the series,
   c. the first 7 terms of the series.

2. To how many decimal places would you expect the approximation for $f(0.2)$ to be accurate if you use only the first 6 terms? Explain.

3. Find a 5-decimal place approximation for $f(1)$, using the first 9 terms of the series for $f(x)$.

4. Think about what happens to the expression

   $$(1 + 1/m)^m$$

   as m becomes very large. The term $1/m$ gets close to 0, so that the base, $(1 + 1/m)$, gets close to 1. If you raise 1 to any power, you get 1. But a number larger than 1 raised to a large power is *large*. Investigate what happens to $(1 + 1/m)^m$ as m gets large by computing the value of the expression for $m = 10$, 100, and 10,000.

5. What do you notice about your answers to Problems 3 and 4? This number is defined to be "*e*" and is an infinite, non-repeating decimal similar to π.

6. Scientific calculators have an e^x key. Evaluate $e^{0.2}$. How does this answer compare with your approximation of $f(0.2)$ from Problem 1?

7. Based on your answer to Problem 6, write an equation expressing $f(x)$ as just *one* term.

8. Let $g(x)$ be the power series

$$g(x) = 1 - \frac{x^2}{2!} + \frac{x^4}{4!} - \frac{x^6}{6!} + \cdots .$$

Demonstrate that you see the pattern of the series by writing the next three terms.

9. Is g an *odd* function or an *even* function? Explain.

10. Calculate $g(0.2)$, using the first four terms of the series. Round off the answer to four decimal places.

11. Calculate $g(-0.2)$ quickly, in *one* step.

12. Let $h(x)$ be the power series

$$h(x) = x - \frac{x^3}{3!} + \frac{x^5}{5!} - \frac{x^7}{7!} + \cdots .$$

Demonstrate that you see the pattern of the series by writing the next three terms.

13. Is h an odd function or an even function? Explain.

14. Calculate $h(0.2)$, using the first four terms of the series. Round off the answer to four decimal places.

15. Calculate $h(-0.2)$ *quickly*, in *one* step.

16. If you have worked Problems 10 and 14 correctly, you should be able to find the answers at very interesting places in Table II. What functions do you suppose that g and h really are?

17. Find $g(0)$ and $h(0)$, and show that these numbers are consistent with the conclusion you reached in Problem 16.

18. *Power Series by Computer:* Write a program to evaluate the function
   $f(x)$ of this seciton. This input should be the value of x and the
   exponent of the last term. The first term in the series will be 1, and
   the first partial sum will equal this first term. The computer should
   then enter a loop in which the next term is calculated. This can be
   done by multiplying the previous term by x, then dividing by the
   new exponent. For this reason you may wish to use the *exponent* as
   the counter in the loop. When the term value has been calculated it
   should be added to the sum of the previous terms. At each pass
   through the loop the computer should print the exponent, the term
   value, and the sum of the terms. When your program is written, use
   it to do the following:

   a. Calculate $f(0.3)$ using 5 terms (last exponent = 4). Confirm that
      the answer is 1.3498375 as shown in this section.
   b. Calculate $f(3)$ using 21 terms (last exponent = 20). Confirm that
      the answer agrees with e^3 as evaluated by calculator.
   c. Calculate $f(-2)$ using 21 terms. Describe what happens to the
      partial sums as the computer goes from term to term.
   d. Modify the program so that it evaluates the function $g(x)$ of this
      section. The new term value is calculated by multiplying the pre-
      vious term by $-x^2$, then dividing by both the new exponent and 1
      less than the new exponent.
   e. Use the program from part (d) to evaluate $g(0.2)$ as in Problem
      10.
   f. Evaluate $g(2)$. How many terms seem to be needed to get a preci-
      sion of 9 significant digits? Confirm that the answer equals the
      circular function cos 2.
   g. Modify the program of part (d) so that it evaluates the function
      $h(x)$ of this section.
   h. Use the program of part (g) to evaluate $h(0.2)$ and $h(2)$. Confirm
      that these answers equal sin 0.2 and sin 2, respectively.

6-9   TAYLOR SERIES FOR SINE, COSINE, AND EXPONENTIAL FUNCTIONS

In Exercise 6-8 you should have discovered that three particular power
series seem to give correct answers for sin x, cos x, and an exponential
function which has a base of approximately 2.7182818, called e. The following equations summarize what you should have discovered.

$$\sin x = x - \frac{x^3}{3!} + \frac{x^5}{5!} - \frac{x^7}{7!} + \cdots$$

$$\cos x = 1 - \frac{x^2}{2!} + \frac{x^4}{4!} - \frac{x^6}{6!} + \cdots$$

$$e^x = 1 + x + \frac{x^2}{2!} + \frac{x^3}{3!} + \frac{x^4}{4!} + \cdots$$

Power series of this form are called "Taylor series." When you study calculus you will learn *why* these particular series are equal to sin x, cos x,
and e^x. For the time being, you will gain further confidence that these series are *reasonable* by drawing graphs and using a computer to print a
table of values which you can compare with Table II. You will also discover a remarkable relationship among sin x, cos x, and e^x.

Objectives:

1. Plot graphs of several terms of the Taylor series for sin x and cos x,
    and show that they resemble the actual sine and cosine graphs.

2. Compute a short table of values of sin x, cos x, and e^x.

3. Write cos x and sin x as exponential functions.

Example 1: Plot a graph of the polynomial function $y = x - x^3/3!$, and
show that it resembles the graph of $y = \sin x$ for values of x close to 0.

    The first thing to do is compute values of y for the polynomial. This
may be done conveniently in table form.

x	x^3	$x^3/3!$	$y = x - x^3/3!$	$\sin x$
0.0	0	0	0	0
0.5	0.125	0.02083	0.47917	0.4794
1.0	1	0.16667	0.83333	0.8415
1.5	3.375	0.56250	0.93750	0.9975
2.0	8	1.33333	0.66667	0.9093
2.5	15.625	2.60417	–0.10417	0.5985
3.0	27	4.5	–1.5	0.1411

Since both sin x and $x - x^3/3!$ are *odd* functions, you can draw the graphs for negative values of x simply by using the *opposites* of the y-values in the table. The graph is shown in Figure 6-9a.

As you can see from the table and from Figure 6-9a, the polynomial and the sine graphs are very close to each other when x is close to 0.

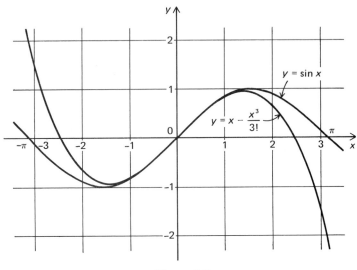

Figure 6-9a

Example 2:   Write cos x in terms of exponential functions.

The Taylor series for e^x and cos x look quite similar. In fact, the cosine series is composed of only the *even* degree terms of the exponential series, and the signs of these terms *alternate*, +, –,+, –, and so forth. So your approach is to think of something to do to the e^x series which will transform it to the cosine series. The transformations must eliminate the unwanted odd-degree terms, and make the signs alternate. Substituting –x for x in the e^x series gives

$$e^x = 1 + (-x) + \frac{(-x)^2}{2!} + \frac{(-x)^3}{3!} + \frac{(-x)^4}{4!} + \cdots$$

$$e^x = 1 - x + \frac{x^2}{2!} - \frac{x^3}{3!} + \frac{x^4}{4!} \cdots .$$

If you now *add* the series for e^x,

$$e^x = 1 + x + \frac{x^2}{2!} + \frac{x^3}{3!} + \frac{x^4}{4!} + \cdots ,$$

to the series for e^{-x}, you get

$$e^x + e^{-x} = 2 + 2 \cdot \frac{x^2}{2!} + 2 \cdot \frac{x^4}{4!} + \cdots .$$

The odd-degree terms cancel out, and the even-degree terms are doubled. Multiplying both members of the equation by 1/2, and assuming that multiplication distributes to all terms of the series, you get

$$\frac{1}{2} (e^x + e^{-x}) = 1 + \frac{x^2}{2!} + \frac{x^4}{4!} + \frac{x^6}{6!} + \frac{x^8}{8!} + \frac{x^{10}}{10!} \cdots .$$

This is the desired series for cosine, except that the signs do not alternate.

Recalling what you learned about powers of the imaginary number i in Seciton 6-4, you know that

$$i^2 = -1, \; i^4 = 1, \; i^6 = -1, \; i^8 = 1, \ldots .$$

Substituting ix for x in the preceding series gives

$$\frac{1}{2} (e^{ix} + e^{-ix}) = 1 + \frac{(ix)^2}{2!} + \frac{(ix)^4}{4!} + \frac{(ix)^6}{6!} + \frac{(ix)^8}{8!} + \frac{(ix)^{10}}{10!}$$

$$= 1 + \frac{i^2 x^2}{2!} + \frac{i^4 x^4}{4!} + \frac{i^6 x^6}{6!} + \frac{i^8 x^8}{8!} + \frac{i^{10} x^{10}}{10!} + \cdots$$

$$= 1 - \frac{x^2}{2!} + \frac{x^4}{4!} - \frac{x^6}{6!} + \frac{x^8}{8!} - \frac{x^{10}}{10!} + \cdots ,$$

which is the Taylor series for $\cos x$. So you can write

$$\cos x = \frac{1}{2} (e^{ix} - e^{-ix})$$

In Problem 13, following, you will perform other transformations on the Taylor series for e^x to show that

$$\sin x = \frac{1}{2i} (e^{ix} - e^{-ix})$$

These two equations are called *Euler's Formulas* after the German mathematician Leonhard Euler (pronounced "oiler"), who lived in the 1700s. Euler's Formulas can be used to derive another form for writing complex numbers, as you will find out by working Problems 14 through 24.

Exercise 6-9

1. Plot a graph of

$$y = 1 - \frac{x^2}{2!}$$

by calculating values of y for each 0.5 unit of x from $x = -2$ through $x = 2$. Use the *same* scales for both axes. On the same set of axes, plot a graph of the circular function $y = \cos x$. For which values of x do the graphs seem to be very close together?

2. Plot a graph of

$$y = 1 - \frac{x^2}{2!} + \frac{x^4}{4!}$$

by calculating values of y for each 0.5 unit of x from $x = -3$ through $x = 3$. You can use the computer program of Problem 18, Section 6-8. Use the same scales for both axes. On the same set of axes, draw a graph of the circular function $y = \cos x$. For which values of x do the two graphs seem to be very close together?

3. Using the techniques of Problem 2, plot graphs of

$$y = x - \frac{x^3}{3!} + \frac{x^5}{5!} \quad \text{and} \quad y = \sin x$$

on the same set of axes. Use values of x from $x + -4$ through $x = 4$. For which values of x do the two graphs seem to be very close together?

For Problems 4 through 9, calculate the circular or exponential function values indicated. Use enough terms of the appropriate Taylor series to get answers which are correct to 5 decimal places. You may use the computer program of Problem 18, Section 6-8.

4. $\sin 0.3$ 5. $\cos 0.3$ 6. $e^{0.3}$
7. $\sin 1$ 8. $\cos 1$ 9. e

10. One reason circular functions are preferred to trigonometric functions is that circular function values are easier to calculate by Taylor series. To calculate a trigonometric function value, you must first convert the degree argument to radians or arc length, as you did in Section 2-6. Demonstrate that you can do this by calculating $\sin 25°$ correct to 5 decimal places, using the appropriate Taylor series.

11. Write a computer program to print a short table of circular sines and cosines, and exponential function values for each 0.1 unit of x, from $x = 0$ through $x = 2.0$. The table should begin

X	SIN X	COS X	EXP X
0.0	0.00000	1.00000	1.00000
0.1	0.09983	0.99500	1.10517

The computer should use enough terms of the series to be sure that the values are correct to 5 decimal places. The program of Problem 18, Section 6-8, can be modified to do this.

12. The *Handbook of Mathematical Functions* published by the National Bureau of Standards lists values of circular functions correct to 23 decimal places. For example, it lists

$$\sin 0.001 \approx 0.00099999999833333334166667.$$

a. Use the Taylor series for $\sin x$ to show that this number is correct.
b. Explain why there are so many repeated digits.

13. By performing the appropriate transformations on the Taylor series for e^x, derive the Euler formula for sine,

$$\sin x = \frac{1}{2i}(e^{ix} - e^{-ix})$$

14. Use Euler's Formulas to show that

a. $e^{ix} = \cos x + i \sin x$
b. $e^{-ix} = \cos x - i \sin x$

The right-hand member of the equation in Problem 14a is the *polar* form of the complex number cis x, which you studied in Section 6-6. Since any complex number, z, can be written $z = r$ cis x, it can also be written in *exponential* form.

$$z = re^{ix}$$

For Problems 15 through 24, write the given complex number in exponential form.

15. $\cos 3 + i \sin 3$
16. $\cos 1.8 + i \sin 1.8$
17. $3(\cos 2 + i \sin 2)$
18. $5(\cos 7 + i \sin 7)$

19. $1 + i$

20. $1 - i$

21. $\sqrt{3} - i$

22. $1 + i\sqrt{3}$

23. i

24. -1

25. From Section 6-6 you recall that if

$$z_1 = r_1 \text{ cis } x_1 \quad \text{and} \quad z_2 = r_2 \text{ cis } x_2,$$

then the product $z_1 z_2$ is

$$z_1 z_2 = r_1 r_2 \text{ cis } (x_1 + x_2).$$

Show that this property follows automatically from the properties of exponentiation by writing z_1 and z_2 in exponential form and multiplying them together.

26. Show that $e^{i\pi} = -1$. This remarkable equation combines four of the most mysterious numbers of mathematics!

27. Show that i^i is a *real* number, and find a decimal approximation for this number.

28. Show that the exponential function with imaginary number exponents is *periodic*. That is, show that

$$e^{i(x + 2\pi)} = e^{ix}.$$

This is a property not possessed by exponential functions which have real-number exponents.

Problems 29 through 32 introduce you to a new kind of function, the *hyperbolic functions*.

29. As you were deriving Euler's Formulas for $\cos x$ in Example 2, and for $\sin x$ in Problem 13, above, you ran across the two series

$$\frac{1}{2}(e^x + e^{-x}) = 1 + \frac{x^2}{2!} + \frac{x^4}{4!} + \frac{x^6}{6!} + \cdots, \text{ and}$$

$$\frac{1}{2}(e^x - e^{-x}) = x + \frac{x^3}{3!} + \frac{x^5}{5!} + \frac{x^7}{7!} + \cdots.$$

These series are the same as the Taylor series for $\cos x$ and $\sin x$, respectively, except that the signs do not alternate. Let

$$u = \frac{1}{2}(e^x + e^{-x}) \quad \text{and} \quad v = \frac{1}{2}(e^x - e^{-x}).$$

Show that $u^2 - v^2 = 1$.

30. The graph of $u^2 - v^2 = 1$ is a *hyperbola.* Figure 6-9b shows the right-hand branch of this hyperbola. Since the vertex is one unit from the origin, the graph is called a *unit* hyperbola. The numbers u and v are the abscissa and ordinate of a point on this hyperbola, the same way that the *circular* functions $\cos x$ and $\sin x$ are coordinates of points

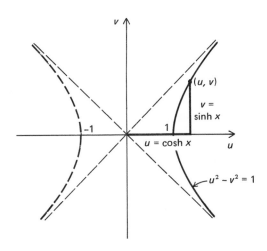

Figure 6-9b

on a unit *circle* (Figure 6-9c). So the new functions are called the *hyperbolic cosine* and *hyperbolic sine,* and are written

$$\cosh x = \frac{1}{2}(e^x + e^{-x})$$

$$\sinh x = \frac{1}{2}(e^x - e^{-x})$$

The letter h in cosh and sinh stands for hyperbolic. *Cosh* is pronounced as it is spelled with a short *o. Sinh* is pronounced "sinch."

Plot graphs of $y = \cosh x$ and $y = \sinh x$ by substituting values of x into these equations. Values of e^x can be found by calculator. The graph of $y = \cosh x$ is called a "catenary," and has the shape taken by a chain hanging freely under its own weight between two supports.

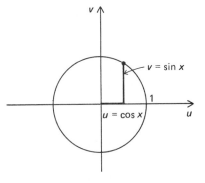

Figure 6-9c

31. There are four other hyperbolic functions, tanh x, coth x, sech x, and csch x. By recalling how the corresponding circular functions were defined in Section 2-6, write definitions for these functions in terms of cosh x and sinh x.

32. Use the technique of composition of ordinates which you studied in Section 4-1, and the definitions of the other hyperbolic functions from Problem 31 to sketch graphs of

 a. $y = \tanh x$
 b. $y = \coth x$
 c. $y = \operatorname{sech} x$
 d. $y = \operatorname{csch} x$

6-10   CHAPTER REVIEW AND TEST

In this chapter you have been introduced to some ways in which the trigonometric and circular functions can be applied to the mathematical world. The specific objectives were

1. Draw graphs in a polar coordinate system.
2. Transform an equation from polar to Cartesian coordinates and back again.
3. Solve systems of polar equations.
4. Do arithmetic with complex numbers written in polar form.
5. Add and subtract vectors by first writing them as complex numbers.
6. Use Taylor series to calculate values of various functions.

   As you progressed through the chapter, you saw how accomplishing the next objective required you to draw upon all of the previous objectives. It is the ability to apply your present knowledge to the gaining of new knowledge which is the most important goal in the educational process. If you have made progress toward being able to accomplish this goal, then taking this course in trigonometry has been worthwhile.
   The following review problems are numbered according to the five objectives so that you can measure your ability to accomplish the objective when you *know* which one is being tested. The Chapter Test is designed to see whether you can put together all of these skills to work problems you have never encountered before.

Review Problems

The following problems are numbered according to the six objectives listed above.

1. Sketch polar graphs of the following equations:

    a. $r = 10 \cos 3\theta$
    b. $r = 10(\cos\theta \cdot |\sin\theta|)$
    c. $r = 2 \sec (\theta - 50°)$
    d. $r = 2 \cos (\theta - 50°)$
    e. $r^2 + 8r \cos (\theta - 50°) - 9 = 0$

2. a. Transform $r = \sin 2\theta$ to Cartesian coordinates, and eliminate any radicals.
    b. Transform $x^2 + y^2 - 6x = 0$ to polar coordinates, and express r in terms of θ.

3. For the equations

    $$r = b \cos \theta$$
    $$r = 5 - 5 \cos \theta$$

    a. Sketch the graph to find approximate intersection points.
    b. Calculate *all* intersection points.

4. Perform the indicated operations and express the answers in the form $a + bi$.

    a. $(2 \text{ cis } 52°)(5 \text{ cis } 38°)$
    b. $(51 \text{ cis } 198°) \div (17 \text{ cis } 228°)$
    c. $(2 \text{ cis } 27°)^5$
    d. $(8 \text{ cis } 120°)^{1/3}$

5. *Airplane Looping Problem:* A stunt pilot is doing a "loop" with his plane. As shown in Figure 6-10a, there are three forces acting on the plane:

    Wing lift, 2500 lb at 127°
    Propeller thrust, 700 lb at 37°
    Gravity, 2000 lb, straight down.

    Find the sum of these three force vectors, and express the answer as a complex number in polar form.

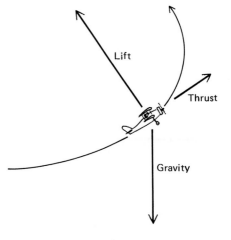

Figure 6-10a

6. a. Calculate a 10-decimal place approximation of sin 0.06 by using a sufficient number of terms of the appropriate Taylor series.

b. By substituting into the appropriate Taylor series, show that $\cos(ix) = \cosh x$.

c. Show that $\cos i$ is a *real* number, *greater* than one. This result should be surprising, since cosines of *real-number* arguments are always less than or equal to one.

Chapter Test

Problems 1 through 5 concern the design of gear teeth. The surfaces of the teeth (Figure 6-10b) are made in the shape of an *involute* of a circle. An involute is the path traced by the end of a string as it is unwound from around the circle.

Suppose than an involute is formed from a circle of radius a. The position vector, $\vec{r} = r \text{ cis } \theta$, of a point on the involute is the sum of vectors $\vec{a}$ and $\vec{v}$. Vector $\vec{a} = a \text{ cis } \phi$. Vector $\vec{v}$ is perpendicular to $\vec{a}$ (Figure 6-10c). θ and ϕ. are in *radians*.

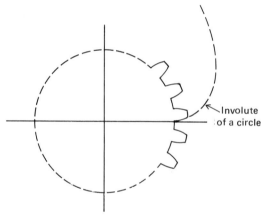

Figure 6-10b

1. The magnitude of $\vec{v}$ is equal to the length of the string which has been unwound. This length is, of course, equal to the *arc length* of the circle subtended by angle ϕ. Recalling that ϕ is measured in *radians*, find the magnitude of $\vec{v}$. Then write $\vec{v}$ as a complex number in polar form.

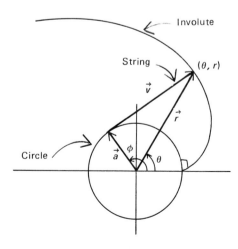

Figure 6-10c

2. Show that

$$\vec{r} = a(\cos \phi + \phi \sin \phi) + ia(\sin \phi - \phi \cos \phi).$$

3. Show that

$$r = a \sqrt{1 + \phi^2}.$$

4. Draw a polar graph of the involute of a *unit* circle centered at the pole by picking each $\pi/2$ units of ϕ from 0 to $5\pi/2$ and by using the corresponding values of $| \vec{v} |$ to plot points.

5. A particular gear is to have radius a = 10 cm, and the teeth are to project an additional 1 cm (i.e., $r = 11$ cm; see Figure 6-10d).

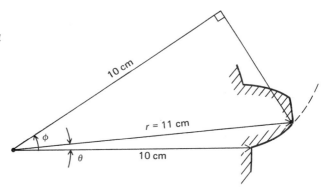

Figure 6-10d

   a. What is the measure of ϕ?

   b. Use the measure of ϕ to find the angle θ which the vector r makes with the polar axis. Convert θ to degrees and minutes.

6. Suppose that $f(x)$ is defined by the power series

$$f(x) = x - \frac{x^3}{3} + \frac{x^5}{5} - \frac{x^7}{7} + \cdots.$$

   a. Write the next three terms of the series.
   b. Using the first three terms of the series, find a decimal approximation for $f(0.3)$.
   c. By calculator find the value of the circular Arctan 0.3.
   d. Based on your answers to parts b and c, what function do you suppose f really is? Show that $f(0)$ confirms your conclusion. Give another piece of evidence to support your conclusion.

7. Figure 6-10e shows these graphs.

$$r = 6 + 4 \cos \theta$$
$$r = -3 + 3 \sin \theta$$

a. The graphs intersect
    at (6, 90°). Is this a
    common solution of
    the two equations?
    Justify your
    answer.
b. Find the coordinates
    of the point in the
    third quadrant
    where the graphs
    intersect.

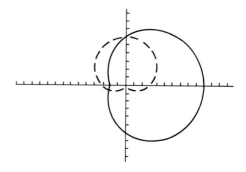

Figure 6-10e

FINAL EXAMINATION

The following exercise may be considered to be a final examination that test your ability to use all you have learned about trigonometric and circular functions. If you are thoroughly familiar with the concepts, you should be able to work all of the problems in about three hours.

Suppose you have joined the Navy and are stationed aboard the nuclear submarine Seawolf. Your boat has been assigned to conduct torpedo target practice in the Gulf of Mexico. Answer the following questions.

1. As you approach the practice area, you travel a displacement vector of 6 kilometers along a bearing of $22°$. Then you turn and go a displacement vector of 15 kilometers along a bearing of $82°$.

   a. Add these two vectors to find your resultant displacement.
   b. What is the area of ocean enclosed by these three vectors?

2. While you wait for the target ships to arrive, you steam submerged in a circle of diameter 100 kilometers, making a complete revolution every 20 hours. The closest you come to the coastline is 30 kilometers (see figure.)

   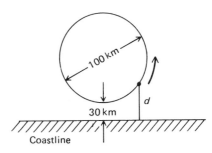

   a. What is your angular velocity in radians per hour?
   b. To the nearest tenth of a kilometer per hour, how fast are you going?
   c. Your distance, d, from the coastline varies sinusoidally with time, t. When $t = 2$ hours, you are at your maximum distance from the coastline. Write an equation expressing d in terms of t.
   d. Predict your distance from the coastline when $t = 9$.
   e. Transform the equation from part c so that t is expressed in terms of d.
   f. What are the first three positive values of t for which $d = 123$?

3. On the fourth day of your patrol, your electronic gear picks up five strange signals:

$$\text{(i)} \quad y_1 = \sec^2 x \sin^2 x + \tan^4 x$$

$$\text{(ii)} \quad y_2 = \frac{\sin^2 x}{\cos^4 x}$$

$$\text{(iii)} \quad y_3 = \cos^2 x$$

$$\text{(iv)} \quad y_4 = \cos 3x \cos 5x$$

$$\text{(v)} \quad y_5 = \cos(x + iz)$$

a. Prove that the expressions for y_1 and y_2 are identical.

b. Before your computer can analyze signals iii and iv, number iii must be expressed in terms of $\cos 2x$ and number iv must be expressed as a sum of sines or cosines. Perform these two transformations.

c. Use the composite argument properties to write y_5 in terms of sines and cosines of x and iz.

d. By transforming the appropriate Taylor series, show that $\cos iz = \cosh z$ and $\sin iz = i \sinh z$.

e. Write y_5 in terms of functions of *real-number* arguments x and z.

f. For what values of x and z will y_5 equal a *real* number?

4. The signals are coming from three unmanned target ships, the Hic, the Haec, and the Hoc. Your sonar detects a sound of varying amplitude coming from Hoc's engines. The sound is described by the equation

$$y = 4 \sin \theta \cdot \sin 4\theta.$$

Sketch one complete cycle of the graph of this function.

5. You can fire torpedoes at any angle θ to the ship's axis in the interval $[-180°, 180°]$, but $\theta \neq 0$. (Firing them straight ahead might give away your position.) However, the best angles are those in the solution set of the trigonometric equation

$$\cos 4\theta - \cos 2\theta = 0.$$

Solve this equation in the given domain.

6. In preparation for firing torpedoes, you must evaluate the following. Leave the answer in *exact* form using π or radicals, if necessary, unless otherwise specified. Assume circular functions unless degrees or θ is specified.

   a.   cos 150°

   b.   sin $\dfrac{5\pi}{4}$

   c.   tan θ, if θ terminates in quadrant IV, and cos $\theta = \dfrac{7}{11}$

   d.   csc 3, to 5 decimal places

   e. θ = Arcsin $\left(\dfrac{1}{2}\right)$

   f. x = Arcos (−1)

   g. $x = \text{Tan}^{-1}\ (-\sqrt{3})$

   h. $x = \text{Sec}^{-1}\left(\dfrac{-2}{\sqrt{3}}\right)$

   i. $\sin\left(\text{Cos}^{-1}\left(\dfrac{-2}{3}\right)\right)$

   j.   cos (cos(cos 2)), to 5 decimal places

7. The last piece of information needed is the value of sin 0.06 correct to *twelve* decimal places. Use enough terms of the Taylor series to find this value. Show that it agrees with the value found by calculator to as many places as your calculator will give.

8. Your first torpedo sinks the Hic. As you set up to fire at the Haec, assume that you are at the pole of a polar coordinate system. The Haec is located at the point (5000, 135°), where the radius is expressed in meters. You fire the torpedo in a circular path, tangent to the polar axis, setting the rudder to pass through (5000, 135°). Find a polar equation of this circular path.

9. The torpedo does not sink the Haec, but damages its rudder so that it steams out of control on the path of the polar equation
       $r = 3000 - 2000 \sin 2\theta$.

   a.   Show that (5000, 135°) is on this path.
   b.   Sketch a Cartesian graph of this equation, letting r be the ordinate and θ the abscissa.
   c.   Sketch the path of the damaged target ship on polar coordinate graph paper.

10. The Haec explodes. The two pieces of the target ship sink at the points whose coordinates are the two square roots of 400i. Write these two numbers as complex numbers in polar form. Then sketch the numbers on a complex plane.

11. The Hoc leaves the practice area along a bearing of Arctan $(-\sqrt{3})$.

    a. Find exactly the inverse *circular* Arctan $(-\sqrt{3})$.
    b. Find exactly the inverse *trigonometric* Arctan $(-\sqrt{3})$.
    c. What are the values of arctan $(-\sqrt{3})$? (Trig or circular.)
    d. What is the value of sin (Arctan 2)?
    e. Sketch a graph of y = Arctan x.

12. On the trip home you dig out an old trigonometry text and see if you can apply your knowledge to a new situation.

    You find stated, without proof, the *Law of Tangents,* which says that in any triangle ABC,

$$\frac{\tan \tfrac{1}{2}(A - B)}{\tan \tfrac{1}{2}(A + B)} = \frac{a - b}{a + b}$$

You decide to prove the Law of Tangents.

    a. Use the Law of Sines and the addition property of equality to show

$$(\text{i}) \quad \frac{\sin A + \sin B}{\sin B} = \frac{a + b}{b} \qquad \text{and} \quad (\text{ii}) \quad \frac{\sin A - \sin B}{\sin B} = \frac{a - b}{b}$$

    b. Divide equation (ii) by equation (i), left member by left member and right member by right member, then simplify. Then use the sum and product properties to express the numerator and denominator of the left member as *products.*
    c. Use the quotient properties to arrive at the Law of Tangents from your work in part b.

TABLES

Instructions for Table I

Table I. Trigonometric Functions and Degrees-to-Radians

Degrees	Radians	sin θ	csc θ	tan θ	cot θ	sec θ	cos θ		
36°00'	.6283	.5878	1.701	.7265	1.376	1.236	.8090	.9425	54°00'
10'	.6312	.5901	1.695	.7310	1.368	1.239	.8073	.9396	50' ← Example 3
20'	.6341	.5925	1.688	.7355	1.360	1.241	.8056	.9367	40' → Example 5
30'	.6370	.5948	1.681	.7400	1.351	1.244	.8039	.9338	30'
40'	.6400	.5972	1.675	.7445	1.343	1.247	.8021	.9308	20'
50'	.6429	.5995	1.668	.7490	1.335	1.249	.8004	.9279	10'
37°00'	.6458	.6018	1.662	.7536	1.427	1.252	.7986	.9250	53°00'
10'	.6487	.6041	1.655	.7581	1.319	1.255	.7969	.9221	50' Example 4
20'	.6516	.6065	1.649	.7627	1.311	1.258	.7951	.9192	40'
30'	.6545	.6088	1.643	.7673	1.303	1.260	.7934	.9163	30'
Example 1 → 40'	.6574	.6111	1.636	.7720	1.295	1.263	.7916	.9134	20'
50'	.6603	.6134	1.630	.7766	1.288	1.266	.7898	.9105	10'
38°00'	.6632	.6157	1.624	.7813	1.280	1.269	.7880	.9076	52°00'
10'	.6661	.6180	1.618	.7860	1.272	1.272	.7862	.9047	50'
20'	.6690	.6202	1.612	.7907	1.265	1.275	.7844	.9018	40'
30'	.6720	.6225	1.606	.7954	1.257	1.278	.7826	.8988	30'
40'	.6749	.6248	1.601	.8002	1.250	1.281	.7808	.8959	20' ← Example 2
50'	.6778	.6271	1.595	.8050	1.242	1.284	.7790	.8930	10'
39°00'	.6807	.6293	1.589	.8098	1.235	1.287	.7771	.8901	51°00'
10'	.6836	.6316	1.583	.8146	1.228	1.290	.7753	.8872	50'
	.6865	.6338			1.220	1.293	.7735	.8843	40'
40			1.423	.9864					
50'	.7825	.7050	1.418	.9942	1.006	1.410	.7092	.7883	10'
45°00'	.7854	.7071	1.414	1.000	1.000	1.414	.7071	.7854	45°00'
	cos θ	sec θ	cot θ	tan θ	csc θ	sin θ	Radians	Degrees	

Example 1: tan 37°40' ≈ 0.7720

Find 37°40' in the column headed $m(\theta)$ on the left. The answer is in the column headed tan θ at the top of the page.

Example 2: cos 51°20' ≈ 0.6248

Find 51°10' by reading *up* the *righthand* column headed $m(\theta)$. The answer is in the column that is headed cos θ at the *bottom* of the page.

Example 3: sec 126°10' ≈ −1.695

Find the reference angle, 180° − 126°10' = 53°50'. Look up 53°50' in the righthand column and use the column labeled sec θ at the bottom of the page. The "−" sign is needed because sec θ is negative in Quadrant II.

Example 4: cos 52°43' ≈ 0.6058

Find cos 52°40' = .6065 and cos 52°50' = .6041. Since 43' is .3 of the way from 40' to 50', assume that cos 52°43' is .3 of the way from .6065 to .6041. The total difference between the numbers, ignoring the decimal point, is −24. (.3)(−24) is about −7. Adding −7 to 6065 gives 6058, which gives the answer above. This process is called *interpolation.*

Example 5: If tan θ = 1.356, then θ ≈ 53°36'

Find the two values in the tan θ column, 1.351 and 1.360, which 1.356 is between. The corresponding angles are 53°30' and 53°40'. Since 1.356 is 5/9 of the way from 1.351 to 1.360 assume that the number of minutes is 5/9 of the way from 30' to 40'. (5/9)(10) is about 6. Adding 6' to 30' gives 36', which gives the above answer. This process is also called interpolation.

Table I. Trigonometric Functions and Degrees-to-Radians

Degrees	Radians	sin θ	csc θ	tan θ	cot θ	sec θ	cos θ		
0° 00′	.0000	.0000	Undef.	.0000	Undef.	1.000	1.0000	1.5708	90° 00′
10′	.0029	.0029	343.8	.0029	343.8	1.000	1.0000	1.5679	50′
20′	.0058	.0058	171.9	.0058	171.9	1.000	1.0000	1.5650	40′
30′	.0087	.0087	114.6	.0087	114.6	1.000	1.0000	1.5621	30′
40′	.0116	.0116	85.95	.0116	85.94	1.000	.9999	1.5592	20′
50′	.0145	.0145	68.76	.0145	68.75	1.000	.9999	1.5563	10′
1° 00′	.0175	.0175	57.30	.0175	57.29	1.000	.9998	1.5533	89° 00′
10′	.0204	.0204	49.11	.0204	49.10	1.000	.9998	1.5504	50′
20′	.0233	.0233	42.98	.0233	42.96	1.000	.9997	1.5475	40′
30′	.0262	.0262	38.20	.0262	38.19	1.000	.9997	1.5446	30′
40′	.0291	.0291	34.38	.0291	34.37	1.000	.9996	1.5417	20′
50′	.0320	.0320	31.26	.0320	31.24	1.001	.9995	1.5388	10′
2° 00′	.0349	.0349	28.65	.0349	28.64	1.001	.9994	1.5359	88° 00′
10′	.0378	.0378	26.45	.0378	26.43	1.001	.9993	1.5330	50′
20′	.0407	.0407	24.56	.0407	24.54	1.001	.9992	1.5301	40′
30′	.0436	.0436	22.93	.0437	22.90	1.001	.9990	1.5272	30′
40′	.0465	.0465	21.49	.0466	21.47	1.001	.9989	1.5243	20′
50′	.0495	.0494	20.23	.0495	20.21	1.001	.9988	1.5213	10′
3° 00′	.0524	.0523	19.11	.0524	19.08	1.001	.9986	1.5184	87° 00′
10′	.0553	.0552	18.10	.0553	18.07	1.002	.9985	1.5155	50′
20′	.0582	.0581	17.20	.0582	17.17	1.002	.9983	1.5126	40′
30′	.0611	.0610	16.38	.0612	16.35	1.002	.9981	1.5097	30′
40′	.0640	.0640	15.64	.0641	15.60	1.002	.9980	1.5068	20′
50′	.0669	.0669	14.96	.0670	14.92	1.002	.9978	1.5039	10′
4° 00′	.0698	.0698	14.34	.0699	14.30	1.002	.9976	1.5010	86° 00′
10′	.0727	.0727	13.76	.0729	13.73	1.003	.9974	1.4981	50′
20′	.0756	.0756	13.23	.0758	13.20	1.003	.9971	1.4952	40′
30′	.0785	.0785	12.75	.0787	12.71	1.003	.9969	1.4923	30′
40′	.0814	.0814	12.29	.0816	12.25	1.003	.9967	1.4893	20′
50.	.0844	.0843	11.87	.0846	11.83	1.004	.9964	1.4864	10′
5° 00′	.0873	.0872	11.47	.0874	11.43	1.004	.9962	1.4835	85° 00′
10′	.0902	.0901	11.10	.0904	11.06	1.004	.9959	1.4806	50′
20′	.0931	.0929	10.76	.0934	10.71	1.004	.9957	1.4777	40′
30′	.0960	.0958	10.43	.0963	10.39	1.005	.9954	1.4748	30′
40′	.0989	.0987	10.13	.0992	10.08	1.005	.9951	1.4719	20′
50′	.1018	.1016	9.839	.1022	9.788	1.005	.9948	1.4690	10′
6° 00′	.1047	.1045	9.567	.1051	9.514	1.006	.9945	1.4661	84° 00′
10′	.1076	.1074	9.309	.1080	9.255	1.006	.9942	1.4632	50′
20′	.1105	.1103	9.065	.1110	9.010	1.006	.9939	1.4603	40′
30′	.1134	.1132	8.834	.1139	8.777	1.006	.9936	1.4573	30′
40′	.1164	.1161	8.614	.1169	8.556	1.007	.9932	1.4544	20′
50′	.1193	.1190	8.405	.1198	8.345	1.007	.9929	1.4515	10′
7° 00′	.1222	.1219	8.206	.1228	8.144	1.008	.9925	1.4486	83° 00′
10′	.1251	.1248	8.016	.1257	7.953	1.008	.9922	1.4457	50′
20′	.1280	.1276	7.834	.1287	7.770	1.008	.9918	1.4428	40′
30′	.1309	.1305	7.661	.1317	7.596	1.009	.9914	1.4399	30′
40′	.1338	.1334	7.496	.1346	7.429	1.009	.9911	1.4370	20′
50′	.1367	.1363	7.337	.1376	7.269	1.009	.9907	1.4341	10′
8° 00′	.1396	.1392	7.185	.1405	7.115	1.010	.9903	1.4312	82° 00′
10′	.1425	.1421	7.040	.1435	6.968	1.010	.9899	1.4283	50′
20′	.1454	.1449	6.900	.1465	6.827	1.011	.9894	1.4254	40′
30′	.1484	.1478	6.765	.1495	6.691	1.011	.9890	1.4224	30′
40′	.1513	.1507	6.636	.1524	6.561	1.012	.9886	1.4195	20′
50′	.1542	.1536	6.512	.1554	6.435	1.012	.9881	1.4166	10
9° 00′	.1571	.1564	6.392	.1584	6.314	1.012	.9877	1.4137	81° 00′
		cos θ	sec θ	cot θ	tan θ	csc θ	sin θ	Radians	Degrees
								m(θ)	

m(θ)

Table I (Continued)

$m(\theta)$ Degrees	$m(\theta)$ Radians	$\sin\theta$	$\csc\theta$	$\tan\theta$	$\cot\theta$	$\sec\theta$	$\cos\theta$		
9°00′	.1571	.1564	6.392	.1584	6.314	1.012	.9877	1.4137	81°00′
10′	.1600	.1593	6.277	.1614	6.197	1.013	.9872	1.4108	50′
20′	.1629	.1622	6.166	.1644	6.084	1.013	.9868	1.4079	40′
30′	.1658	.1650	6.059	.1673	5.976	1.014	.9863	1.4050	30′
40′	.1687	.1679	5.955	.1703	5.871	1.014	.9858	1.4021	20′
50′	.1716	.1708	5.855	.1733	5.769	1.015	.9853	1.3992	10′
10°00′	.1745	.1736	5.759	.1763	5.671	1.015	.9848	1.3963	80°00′
10′	.1774	.1765	5.665	.1793	5.576	1.016	.9843	1.3934	50′
20′	.1804	.1794	5.575	.1823	5.485	1.016	.9838	1.3904	40′
30′	.1833	.1822	5.487	.1853	5.396	1.017	.9833	1.3875	30′
40′	.1862	.1851	5.403	.1883	5.309	1.018	.9827	1.3846	20′
50′	.1891	.1880	5.320	.1914	5.226	1.018	.9822	1.3817	10′
11°00′	.1920	.1908	5.241	.1944	5.145	1.019	.9816	1.3788	79°00′
10′	.1949	.1937	5.164	.1974	5.066	1.019	.9811	1.3759	50′
20′	.1978	.1965	5.089	.2004	4.989	1.020	.9805	1.3730	40′
30′	.2007	.1994	5.016	.2035	4.915	1.020	.9799	1.3701	30′
40′	.2036	.2022	4.945	.2065	4.843	1.021	.9793	1.3672	20′
50′	.2065	.2051	4.876	.2095	4.773	1.022	.9787	1.3643	10′
12°00′	.2094	.2079	4.810	.2126	4.705	1.022	.9781	1.3614	78°00′
10′	.2123	.2108	4.745	.2156	4.638	1.023	.9775	1.3584	50′
20′	.2153	.2136	4.682	.2186	4.574	1.024	.9769	1.3555	40′
30′	.2182	.2164	4.620	.2217	4.511	1.024	.9763	1.3526	30′
40′	.2211	.2193	4.560	.2247	4.449	1.025	.9757	1.3497	20′
50′	.2240	.2221	4.502	.2278	4.390	1.026	.9750	1.3468	10′
13°00′	.2269	.2250	4.445	.2309	4.331	1.026	.9744	1.3439	77°00′
10′	.2298	.2278	4.390	.2339	4.275	1.027	.9737	1.3410	50′
20′	.2327	.2306	4.336	.2370	4.219	1.028	.9730	1.3381	40′
30′	.2356	.2334	4.284	.2401	4.165	1.028	.9724	1.3352	30′
40′	.2385	.2363	4.232	.2432	4.113	1.029	.9717	1.3323	20′
50′	.2414	.2391	4.182	.2462	4.061	1.030	.9710	1.3294	10′
14°00′	.2443	.2419	4.134	.2493	4.011	1.031	.9703	1.3265	76°00′
10′	.2473	.2447	4.086	.2524	3.962	1.031	.9696	1.3235	50′
20′	.2502	.2476	4.039	.2555	3.914	1.032	.9689	1.3206	40′
30′	.2531	.2504	3.994	.2586	3.867	1.033	.9681	1.3177	30′
40′	.2560	.2532	3.950	.2617	3.821	1.034	.9674	1.3148	20′
50′	.2589	.2560	3.906	.2648	3.776	1.034	.9667	1.3119	10′
15°00′	.2618	.2588	3.864	.2679	3.732	1.035	.9659	1.3090	75°00′
10′	.2647	.2616	3.822	.2711	3.689	1.036	.9652	1.3061	50′
20′	.2676	.2644	3.782	.2742	3.647	1.037	.9644	1.3032	40′
30′	.2705	.2672	3.742	.2773	3.606	1.038	.9636	1.3003	30′
40′	.2734	.2700	3.703	.2805	3.566	1.039	.9628	1.2974	20′
50′	.2763	.2728	3.665	.2836	3.526	1.039	.9621	1.2945	10′
16°00′	.2793	.2756	3.628	.2867	3.487	1.040	.9613	1.2915	74°00′
10′	.2822	.2784	3.592	.2899	3.450	1.041	.9605	1.2886	50′
20′	.2851	.2812	3.556	.2931	3.412	1.042	.9596	1.2857	40′
30′	.2880	.2840	3.521	.2962	3.376	1.043	.9588	1.2828	30′
40′	.2909	.2868	3.487	.2994	3.340	1.044	.9580	1.2799	20′
50′	.2938	.2896	3.453	.3026	3.305	1.045	.9572	1.2770	10′
17°00′	.2967	.2924	3.420	.3057	3.271	1.046	.9563	1.2741	73°00′
10′	.2996	.2952	3.388	.3089	3.237	1.047	.9555	1.2712	50′
20′	.3025	.2979	3.356	.3121	3.204	1.048	.9546	1.2683	40′
30′	.3054	.3007	3.326	.3153	3.172	1.049	.9537	1.2654	30′
40′	.3083	.3035	3.295	.3185	3.140	1.049	.9528	1.2625	20′
50′	.3113	.3062	3.265	.3217	3.108	1.050	.9520	1.2595	10′
18°00′	.3142	.3090	3.236	.3249	3.078	1.051	.9511	1.2566	72°00′
		$\cos\theta$	$\sec\theta$	$\cot\theta$	$\tan\theta$	$\csc\theta$	$\sin\theta$	Radians	Degrees
								$m(\theta)$	

Table I (Continued)

m(θ) Degrees	m(θ) Radians	sin θ	csc θ	tan θ	cot θ	sec θ	cos θ		
18°00'	.3142	.3090	3.236	.3249	3.078	1.051	.9511	1.2566	72°00'
10'	.3171	.3118	3.207	.3281	3.047	1.052	.9502	1.2537	50'
20'	.3200	.3145	3.179	.3314	3.018	1.053	.9492	1.2508	40'
30'	.3229	.3173	3.152	.3346	2.989	1.054	.9483	1.2479	30'
40'	.3258	.3201	3.124	.3378	2.960	1.056	.9474	1.2450	20'
50'	.3287	.3228	3.098	.3411	2.932	1.057	.9465	1.2421	10'
19°00'	.3316	.3256	3.072	.3443	2.904	1.058	.9455	1.2392	71°00'
10'	.3345	.3283	3.046	.3476	2.877	1.059	.9446	1.2363	50'
20'	.3374	.3311	3.021	.3508	2.850	1.060	.9436	1.2334	40'
30'	.3403	.3338	2.996	.3541	2.824	1.061	.9426	1.2305	30'
40'	.3432	.3365	2.971	.3574	2.798	1.062	.9417	1.2275	20'
50'	.3462	.3393	2.947	.3607	2.773	1.063	.9407	1.2246	10'
20°00'	.3491	.3420	2.924	.3640	2.747	1.064	.9397	1.2217	70°00'
10'	.3520	.3448	2.901	.3673	2.723	1.065	.9387	1.2188	50'
20'	.3549	.3475	2.878	.3706	2.699	1.066	.9377	1.2159	40'
30'	.3578	.3502	2.855	.3739	2.675	1.068	.9367	1.2130	30'
40'	.3607	.3529	2.833	.3772	2.651	1.069	.9356	1.2101	20'
50'	.3636	.3557	2.812	.3805	2.628	1.070	.9346	1.2072	10'
21°00'	.3665	.3584	2.790	.3839	2.605	1.071	.9336	1.2043	69°00'
10'	.3694	.3611	2.769	.3872	2.583	1.072	.9325	1.2014	50'
20'	.3723	.3638	2.749	.3906	2.560	1.074	.9315	1.1985	40'
30'	.3752	.3665	2.729	.3939	2.539	1.075	.9304	1.1956	30'
40'	.3782	.3692	2.709	.3973	2.517	1.076	.9293	1.1926	20'
50'	.3811	.3719	2.689	.4006	2.496	1.077	.9283	1.1897	10'
22°00'	.3840	.3746	2.669	.4040	2.475	1.079	.9272	1.1868	68°00'
10'	.3869	.3773	2.650	.4074	2.455	1.080	.9261	1.1839	50'
20'	.3898	.3800	2.632	.4108	2.434	1.081	.9250	1.1810	40'
30'	.3927	.3827	2.613	.4142	2.414	1.082	.9239	1.1781	30'
40'	.3956	.3854	2.595	.4176	2.394	1.084	.9228	1.1752	20'
50'	.3985	.3881	2.577	.4210	2.375	1.085	.9216	1.1723	10'
23°00'	.4014	.3907	2.559	.4245	2.356	1.086	.9205	1.1694	67°00'
10'	.4043	.3934	2.542	.4279	2.337	1.088	.9194	1.1665	50'
20'	.4072	.3961	2.525	.4314	2.318	1.089	.9182	1.1636	40'
30'	.4102	.3987	2.508	.4348	2.300	1.090	.9171	1.1606	30'
40'	.4131	.4014	2.491	.4383	2.282	1.092	.9159	1.1577	20'
50'	.4160	.4041	2.475	.4417	2.264	1.093	.9147	1.1548	10'
24°00'	.4189	.4067	2.459	.4452	2.246	1.095	.9135	1.1519	66°00'
10'	.4218	.4094	2.443	.4487	2.229	1.096	.9124	1.1490	50'
20'	.4247	.4120	2.427	.4522	2.211	1.097	.9112	1.1461	40'
30'	.4276	.4147	2.411	.4557	2.194	1.099	.9100	1.1432	30'
40'	.4305	.4173	2.396	.4592	2.177	1.100	.9088	1.1403	20'
50'	.4334	.4200	2.381	.4628	2.161	1.102	.9075	1.1374	10'
25°00'	.4363	.4226	2.366	.4663	2.145	1.103	.9063	1.1345	65°00'
10'	.4392	.4253	2.352	.4699	2.128	1.105	.9051	1.1316	50'
20'	.4422	.4279	2.337	.4734	2.112	1.106	.9038	1.1286	40'
30'	.4451	.4305	2.323	.4770	2.097	1.108	.9026	1.1257	30'
40'	.4480	.4331	2.309	.4806	2.081	1.109	.9013	1.1228	20'
50'	.4509	.4358	2.295	.4841	2.066	1.111	.9001	1.1199	10'
26°00'	.4538	.4384	2.281	.4877	2.050	1.113	.8988	1.1170	64°00'
10'	.4567	.4410	2.268	.4913	2.035	1.114	.8975	1.1141	50'
20'	.4596	.4436	2.254	.4950	2.020	1.116	.8962	1.1112	40'
30'	.4625	.4462	2.241	.4986	2.006	1.117	.8949	1.1083	30'
40'	.4654	.4488	2.228	.5022	1.991	1.119	.8936	1.1054	20'
50'	.4683	.4514	2.215	.5059	1.977	1.121	.8923	1.1025	10'
27°00'	.4712	.4540	2.203	.5095	1.963	1.122	.8910	1.0996	63°00'
		cos θ	sec θ	cot θ	tan θ	csc θ	sin θ	Radians m(θ)	Degrees

Table I (Continued)

m(θ) Degrees	m(θ) Radians	sin θ	csc θ	tan θ	cot θ	sec θ	cos θ		
27° 00′	.4712	.4540	2.203	.5095	1.963	1.122	.8910	1.0996	63° 00′
10′	.4741	.4566	2.190	.5132	1.949	1.124	.8897	1.0966	50′
20′	.4771	.4592	2.178	.5169	1.935	1.126	.8884	1.0937	40′
30′	.4800	.4617	2.166	.5206	1.921	1.127	.8870	1.0908	30′
40′	.4829	.4643	2.154	.5243	1.907	1.129	.8857	1.0879	20′
50′	.4858	.4669	2.142	.5280	1.894	1.131	.8843	1.0850	10′
28° 00′	.4887	.4695	2.130	.5317	1.881	1.133	.8829	1.0821	62° 00′
10′	.4916	.4720	2.118	.5354	1.868	1.134	.8816	1.0792	50′
20′	.4945	.4746	2.107	.5392	1.855	1.136	.8802	1.0763	40′
30′	.4974	.4772	2.096	.5430	1.842	1.138	.8788	1.0734	30′
40′	.5003	.4797	2.085	.5467	1.829	1.140	.8774	1.0705	20′
50′	.5032	.4823	2.074	.5505	1.816	1.142	.8760	1.0676	10′
29° 00′	.5061	.4848	2.063	.5543	1.804	1.143	.8746	1.0647	61° 00′
10′	.5091	.4874	2.052	.5581	1.792	1.145	.8732	1.0617	50′
20′	.5120	.4899	2.041	.5619	1.780	1.147	.8718	1.0588	40′
30′	.5149	.4924	2.031	.5658	1.767	1.149	.8704	1.0559	30′
40′	.5178	.4950	2.020	.5696	1.756	1.151	.8689	1.0530	20′
50′	.5207	.4975	2.010	.5735	1.744	1.153	.8675	1.0501	10′
30° 00′	.5236	.5000	2.000	.5774	1.732	1.155	.8660	1.0472	60° 00′
10′	.5265	.5025	1.990	.5812	1.720	1.157	.8646	1.0443	50′
20′	.5294	.5050	1.980	.5851	1.709	1.159	.8631	1.0414	40′
30′	.5323	.5075	1.970	.5890	1.698	1.161	.8616	1.0385	30′
40′	.5352	.5100	1.961	.5930	1.686	1.163	.8601	1.0356	20′
50′	.5381	.5125	1.951	.5969	1.675	1.165	.8587	1.0327	10′
31° 00′	.5411	.5150	1.942	.6009	1.664	1.167	.8572	1.0297	59° 00′
10′	.5440	.5175	1.932	.6048	1.653	1.169	.8557	1.0268	50′
20′	.5469	.5200	1.923	.6038	1.643	1.171	.8542	1.0239	40′
30′	.5498	.5225	1.914	.6128	1.632	1.173	.8526	1.0210	30′
40′	.5527	.5250	1.905	.6168	1.621	1.175	.8511	1.0181	20′
50′	.5556	.5275	1.896	.6208	1.611	1.177	.8496	1.0152	10′
32° 00′	.5585	.5299	1.887	.6249	1.600	1.179	.8480	1.0123	58° 00′
10′	.5614	.5324	1.878	.6289	1.590	1.181	.8465	1.0094	50′
20′	.5643	.5348	1.870	.6330	1.580	1.184	.8450	1.0065	40′
30′	.5672	.5373	1.861	.6371	1.570	1.186	.8434	1.0036	30′
40′	.5701	.5398	1.853	.6412	1.560	1.188	.8418	1.0007	20′
50′	.5730	.5422	1.844	.6453	1.550	1.190	.8403	.9977	10′
33° 00′	.5760	.5446	1.836	.6494	1.540	1.192	.8387	.9948	57° 00′
10′	.5789	.5471	1.828	.6536	1.530	1.195	.8371	.9919	50′
20′	.5818	.5495	1.820	.6577	1.520	1.197	.8355	.9890	40′
30′	.5847	.5519	1.812	.6619	1.511	1.199	.8339	.9861	30′
40′	.5876	.5544	1.804	.6661	1.501	1.202	.8323	.9832	20′
50′	.5905	.5568	1.796	.6703	1.492	1.204	.8307	.9803	10′
34° 00′	.5934	.5592	1.788	.6745	1.483	1.206	.8290	.9774	56° 00′
10′	.5963	.5616	1.781	.6787	1.473	1.209	.8274	.9745	50′
20′	.5992	.5640	1.773	.6830	1.464	1.211	.8258	.9716	40′
30′	.6021	.5664	1.766	.6873	1.455	1.213	.8241	.9687	30′
40′	.6050	.5688	1.758	.6916	1.446	1.216	.8225	.9657	20′
50′	.6080	.5712	1.751	.6959	1.437	1.218	.8208	.9628	10′
35° 00′	.6109	.5736	1.743	.7002	1.428	1.221	.8192	.9599	55° 00′
10′	.6138	.5760	1.736	.7046	1.419	1.223	.8175	.9570	50′
20′	.6167	.5783	1.729	.7089	1.411	1.226	.8158	.9541	40′
30′	.6196	.5807	1.722	.7133	1.402	1.228	.8141	.9512	30′
40′	.6225	.5831	1.715	.7177	1.393	1.231	.8124	.9483	20′
50′	.6254	.5854	1.708	.7221	1.385	1.233	.8107	.9454	10′
36° 00′	.6283	.5878	1.701	.7265	1.376	1.236	.8090	.9425	54° 00′
		cos θ	sec θ	cot θ	tan θ	csc θ	sin θ	Radians	Degrees
								m(θ)	

Table I (Concluded)

m(θ) Degrees	m(θ) Radians	sin θ	csc θ	tan θ	cot θ	sec θ	cos θ		
36°00′	.6283	.5878	1.701	.7265	1.376	1.236	.8090	.9425	54°00′
10′	.6312	.5901	1.695	.7310	1.368	1.239	.8073	.9396	50′
20′	.6341	.5925	1.688	.7355	1.360	1.241	.8056	.9367	40′
30′	.6370	.5948	1.681	.7400	1.351	1.244	.8039	.9338	30′
40′	.6400	.5972	1.675	.7445	1.343	1.247	.8021	.9308	20′
50′	.6429	.5995	1.668	.7490	1.335	1.249	.8004	.9279	10′
37°00′	.6458	.6018	1.662	.7536	1.327	1.252	.7986	.9250	53°00′
10′	.6487	.6041	1.655	.7581	1.319	1.255	.7969	.9221	50′
20′	.6516	.6065	1.649	.7627	1.311	1.258	.7951	.9192	40′
30′	.6545	.6088	1.643	.7673	1.303	1.260	.7934	.9163	30′
40′	.6574	.6111	1.636	.7720	1.295	1.263	.7916	.9134	20′
50′	.6603	.6134	1.630	.7766	1.288	1.266	.7898	.9105	10′
38°00′	.6632	.6157	1.624	.7813	1.280	1.269	.7880	.9076	52°00′
10′	.6661	.6180	1.618	.7860	1.272	1.272	.7862	.9047	50′
20′	.6690	.6202	1.612	.7907	1.265	1.275	.7844	.9018	40′
30′	.6720	.6225	1.606	.7954	1.257	1.278	.7826	.8988	30′
40′	.6749	.6248	1.601	.8002	1.250	1.281	.7808	.8959	20′
50′	.6778	.6271	1.595	.8050	1.242	1.284	.7790	.8930	10′
39°00′	.6807	.6293	1.589	.8098	1.235	1.287	.7771	.8901	51°00′
10′	.6836	.6316	1.583	.8146	1.228	1.290	.7753	.8872	50′
20′	.6865	.6338	1.578	.8195	1.220	1.293	.7735	.8843	40′
30′	.6894	.6361	1.572	.8243	1.213	1.296	.7716	.8814	30′
40′	.6923	.6383	1.567	.8292	1.206	1.299	.7698	.8785	20′
50′	.6952	.6406	1.561	.8342	1.199	1.302	.7679	.8756	10′
40°00′	.6981	.6428	1.556	.8391	1.192	1.305	.7660	.8727	50°00′
10′	.7010	.6450	1.550	.8441	1.185	1.309	.7642	.8698	50′
20′	.7039	.6472	1.545	.8491	1.178	1.312	.7623	.8668	40′
30′	.7069	.6494	1.540	.8541	1.171	1.315	.7604	.8639	30′
40′	.7098	.6517	1.535	.8591	1.164	1.318	.7585	.8610	20′
50′	.7127	.6539	1.529	.8642	1.157	1.322	.7566	.8581	10′
41°00′	.7156	.6561	1.524	.8693	1.150	1.325	.7547	.8552	49°00′
10′	.7185	.6583	1.519	.8744	1.144	1.328	.7528	.8523	50′
20′	.7214	.6604	1.514	.8796	1.137	1.332	.7509	.8494	40′
30′	.7243	.6626	1.509	.8847	1.130	1.335	.7490	.8465	30′
40′	.7272	.6648	1.504	.8899	1.124	1.339	.7470	.8436	20′
50′	.7301	.6670	1.499	.8952	1.117	1.342	.7451	.8407	10′
42°00′	.7330	.6691	1.494	.9004	1.111	1.346	.7431	.8378	48°00′
10′	.7359	.6713	1.490	.9057	1.104	1.349	.7412	.8348	50′
20′	.7389	.6734	1.485	.9110	1.098	1.353	.7392	.8319	40′
30′	.7418	.6756	1.480	.9163	1.091	1.356	.7373	.8290	30′
40′	.7447	.6777	1.476	.9217	1.085	1.360	.7353	.8261	20′
50′	.7476	.6799	1.471	.9271	1.079	1.364	.7333	.8232	10′
43°00′	.7505	.6820	1.466	.9325	1.072	1.367	.7314	.8203	47°00′
10′	.7534	.6841	1.462	.9380	1.066	1.371	.7294	.8174	50′
20′	.7563	.6862	1.457	.9435	1.060	1.375	.7274	.8145	40′
30′	.7592	.6884	1.453	.9490	1.054	1.379	.7254	.8116	30′
40′	.7621	.6905	1.448	.9545	1.048	1.382	.7234	.8087	20′
50′	.7650	.6926	1.444	.9601	1.042	1.386	.7214	.8058	10′
44°00′	.7679	.6947	1.440	.9657	1.036	1.390	.7193	.8029	46°00′
10′	.7709	.6967	1.435	.9713	1.030	1.394	.7173	.7999	50′
20′	.7738	.6988	1.431	.9770	1.024	1.398	.7153	.7970	40′
30′	.7767	.7009	1.427	.9827	1.018	1.402	.7133	.7941	30′
40′	.7796	.7030	1.423	.9884	1.012	1.406	.7112	.7912	20′
50′	.7825	.7050	1.418	.9942	1.006	1.410	.7092	.7883	10′
45°00′	.7854	.7071	1.414	1.000	1.000	1.414	.7071	.7854	45°00′
		cos θ	sec θ	cot θ	tan θ	csc θ	sin θ	Radians	Degrees
								m(θ)	

Table II.   Circular Functions and Radians-to-Degrees

Real Number x or $m^R(\theta)$	$m^o(\theta)$	sin x or sin θ	csc x or csc θ	tan x or tan θ	cot x or cot θ	sec x or sec θ	cos x or cos θ
0	0°	0	Undef.	0	Undef.	1	1
0.01	0° 34′	0.0100	100.0	0.0100	100.0	1.000	1.000
.02	1° 09′	.0200	50.00	.0200	49.99	1.000	0.9998
.03	1° 43′	.0300	33.34	.0300	33.32	1.000	0.9996
.04	2° 18′	.0400	25.01	.0400	24.99	1.001	0.9992
0.05	2° 52′	0.0500	20.01	0.0500	19.98	1.001	0.9988
.06	3° 26′	.0600	16.68	.0601	16.65	1.002	.9982
.07	4° 01′	.0699	14.30	.0701	14.26	1.002	.9976
.08	4° 35′	.0799	12.51	.0802	12.47	1.003	.9968
.09	5° 09′	.0899	11.13	.0902	11.08	1.004	.9960
0.10	5° 44′	0.0998	10.02	0.1003	9.967	1.005	0.9950
.11	6° 18′	.1098	9.109	.1104	9.054	1.006	.9940
.12	6° 53′	.1197	8.353	.1206	8.293	1.007	.9928
.13	7° 27′	.1296	7.714	.1307	7.649	1.009	.9916
.14	8° 01′	.1395	7.166	.1409	7.096	1.010	.9902
0.15	8° 36′	0.1494	6.692	0.1511	6.617	1.011	0.9888
.16	9° 10′	.1593	6.277	.1614	6.197	1.013	.9872
.17	9° 44′	.1692	5.911	.1717	5.826	1.015	.9856
.18	10° 19′	.1790	5.586	.1820	5.495	1.016	.9838
.19	10° 53′	.1889	5.295	.1923	5.200	1.018	.9820
0.20	11° 28′	0.1987	5.033	0.2027	4.933	1.020	0.9801
.21	12° 02′	.2085	4.797	.2131	4.692	1.022	.9780
.22	12° 36′	.2182	4.582	.2236	4.472	1.025	.9759
.23	13° 11′	.2280	4.386	.2341	4.271	1.027	.9737
.24	13° 45′	.2377	4.207	.2447	4.086	1.030	.9713
0.25	14° 19′	0.2474	4.042	0.2553	3.916	1.032	0.9689
.26	14° 54′	.2571	3.890	.2660	3.759	1.035	.9664
.27	15° 28′	.2667	3.749	.2768	3.613	1.038	.9638
.28	16° 03′	.2764	3.619	.2876	3.478	1.041	.9611
.29	16° 37′	.2860	3.497	.2984	3.351	1.044	.9582
0.30	17° 11′	0.2955	3.384	0.3093	3.233	1.047	0.9553
.31	17° 46′	.3051	3.278	.3203	3.122	1.050	.9523
.32	18° 20′	.3146	3.179	.3314	3.018	1.053	.9492
.33	18° 54′	.3240	3.086	.3425	2.919	1.057	.9460
.34	19° 29′	.3335	2.999	.3537	2.827	1.061	.9428
0.35	20° 03′	0.3429	2.916	0.3650	2.740	1.065	0.9394
.36	20° 38′	.3523	2.839	.3764	2.657	1.068	.9359
.37	21° 12′	.3616	2.765	.3879	2.578	1.073	.9323
.38	21° 46′	.3709	2.696	.3994	2.504	1.077	.9287
.39	22° 21′	.3802	2.630	.4111	2.433	1.081	.9249
0.40	22° 55′	0.3894	2.568	0.4228	2.365	1.086	0.9211
.41	23° 29′	.3986	2.509	.4346	2.301	1.090	.9171
.42	24° 04′	.4078	2.452	.4466	2.239	1.095	.9131
.43	24° 38′	.4169	2.399	.4586	2.180	1.100	.9090
.44	25° 13′	.4259	2.348	.4708	2.124	1.105	.9048
0.45	25° 47′	0.4350	2.299	0.4831	2.070	1.111	0.9004
.46	26° 21′	.4439	2.253	.4954	2.018	1.116	.8961
.47	26° 56′	.4529	2.208	.5080	1.969	1.122	.8916
.48	27° 30′	.4618	2.166	.5206	1.921	1.127	.8870
.49	28° 04′	.4706	2.125	.5334	1.875	1.133	.8823

Table II (Continued)

Real Number x or $m^R(\theta)$	$m^O(\theta)$	sin x or sin θ	csc x or csc θ	tan x or tan θ	cot x or cot θ	sec x or sec θ	cos x or cos θ
0.50	28°39'	0.4794	2.086	0.5463	1.830	1.139	0.8776
.51	29°13'	.4882	2.048	.5594	1.788	1.146	.8727
.52	29°48'	.4969	2.013	.5726	1.747	1.152	.8678
.53	30°22'	.5055	1.978	.5859	1.707	1.159	.8628
.54	30°56'	.5141	1.945	.5994	1.668	1.166	.8577
0.55	31°31'	0.5227	1.913	0.6131	1.631	1.173	0.8525
.56	32°05'	.5312	1.883	.6269	1.595	1.180	.8473
.57	32°40'	.5396	1.853	.6410	1.560	1.188	.8419
.58	33°14'	.5480	1.825	.6552	1.526	1.196	.8365
.59	33°48'	.5564	1.797	.6696	1.494	1.203	.8309
0.60	34°23!	0.5646	1.771	0.6841	1.462	1.212	0.8253
.61	34°57'	.5729	1.746	.6989	1.431	1.220	.8196
.62	35°31'	.5810	1.721	.7139	1.401	1.229	.8139
.63	36°06'	.5891	1.697	.7291	1.372	1.238	.8080
.64	36°40'	.5972	1.674	.7445	1.343	1.247	.8021
0.65	37°15'	0.6052	1.652	0.7602	1.315	1.256	0.7961
.66	37°49'	.6131	1.631	.7761	1.288	1.266	.7900
.67	38°23'	.6210	1.610	.7923	1.262	1.276	.7838
.68	38°58'	.6288	1.590	.8087	1.237	1.286	.7776
.69	39°32'	.6365	1.571	.8253	1.212	1.297	.7712
0.70	40°06'	0.6442	1.552	0.8423	1.187	1.307	0.7648
.71	40°41'	.6518	1.534	.8595	1.163	1.319	.7584
.72	41°15'	.6594	1.517	.8771	1.140	1.330	.7518
.73	41°50'	.6669	1.500	.8949	1.117	1.342	.7452
.74	42°24'	.6743	1.483	.9131	1.095	1.354	.7385
0.75	42°58'	0.6816	1.467	0.9316	1.073	1.367	0.7317
.76	43°33'	.6889	1.452	.9505	1.052	1.380	.7248
.77	44°07'	.6961	1.437	.9697	1.031	1.393	.7179
.78	44°41'	.7033	1.422	.9893	1.011	1.407	.7109
.79	45°16'	.7104	1.408	1.009	.9908	1.421	.7038
0.80	45°50'	0.7174	1.394	1.030	0.9712	1.435	0.6967
.81	46°25'	.7243	1.381	1.050	.9520	1.450	.6895
.82	46°59'	.7311	1.368	1.072	.9331	1.466	.6822
.83	47°33'	.7379	1.355	1.093	.9146	1.482	.6749
.84	48°08'	.7446	1.343	1.116	.8964	1.498	.6675
0.85	48°42!	0.7513	1.331	1.138	0.8785	1.515	0.6600
.86	49°16'	.7578	1.320	1.162	.8609	1.533	.6524
.87	49°51'	.7643	1.308	1.185	.8437	1.551	.6448
.88	50°25'	.7707	1.297	1.210	.8267	1.569	.6372
.89	51°00'	.7771	1.287	1.235	.8100	1.589	.6294
0.90	51°34'	0.7833	1.277	1.260	0.7936	1.609	0.6216
.91	52°08'	.7895	1.267	1.286	.7774	1.629	.6137
.92	52°43'	.7956	1.257	1.313	.7615	1.651	.6058
.93	53°17'	.8016	1.247	1.341	.7458	1.673	.5978
.94	53°51'	.8076	1.238	1.369	.7303	1.696	.5898
0.95	54°26'	0.8134	1.229	1.398	0.7151	1.719	0.5817
.96	55°00'	.8192	1.221	1.428	.7001	1.744	.5735
.97	55°35'	.8249	1.212	1.459	.6853	1.769	.5653
.98	56°09'	.8305	1.204	1.491	.6707	1.795	.5570
.99	56°43'	.8360	1.196	1.524	.6563	1.823	.5487
1.00	57°18'	0.8415	1.188	1.557	0.6421	1.851	0.5403
1.01	57°52'	.8468	1.181	1.592	.6281	1.880	.5319
1.02	58°27'	.8521	1.174	1.628	.6142	1.911	.5234
1.03	59°01'	.8573	1.166	1.665	.6005	1.942	.5148
1.04	59°35'	.8624	1.160	1.704	.5870	1.975	.5062

Table II   (Concluded)

Real Number x or $m^R(\theta)$	$m^O(\theta)$	sin x or sin θ	csc x or csc θ	tan x or tan θ	cot x or cot θ	sec x or sec θ	cos x or cos θ
1.05	60°10′	0.8674	1.153	1.743	0.5736	2.010	0.4976
1.06	60°44′	.8724	1.146	1.784	.5604	2.046	.4889
1.07	61°18′	.8772	1.140	1.827	.5473	2.083	.4801
1.08	61°53′	.8820	1.134	1.871	.5344	2.122	.4713
1.09	62°27′	.8866	1.128	1.917	.5216	2.162	.4625
1.10	63°02′	0.8912	1.122	1.965	0.5090	2.205	0.4536
1.11	63°36′	.8957	1.116	2.014	.4964	2.249	.4447
1.12	64°10′	.9001	1.111	2.066	.4840	2.295	.4357
1.13	64°45′	.9044	1.106	2.120	.4718	2.344	.4267
1.14	65°19′	.9086	1.101	2.176	.4596	2.395	.4176
1.15	65°53′	0.9128	1.096	2.234	0.4475	2.448	0.4085
1.16	66°28′	.9168	1.091	2.296	.4356	2.504	.3993
1.17	67°02′	.9208	1.086	2.360	.4237	2.563	.3902
1.18	67°37′	.9246	1.082	2.427	.4120	2.625	.3809
1.19	68°11′	.9284	1.077	2.498	.4003	2.691	.3717
1.20	68°45′	0.9320	1.073	2.572	0.3888	2.760	0.3624
1.21	69°20′	.9356	1.069	2.650	.3773	2.833	.3530
1.22	69°54′	.9391	1.065	2.733	.3659	2.910	.3436
1.23	70°28′	.9425	1.061	2.820	.3546	2.992	.3342
1.24	71°03′	.9458	1.057	2.912	.3434	3.079	.3248
1.25	71°37′	0.9490	1.054	3.010	0.3323	3.171	0.3153
1.26	72°12′	.9521	1.050	3.113	.3212	3.270	.3058
1.27	72°46′	.9551	1.047	3.224	.3102	3.375	.2963
1.28	73°20′	.9580	1.044	3.341	.2993	3.488	.2867
1.29	73°55′	.9608	1.041	3.467	.2884	3.609	.2771
1.30	74°29′	0.9636	1.038	3.602	0.2776	3.738	0.2675
1.31	75°03′	.9662	1.035	3.747	.2669	3.878	.2579
1.32	75°38′	.9687	1.032	3.903	.2562	4.029	.2482
1.33	76°12′	.9711	1.030	4.072	.2456	4.193	.2385
1.34	76°47′	.9735	1.027	4.256	.2350	4.372	.2288
1.35	77°21′	0.9757	1.025	4.455	0.2245	4.566	0.2190
1.36	77°55′	.9779	1.023	4.673	.2140	4.779	.2092
1.37	78°30′	.9799	1.021	4.913	.2035	5.014	.1994
1.38	79°04′	.9819	1.018	5.177	.1931	5.273	.1896
1.39	79°38′	.9837	1.017	5.471	.1828	5.561	.1798
1.40	80°13′	0.9854	1.015	5.798	0.1725	5.883	0.1700
1.41	80°47′	.9871	1.013	6.165	.1622	6.246	.1601
1.42	81°22′	.9887	1.011	6.581	.1519	6.657	.1502
1.43	81°56′	.9901	1.010	7.055	.1417	7.126	.1403
1.44	82°30′	.9915	1.009	7.602	.1315	7.667	.1304
1.45	83°05′	0.9927	1.007	8.238	0.1214	8.299	0.1205
1.46	83°39′	.9939	1.006	8.989	.1113	9.044	.1106
1.47	84°13′	.9949	1.005	9.887	.1011	9.938	.1006
1.48	84°48′	.9959	1.004	10.98	.0910	11.03	.0907
1.49	85°22′	.9967	1.003	12.35	.0810	12.39	.0807
1.50	85°57′	0.9975	1.003	14.10	0.0709	14.14	0.0707
1.51	86°31′	.9982	1.002	16.43	.0609	16.46	.0608
1.52	87°05′	.9987	1.001	19.67	.0508	19.70	.0508
1.53	87°40′	.9992	1.001	24.50	.0408	24.52	.0408
1.54	88°14′	.9995	1.000	32.46	.0308	32.48	.0308
1.55	88°49′	0.9998	1.000	48.08	0.0208	48.09	0.0208
1.56	89°23′	.9999	1.000	92.62	.0108	92.63	.0108
1.57	89°57′	1.000	1.000	1256	.0008	1256	.0008
$\frac{\pi}{2}$	90°	1	1	Undef.	0	Undef.	0

GLOSSARY

Absolute value of a complex number: If $z = a + bi$ where a and b stand for real numbers, then

$$|z| = a^2 + b^2.$$

Adjacent side to an angle in a right triangle: The leg of a right triangle which forms one side of the given angle.

Ambiguous case: A term applied to SSA. *Ambiguous* means "two or more possible meanings."

Amplitude of a sinusoid: The distance from sinusoidal axis to a maximum or minimum point on the graph.

Angular velocity: Angle-per-unit time turned through by a rotating object.

Argument of a complex number: If $z = r(\cos \theta + i \sin \theta)$, then θ is called the argument of z.

Argument of a function: The variable or expression upon which a function operates. For $\cos 3(x-7)$, the expression $3(x-7)$ is the argument of cos.

Asymptote: A line that a graph gets closer and closer to but never touches as x or y get very large.

BASIC: An acronym for "Beginners All-purpose Symbolic Instruction Code," an easily-learned computer language.

Cardioid: A heart-shaped curve, described in polar form as $r = a \cos \theta + b$, and traced by a point on the circumference of a circle of radius a that rolls around the circumference of another circle of radius a. A special case of *limaçon*, where $b = a$.

Cartesian coordinate system: A system of coordinates, named after René Descartes, in which the position of a point is measured by its horizontal and vertical distances from the two axes.

Circular function: A function (sin, cos, tan, cot, sec, or csc) whose independent variable, x, is a real number representing the length of an arc of a unit circle.

Closed interval: The set of all the real numbers between and including two given numbers.

Complex conjugate of a complex number: If $a + bi$ is a complex number, then its complex conjugate is $a - bi$ and vice-versa.

Complex number: A number of the form $g + bi$, where a and b stand for real numbers and

$$i = \sqrt{-1}.$$

Composite argument: An argument composed of measures of two arcs or angles.

Composition of ordinates: Graphing a function involving a sum or product of other functions, at least one of which is a sinusoid.

Conchoid: A shell-shaped curve traced by the endpoint of a line segment of constant length located on a straight line that revolves about a fixed point, while the other end of the segment moves along a fixed line not containing the fixed point. In polar form the equation is $r = b + a \sec \theta$ where a is the distance from the fixed point to the fixed line and b is the length of the segment.

Conditional equation: An equation which is true only for certain values of the variable.

Coterminal: Two angles are coterminal if they terminate at the same place.

Cycle: A portion of a periodic function from one point to the point where the graph first starts repeating itself.

DeMoivre's Theorem: If complex number $z = r(\cos \theta + i \sin \theta)$, then

$$z^n = r^n (\cos n\theta + i \sin n\theta).$$

Direct variation function: A function defined by the equation $y = mx$ where y varies directly with x.

Distance formula: If (x_1, y_1) and (x_2, y_2) are points in a Cartesian coordinate system, then the distance, d, between the points is

$$d = \sqrt{(x_2-x_1)^2 + (y_2-y_1)^2}.$$

373

Domain of a function: The set of all possible values of the independent variable of an ordered pair.

Euler's Formulas: Two equations used to derive another form for writing complex numbers; named after the eighteenth-century German mathematician Leonhard Euler.

Even function: If $f(-x) = f(x)$ for all x in the domain of f, then f is an even function.

Exponential function: A function defined by an equation of the form $y = a \cdot b^x$ or $y = a\ 10^{kx}$ where a, b, and k stand for constants.

Folium: A plane cubic curve consisting of a single loop, a node, and two branches asymptotic to the same line. Its rectangular Cartesian equation is $x^3 + y^3 = 3axy$, where the curve passes through the origin and is asymptotic to the line $x + y + a = 0$.

Frequency of a periodic function: Reciprocal of the period of the function.

Function: A set of ordered pairs for which each value of the independent variable takes on a unique value of the dependent variable.

Graph: A picture of a set of ordered pairs in a relation.

Harmonic analysis: Finding sinusoids that lead to a given periodic function.

Heron's Formula: A formula used to find the area of a triangle in one computation. The formula is

$$\text{Area} = \sqrt{s(s-a)(s-b)(s-c)},$$

where s (for *semiperimeter*) equals half the perimeter of the triangle.

Higher degree variation function: A function defined by the equation $y = ax^2$ or $y = ax^3$ where y varies directly with the square or cube of x.

Hypotenuse: The side of a right triangle which is opposite to the right angle (the longest side).

Identity: An equation which is true for all values of the variable (for which both members are defined).

Imaginary number: A square root of a negative real number.

Imaginary part of a complex number: If complex number $z = z + bi$, where a and b stand for real numbers, then the real number b is called the imaginary part of z.

Interval: A set of all the real numbers between (and sometimes including) two given numbers.

Inverse of a function: The inverse of a function is the relation obtained by interchanging the independent variables.

Inverse variation function: An equation of the form

$$y = \frac{a}{x}, y = \frac{a}{x^n}$$

where y varies inversely with x, y is directly proportional to x, or y varies inversely with the nth power of x.

Law of Cosines: In Triangle ABC, $a^2 = b^2 + c^2 - 2bc \cos A$.

Law of Sines: In Triangle ABC,

$$\frac{\sin A}{a} = \frac{\sin B}{b} = \frac{\sin C}{c}$$

Lemniscate: A lazy-eight curve described by the polar equation $r^2 = a^2 \cos 2\theta$, where a is the maximum distance from the origin.

Limaçon: A family of curves of the polar form $r = a \cos \theta + b$. When $b < a$, the curve is a pear-shaped loop within a heart-shaped loop with a node at the origin. When $b = a$, it is a single heart-shaped loop (see *cardioid*). When $b > a$, it is a single loop tending from heart-shaped to circular form as b increases.

Linear combination of two functions: If f and g are two functions, then a linear combination of $f(x)$ and $g(x)$ is an expression of the form $af(x) + bg(x)$ where a and b stand for constants.

Linear function: A function defined by the equation $y = mx + b$ where y varies linearly with x.

Linear velocity: The distance traveled per unit time by a point on a rotating object.

Mathematical model: A representation in the mathematical world of some phenomenon in the real world.

Oblique triangle: A triangle with no right angle.

Odd function: If $f(-x) = -f(x)$ for all x in the domain of f, then f is called an odd function.

Ordered pair: A pair of numbers in which the first number is a value of the independent variable and the second number is the corresponding value of the dependent variable.

Period of a function: The change in the independent variable of a function corresponding to one cycle.

Periodic function: A function in which the dependent variable has values that repeat themselves as the independent variable changes.

Phase displacement: The value of the independent variable of a function which makes the argument of the function equal zero.

Pixels: Tiny squares into which a computer screen is divided.

Polar coordinate system: A coordinate system in which the position of a point is measured by an ordered pair (θ, r), where θ is an angle in standard position, and r is the distance (positive or negative) from the origin (the "pole") to the point.

Polar form of a complex number: If complex number $z = a + bi$, then its polar form is $z = r(\cos \theta + i \sin \theta)$, where

$r = \sqrt{a^2 + b^2}$, $\sin \theta = b/r$, and $\cos \theta = a/r$.

Power series: An expression consisting of the sum of an infinite number of monomials.

Quadratic function: A function defined by an equation of the form

$y = ax^2 + bx + c$

where a, b, and c stand for constants.

Radian: A unit of angular measure equal to 1 (2π) of a complete revolution.

Range of a function: The set of values of the dependent variable of a function.

Real part of a complex number: If complex number $z = a + bi$, where a and b stand for real numbers, then a is called the real part of z.

Reference angle: The positive acute angle or right angle between the x-axis and the terminal side of the angle.

Relation: Any set of ordered pairs.

Resolution of a vector: Expressing a vector as a linear combination of two other vectors, usually parallel to the x- and y-axes.

Resultant of two vectors: The sum of the two vectors.

Right triangle: A triangle with one angle measuring 90°.

SAS: An abbreviation for "side, angle, side."

Scalar: A quantity, such as volume or mass, which has magnitude (size) but no direction.

Sinusoid: A graph of a sine or a cosine function.

Solution of a trigonometric equation: The set of all values of the variable in the domain which make the equation a true statement.

SSA: An abbreviation for "side, side, angle."

Standard position: An angle is in standard position in a Cartesian coordinate system if its initial side is along the positive x-axis, its vertex is at the origin, and it is measured counterclockwise from the x-axis if its measure is positive and clockwise if negative.

Taylor series: A particular class of power series.

Translation: The movement of a graph to a new position without changing its shape or rotating it.

Trigonometric equation: An equation involving one or more trigonometric or circular functions.

Trigonometric function: A function (sin, cos, tan, cot, sec, or csc) whose independent variable is an angle measure (usually in degrees or radians).

Unit vector: A vector of magnitude 1.

Vector quantity: A quantity, such as force or velocity, which has both magnitude (size) and direction.

Vertical displacement: Distance from the x- or θ-axis to the sinusoidal axis.

Vertical magnification of a function: Transforming a function $y = f(x)$ to $y = A \cdot f(x)$ by multiplying by a constant A.

Wavelength: The distance traveled by a wave in one period.

INDEX OF PROBLEM TITLES

CHAPTER 1.   Trigonometric Functions

Exercise 1-1, pages 5-6;   Review of Functions

1. a. Linear
    b.
x	y
−4	−5
−2	−1
0	3
2	7
4	11
    c. (Graph.)

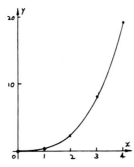

3. a. Direct
        variation
    b.
x	y
0	0
3	2
6	4
9	6
12	8
    c. (Graph.)

5. a. Quadratic
x	y
−1	10
0	4
1	0
2	−2
3	−2
4	0
5	4
6	10
    c. (Graph.)

7. a. Direct
        cube
        variation
    b.
x	y
0	0
1	0.3
2	2.4
3	8.1
4	19.2
    c. (Graph.)

9. a. Inverse
        variation
    b.
x	y
1	12
2	6
3	4
4	3
6	2
12	1
    c. (Graph.)

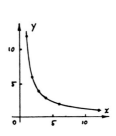

11. a. Exponential
     b.
x	y
3	8
2	4
1	2
0	1
−1	$\frac{1}{2}$
−2	$\frac{1}{4}$
     c. (Graph.)

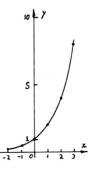

13. a. Rational
         algebraic
     b.
x	y
−2	0.25
−1	0
0	−0.5
1	−2
1.9	−29
2.1	31
3	4
4	2.5
     c. (Graph.)
         Vertical
         asymptote
         at $x = 2$

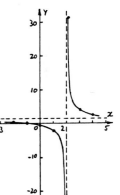

15. Approx. 14.8 cm

17. Pythagorean
     Theorem

Exercise 1-2, pages 8-10; Mathematical Models and Periodic Functions

1. a. Graph.
   b. Periodic

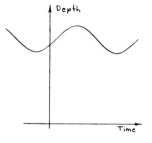

3. a. Graph.
   b. Not periodic

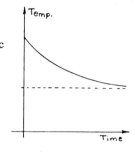

5. a. Graph.
   b. Periodic

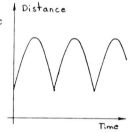

7. a. Graph.
   b. Periodic

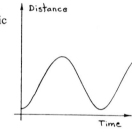

9. a. Graph.
   b. Periodic

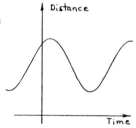

11.

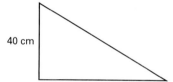

40 cm

   a. Hypotenuse is 80 cm, twice 40.
   b. $L = \sqrt{80^2 - 40^2}$

   $= \sqrt{4800}$ cm

   c. $\sqrt{4800} = 69.28...$
   Shorter leg measures about 69.3 cm, which confirms the calculation.

13. a. 210°

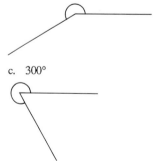

   c. 300°

15. $y = ax^2 + bx + c$

Exercise 1-3, pages 14-16;   Measurement of Rotation

1.   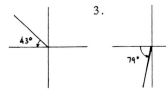   3.   5.   7.

9.      11.   13.   15.

17.   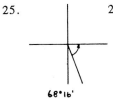   19.      21.   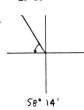   23.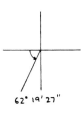

25°23'   33°16'

25.      27.      29.   31.

68°16'   13°51'   58°14'   62°19'27"

33.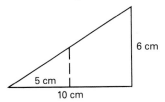

67° 11' 47"

35. *Similar Triangles Problem*

a. Smaller angle is approximately 31°.

b. Ratio is the *same* for both triangles. Corresponding parts of similar triangles are proportional.

c. $\dfrac{\text{Vertical}}{\text{Horizontal}} = \dfrac{3}{5}$, or 0.6.

$\dfrac{\text{Vertical}}{\text{Horizontal}} = \dfrac{6}{10} = \dfrac{3}{5}$, which confirms the conclusion.

Exercise 1-4, pages 21-22; Definition of the Trigonometric Functions

	1.	3.	5.	7.
sin θ	$-\dfrac{3}{5}$	$-\dfrac{7}{\sqrt{74}}$	$\dfrac{4}{5}$	$-\dfrac{\sqrt{15}}{4}$
cos θ	$\dfrac{4}{5}$	$-\dfrac{5}{\sqrt{74}}$	$-\dfrac{3}{5}$	$\dfrac{1}{4}$
tan θ	$-\dfrac{3}{4}$	$\dfrac{7}{5}$	$-\dfrac{4}{3}$	$-\sqrt{15}$
cot θ	$-\dfrac{4}{3}$	$\dfrac{5}{7}$	$-\dfrac{3}{4}$	$-\dfrac{1}{\sqrt{15}}$
sec θ	$\dfrac{5}{4}$	$-\dfrac{\sqrt{74}}{5}$	$-\dfrac{5}{3}$	4
csc θ	$-\dfrac{5}{3}$	$-\dfrac{\sqrt{74}}{7}$	$\dfrac{5}{4}$	$-\dfrac{4}{\sqrt{15}}$

	θ	sin θ	cos θ	tan θ	cot θ	sec θ	csc θ
9.	60°	$\dfrac{\sqrt{3}}{2}$	$\dfrac{1}{2}$	$\sqrt{3}$	$\dfrac{\sqrt{3}}{3}$	2	$\dfrac{2\sqrt{3}}{3}$
11.	−315°	$\dfrac{\sqrt{2}}{2}$	$\dfrac{\sqrt{2}}{2}$	1	1	$\sqrt{2}$	$\sqrt{2}$
13.	180°	0	-1	0	und.	-1	und.

15. 0   17. $-\dfrac{1}{2}$ 19. −1   21. undefined

23. $\dfrac{-2\sqrt{3}}{3}$ 25. $\sqrt{2}$ 27. 1   29. $-2\sqrt{3}$

31. 6   33. 0   35. 2   37. 1

39. -1   41. 0   43. $\dfrac{4}{3}$ 45. 0

47. a. 0°, 180°, 360°   b. 90°, 270°

c. 0°, 180°, 360°   d. 90°, 270°

e. no values

f. no values

49. a. 30°

b. cos 60° = $\dfrac{1}{2}$; sin 30° = $\dfrac{1}{2}$

c. cos 60° = sin 30°

d. "co–" stands for "complement."

51. cos 30° = 0.866025...   53. 216° reflex angle

$\dfrac{\sqrt{3}}{2}$ = 0.866025..., which agrees.

Exercise 1-5, pages 25-26;   Approx. Values of Trig. Functions

1. 0.4602

3. 0.2096

5. 1.134

7. 0.08397

9. 1.023

11. 11.71

13. a. $u \approx 0.90$
         $y \approx 0.44$

    b. $\frac{v}{u} \approx 0.49$

15. a. 28.63°
     b. 28°38'

17. a. 24.15°
     b. 24°9'

19. a. 47.04°
     b. 47°3'

21. a. 62.37°
     b. 62°22'

23. a. 67.20°
     b. 67°12'

25. a. 70.33°
     b. 70°20'

27. $\theta = 53.13...°$
     sin 53.13...° = 0.8
     $\frac{4}{5} = 0.8$

29. $\theta = 64.62...$
     tan 64.62...° = 2.108
     $= \frac{\sqrt{40}}{3} = 2.108$

31. $\theta = 67.97...°$
     sec 67.97...° = 2.666...
     $\frac{8}{3} = 2.666...$

33. a. 139.70°
     b. 139°42'

35. a. 349.55°
     b. 349°33'

37. a. 94.47°
     b. 94°28'

39. Direct square variation:

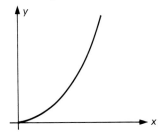

41. Approximately 25.6 yd

Exercise 1-6, pages 29-37; Right Triangle Problems

1. *Construction Problem No. 1*

    a.

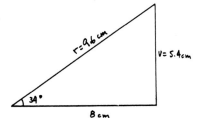

    b. $v \approx 5.4$ cm
       $r \approx 9.6$ cm

3. *Ladder Problem*

    6.0m

5. *Cat Problem*

    76°

7. *The Grapevine Problem*

   a. 4.53° or 4°32'

   b. Slope is assumed to be constant.

11. *Airplane Landing Problem*

   a. 191 km

   b. 1.91° or 1°55'

15. *Guy Wire Problem*

   a. 2245 ft

   b. 1019 ft

19. *Submarine Problem*

   a. $v \approx 108$ m

     $u \approx 280$ m

   b. 2790 m

23. *Grand Piano Problem*

   a. 30.6° or 30°40'

   b. 47.3 in.

   c. 53.4 in.

9. *Moon Crater Problem*

   142m

13. *Triangular Block Problem*

   a. 35.3° or 35°20'

   b. 72 paces

17. *Highland Drive Problem*

   a. 11°28'   c. 74 ft

   b. 7 ft

21. *Window Problem*

   a. 1.4 ft

   b. 8.2 ft

   c. 6.8 ft

Exercise 1-7, pages 38-40; Chapter Review and Test

Review Problems

R1. a.

x	y
-3	-6
0	-4
3	-2
6	0

   b. (Graph.)

   c. Linear function

R2. a.

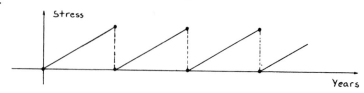

   b. Periodic function

R3. a. $\sin 150° = \frac{1}{2}$

    $\cos 150° = \frac{-\sqrt{3}}{2}$

    $\tan 150° = \frac{-\sqrt{3}}{3}$

    $\cot 150° = -\sqrt{3}$

    $\sec 150° = \frac{-2}{\sqrt{3}}$

    $\csc 150° = 2$

           b. $-\sqrt{2}$

           c. $\frac{-3}{\sqrt{34}}$

           d. $-2\sqrt{2}$

           e. -2

           f. 0

           g. $\sqrt{3}$

           h. $-3\frac{2}{3}$

R4. a. 1.039

   b. 13.95

   c. 0.9252

   d. −11.47

   e. 0.9945

   f. −1.443

R5. a. 36°30'

   b. 108°20'

   c. 268°10'

   d. 339°0'

   e. 40°5'

   f. 126°7'

R6. a. 319 m deep

   b. 604 m away

   c. 75.25° or 75°15'

Chapter 1 Test

T1.

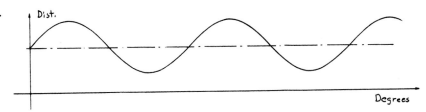

Objective: 2

T2. a. $\tan 120° = -\sqrt{3}$

    $\cot 120° = \frac{-\sqrt{3}}{3}$

    $\sin 120° = \frac{\sqrt{3}}{2}$

    $\cos 120° = \frac{-1}{2}$

    $\sec 120° = -2$

    $\csc 120° = \frac{2\sqrt{3}}{3}$

   b. $\tan 270°$ is und.

    $\cot 270° = 0$

    $\sin 270° = -1$

    $\cos 270° = 0$

    $\sec 270°$ is und.

    $\csc 270° = -1$

   c. $\tan 315° = -1$

    $\cot 315° = -1$

    $\sin 315° = \frac{-\sqrt{2}}{2}$

    $\cos 315° = \frac{\sqrt{2}}{2}$

    $\sec 315° = \sqrt{2}$

    $\csc 315° = -\sqrt{2}$

Objective: 3

T3. a. $\tan \theta = \frac{-\sqrt{5}}{2}$ $\cos \theta = \frac{2}{3}$

$\cot \theta = \frac{-2\sqrt{5}}{5}$ $\sec \theta = \frac{3}{2}$

$\sin \theta = \frac{-\sqrt{5}}{3}$ $\csc \theta = \frac{-3\sqrt{5}}{5}$

b. 48°11'

c. 311°49'

d. 18,311°49'

Objectives: 3, 5

T4. $u \approx -133.2$ cm

$y \approx 69.0$ cm

Objectives: 4, 6, New Concept

T5. 329 cm

Objective: New Concept

CHAPTER 2.   Applications of Trigonometric and Circular Functions

Exercise 2-1, page 43;   Introduction to Sine and Cosine Graphs

Read ahead to see what the graphs look like!

Exercise 2-2, pages 47-48;   Sinusoids—Amplitude and Period

1.
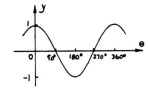

3.
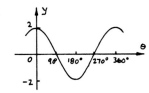

5.
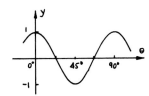

7.
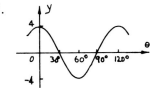

9.
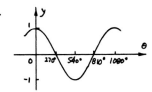

11.
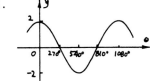

13. b. $y \approx 2.16$
Graph.

c. $\theta \approx 18.4°$
Graph.

15. 81.1 in.

17. $\theta = 43.22661...°$

tan 43.22661...° = 0.93993...

19. $\dfrac{-1}{\sqrt{3}}$

Exercise 2-3, pages 51-52;   Sinusoids—Phase Shift and Vertical Shift

1.
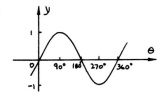

3.
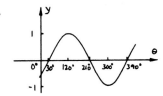

391

5.

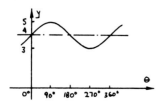

7.

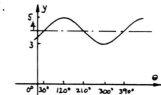

9.

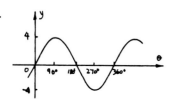

11.

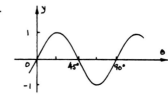

13. b. $y \approx 3.26$

c. $\theta \approx 75.6°$

15. Triangle is a *right* triangle.

$\theta = 53.1301$

17. $-\dfrac{\sqrt{3}}{2}$

19. $57.2957...°$

Exercise 2-4, pages 56–59; General Sinusoidal Graphs

1.

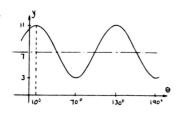

$y = 7 + 4 \cos 3(\theta - 10°)$
Per. = 120°, Amp. = 4,
Ph. disp. = 10°, V. disp. = 7

3.

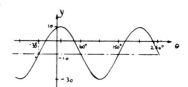

$y = -10 + 20 \sin 2(\theta + 30°)$
Per. = 180°, Amp. = 20,
Ph. d. = –30°, V. d. = –10

5.

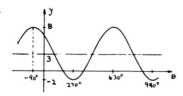

$y = 3 + 5 \cos \frac{1}{2}(\theta + 90°)$
Per. = 720°, Amp. = 5
Ph. d. = –90°, V. d. = 3

7.

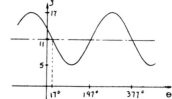

$y = 11 - 6 \sin (\theta - 17°)$
Per. = 360°, Amp. = 6,
Ph. d. = 17°, V. d. = 11

9. $y = 9 + 6 \cos 2(\theta - 20°)$

Per. = 180°, Freq. = $\frac{1}{180}$, Amp. = 6, Ph. d. = 20°, V. d. = 9

11. $y = -3 + 5 \cos 3(\theta - 10°)$

Per. = 120°, Freq. = $\frac{1}{120}$, Amp. = 5, Ph. d. = 10°, V. d. = -3

13. $y = 1.45 + 1.11 \cos 10(\theta + 7°)$

Per. = 36°, Freq. = $\frac{1}{36}$, Amp. = 1.11, Ph. d. = -7°, V. d. = 1.45

15. $y = \sqrt{3} \cos (\theta - 30°)$

Per. = 360°, Freq. = $\frac{1}{360}$, Amp. = $\sqrt{3}$, Ph. d. = 30°, V. d. = 0

17. $r = 7 \cos 3\alpha$

Per. = 120°, Freq. = $\frac{1}{120}$, Amp. = 7, Ph. d. = 0°, V. d. = 0

19.

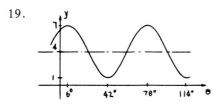

$y = 4 + 3 \cos 5(\theta - 6°)$

21. b. $y \approx 4.34$
c. $\theta \approx 10.3°$

25. Triangle is a *right* triangle.
22.61986...°

27. no value

29. a. $f(3) = 2$
b. $f(-5) = 18$
c. $x = 8$ or -8

Exercise 2-5, pages 62-64; Radian Measure of Angles

1. $\frac{\pi}{3}$ 3. $\frac{\pi}{6}$ 5. π 7. $-\frac{5\pi}{4}$
9. 0.65 11. 2.15 13. 0.72 15. 60°
17. 30° 19. 45° 21. 135° 23. 270°
25. 19°29' 27. 72°12' 29. 57°18' 31. $\frac{\sqrt{3}}{2}$
33. 0 35. 1 37. 4 39. $\sqrt{3}$

41. $1 + \frac{2\sqrt{3}}{3}$　　43. $\frac{-11}{3}$　　　45. $\frac{-\sqrt{3}}{3}$　　　47. 18.5 furlongs

49. $\frac{-1}{\sqrt{3}}$　　　51. sin 41° = 0.65605...

$\sin^{-1} 0.65605... = 41°$

Surprising, until you realize that the inverse of a function "undoes" what the function did to a number, leaving the original number as a result.

Exercise 2-6, pages 67-70;　Circular Functions and Inverses

1. $\frac{\pi}{6}$　　　　3. $\frac{\pi}{3}$　　　　5. π　　　　7. $\frac{2\pi}{3}$

9. 60°　　　11. 360°　　　13. 30°　　　15. 150°

17. $\frac{\pi}{3}$　　　19. 2　　　21. $\frac{\sqrt{3}}{2}$

　　　　　　　　　　　　　　　　　　　23. −1

25. $\frac{-2\sqrt{3}}{3}$　　27. undefined　　29. $\frac{\sqrt{3}}{2} + 3\sqrt{2}$　　31. 1

33. 2　　　35. undefined　　37. $\frac{1}{2}$　　　39. 0.6743

41. −1.5013　　43. −1.2482　　45. 0.8415　　47. 0.6700

49. 0.6393　　51. 1.2971　　53. 0.5627　　55. 15.6 ft

57.

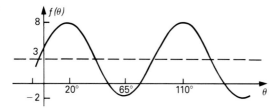

59. *Wrapping Function*

a. $W(\frac{\pi}{2}) = (0, 1)$

$W(\frac{3\pi}{2}) = (0, -1)$

$W(\frac{-\pi}{2}) = (0, -1)$

$W(2\pi) = (1, 0)$

b. False. There is an infinite number of values of x for each point. The values are spaced 2π units apart.

c. Since the circle is a unit circle,

$u = u/r = \cos x$, and $v = v/r = \sin x$.

$\therefore W(x) = (\cos x, \sin x)$

d. $W(\frac{\pi}{3}) = (\frac{1}{2}, \frac{\sqrt{3}}{2})$

$W(\frac{5\pi}{6}) = (\frac{-\sqrt{3}}{2}, \frac{1}{2})$

$W(\frac{-3\pi}{4}) = (\frac{-\sqrt{2}}{2}, \frac{-\sqrt{2}}{2})$

e. $W(5) = (0.2836..., -0.9589...)$

f. $0.6^2 + 0.8^2 = 1$
∴ (0.6,0.8) *can* be a value of $W(x)$.
$0.3^2 + 0.9^2 = 0.9 \neq 1$
∴ (0.3, 0.9) *cannot* be a value of $W(x)$.

g. $W(x) = (0.6, 0.8)$
∴ cos $x = 0.6$ and sin $x = 0.8$
∴ $x = 0.9279... \neq 2\pi n$
$= 0.9279..., 7.2104..., 13.4936...,$ etc.

h. $W(x) = (0.28, 0.96)$
$W(x + \pi) = (-0.28, -0.96)$
$W(-x) = (0.28, -0.96)$
$W(2\pi + x) = (0.28, 0.96)$

Exercise 2-7, pages 71-73;   Graphs of Circular Function Sinusoids

1.

$y = 3 + 2 \cos \frac{1}{5}(x - \pi)$

Per. $= \dfrac{2\pi}{\frac{1}{5}} = 10\pi$

3.

$y = 2 + 6 \sin \frac{\pi}{4}(x - 1)$

Per. $= \dfrac{2\pi}{\frac{\pi}{4}} = 8$

5. $y = 5 + 2 \cos 2(x - \frac{\pi}{6})$

7. $y = -2 + 5 \cos \frac{\pi}{15}(x + 5)$

9. $z = -8 + 2 \cos 5\pi(t + 0.13)$

11. 172.04°

13. cos 3 = −0.989992...

14. cos 3° = 0.998629...

15. 21.6 mm

16. For small x, sin $x \approx x \approx$ tan x.
As shown in the sketch, these three lengths are approximately equal.

Exercise 2-8, pages 76-79;   Sinusoids by Computer Graphics

1.

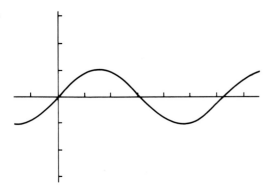

   a. Approximately 6.3

   b. 1

   c. Approximately 1.6

3.   a.

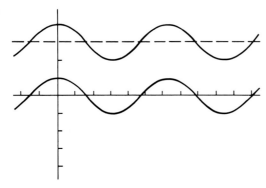

   b. sinusoid axis

5.   a. Graph of *g* should have 3 times the amplitude of *f*.

     b. Graphs are as predicted.

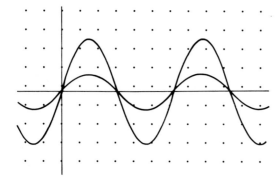

7. a. Adding 3 to cos x should raise the graph up 3 units, without changing its shape. Multiplying cos x by 3 should triple its amplitude.

   b. Graphs are as predicted.

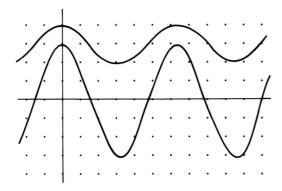

9. a. See graph in problem 1, above.
   b. $D = \frac{\pi}{2} = 1.57079...$

11. $g(x) = \cos 2x$ should have *half* the period of $f(x) = \cos x$.

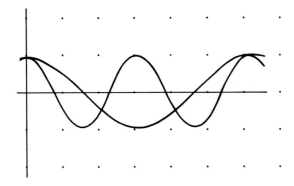

13. a. 6
    b. $\frac{\pi}{3} = 1.047197...$

    Period *is* 6.

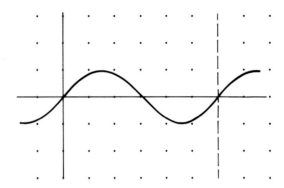

15. a. $B = \frac{\pi}{2}$

   b. Period *is* 4.

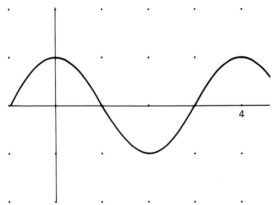

17. $y = -3 + 5 \cos \frac{2\pi}{13} (x + 4)$

19. a. period = 10

   amplitude = 4

   phase disp. = -1 (for sine)

   vert. shift = 3

   b.

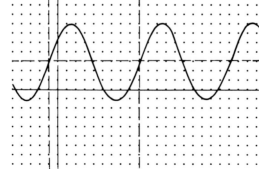

21. *Quadratic Function Problem*

   a. parabola

   b. (1, –4)

   c. $x = 0$: $y = -3$

   $y = 0$: $x = 3$, $x = -1$

   d. All predictions are correct.

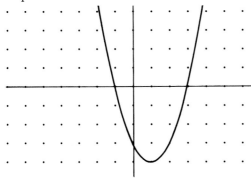

27. *Asymptotic Behavior Problem*
   As the argument approaches the asymptote, the graph "shoots off to infinity." Then it comes back from infinity in the opposite direction.

Exercise 2-9, pages 84-86;   Graphs of Tan, Cot, Sec, and Csc Functions

5.

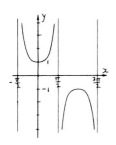

7.

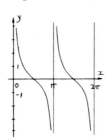

9.

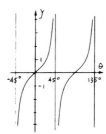

11.

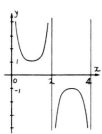

13.

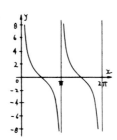

15.

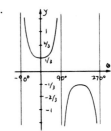

17.

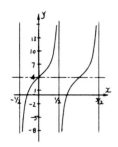

19.

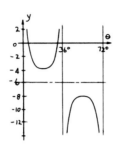

21.

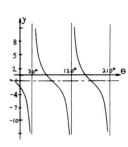

23.

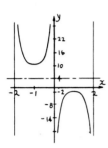

Exercise 2-10, pages 90-91;   General Inverse Sine and Cosine Relations

1. 11.24°   3. 106.52°   5. 0.5642   7. −1.3252

9. a. $\theta \approx \pm 24.49° + 360n°$ 11. a. $\theta \approx 32.01° + 360n°$ or
    b. $\theta \approx 24.49°, 335.51°, 384.49°$ $147.99° + 360n°$
                                                   b. $\theta \approx 32.01°, 147.99°, 392.01°$

13. a. $\theta \approx \pm 98.63° + 360n°$ 15. a. $\theta \approx -49.46° + 360n°$ or
     b. $\theta \approx 98.63°, 261.37°, 458.63°$ $229.46° + 360n°$
                                                    b. $\theta \approx 229.46°, 310.54°, 589.46°$

17. a. $x \approx \pm 1.3078 + 2\pi n$ 19. a. $x \approx 1.3705 + 2\pi n$ or
     b. $x \approx 1.3078, 4.9754, 7.5910$ $1.7711 + 2\pi n$
                                                b. $x \approx 1.3705, 1.7711, 7.6536$

21. a. $x \approx \pm 1.6710 + 2\pi n$ 23. a. $x \approx -0.6816 + 2\pi n$ or
     b. $x \approx 1.6710, 4.6122, 7.9541$ $3.8231 + 2\pi n$
                                                b. $x \approx 3.8231, 5.6016, 10.1063$

25. 30°   27. −30°   29. 90°   31. $\frac{\pi}{2}$

33. $\frac{\pi}{4}$ 35. π 37. 0   39. no value

41. a. 5.37305...
     b. 29.295...°, 70.704...°, 209.295...°

Exercise 2-11, pages 94-95;   Evaluation of Sinusoidal Functions

1. a. 2.31

   b. 0.95, 5.05, 20.95

   c.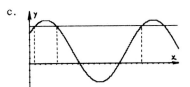

3. a. −3.82

   b. 0.76, 3.84, 4.76

   c.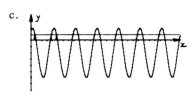

5. a. −0.15

   b. 5.43, 12.57, 21.43

   c.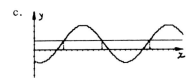

7. a. 6.71

   b. 1.29, 2.71, 9.29

   c.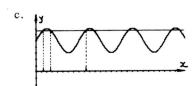

9. a. −1.33

   b. 2.58, 10.42, 20.58

   c.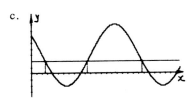

11. *Tangent Function Evaluation Problem*

    a. 1.79289...

    b. 6.7469..., 14.7469..., 22.7469...

    c. Answers check.

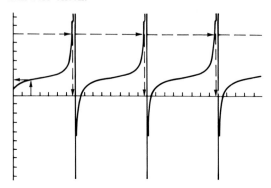

Exercise 2-12, pages 98-111; Sinusoidal Functions as Mathematical Models

1. *Ferris Wheel Problem*

    a. Graph.

    b. The lowest you go is 3 feet above the ground, because seats in a Ferris wheel do not scrape the ground.

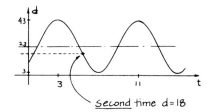

Second time d = 18

    c. Let d = no. of feet above ground.

$$d = 23 + 20 \cos \tfrac{\pi}{4}(t - 3)$$

    d. i.   8.86 ft   ii.   23 ft

        ii.   33 ft   iv. 8.86 ft

    e. 5.32 s

3. *Extraterrestrial Being Problem*

    a. Graph.

    b. Let y = no. of degrees temp. Let t = no. of min.

$$y = 112 + 8 \cos \tfrac{\pi}{20}(t - 35)$$

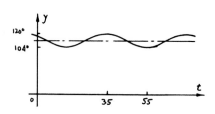

    c. 117.7°

    d. 3.39 min, 26.61 min, 43.39 min

5. *Bouncing Spring Problem*

   a. Graph.

   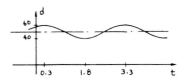

   b. Let d = no. of cm from floor.
      Let t = no. of seconds on watch.
      $$d = 50 + 10 \cos \frac{2\pi}{3}(t - 0.3)$$

   c. 43.3 cm

   d. 58.1 cm

   e. 0.08 s

7. *Roller Coaster Problem*

   a. $y = 12 + 15 \cos \frac{\pi}{50} x$

   b.   i. 27 m

        ii. 26.53 m

        iii. 5.61 m

   c.   i. $y = 25$: 8.31m

        ii. $y = 5$: 32.73 m

   d. 39.76 m

9. *Sunspot Problem*

   a. 11 years

   b. Graph.

   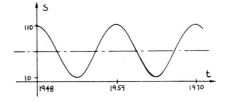

   c. Let t = year.
      Let S = no. of sunspots.
      $$S = 60 + 50 \cos \frac{2\pi}{11}(t - 1948)$$

   d.   i. 53 spots

        ii. Answers will depend on
            the year you work the
            problem.

   e.   i. 2007

        ii. 2003

   f. Check the Scientific American article!

11. *Tidal Wave Problem*
    Let y = no. of meters deep.
    Let t = no. of minutes since
    tsunami first reached pier.
    $y = 9 - 10 \sin \frac{2\pi}{15}t$

    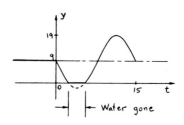

    a.   i. 1.57m
        ii. The water has receded beyond
            the point at which the depth is
            being measured, meaning that the
            depth at that point is *zero*.

        iii. 18.51 m

    b. According to the model, the minimum depth is −1 meter. So there is a time
       interval, represented by the dotted part of the graph above, during which the water
       is all gone.

    c. between 2.7 and 4.8 minutes

    d. 300 km

    e. Since the wave length is so long compared to the amplitude, a person on a ship at
       sea would not even notice that a tsunami had passed. Note that the motion of the
       water is up-and-down. It is only the location of the crest of the distrubance which
       moves horizontally at 1200 km. per hour.

13. *Spaceship Problem*

    a. Graph.

    b. $y = 4000 \cos \frac{\pi}{45}(t - 10)$

    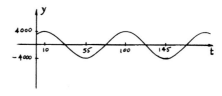

    c.   i. 2000 km

        ii. −2237 km

        iii. −1236 km

    d. about 38.4 min

    e. 3064 km

    f. You check the map!

15. *Biorhythm Problem*

    a. Let t = no. of days after the present.
       Let P = physical function value.
       Let E = emotional function value.
       Let I = intellectual function value.
       $$P = 100 \cos \tfrac{2\pi}{23} t \quad E = 100 \cos \tfrac{2\pi}{28} t \quad I = 100 \cos \tfrac{2\pi}{33} t$$

    b. $P \approx -91.7 \qquad E \approx 43.4$

    c. P: 5.75 days $\qquad$ E: 7 days $\qquad$ I: 8.25 days

17. *Electrical Current and Voltage Problem*

    a. Let t = no. of seconds.
       Let I = no. of amps current.
       Let V = no. of volts voltage.
       $I = 5 \cos 120\pi t$

    b. $V = 180 \cos 120\pi \, (t + 0.003)$

    c. 76.6 volts

    d. 2.13 amps

    e. 0.0128 s

19. *Sun Elevation Problem*

    a. Graph.

    b. The t-intercepts are the
       times of sunrise and sunset.

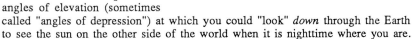

    c. The portion of the graph below
       the t-axis indicates *negative*
       angles of elevation (sometimes
       called "angles of depression") at which you could "look" *down* through the Earth
       to see the sun on the other side of the world when it is nighttime where you are.

    d. $E = -5 + 60 \cos \tfrac{\pi}{12} (t - 12.75)$

       i. 34.0°
       ii. 48.8°

    e. 7:04 a.m.

    f. Instead of C being a *constant* in $E = C + A \cos B(t - D)$, make C vary sinusoidally
       with time. The period would be 365 days (or 365.24 days), amplitude 23°27' (the
       tilt of the Earth to the Ecliptic Plane), and the phase displacement 172 days (to
       June 21). Problems 5 and 6 of Exercise 4-2 have graphs with similar
       characteristics.

21. *Variable Amplitude Pendulum Problem*

    a. $A = 20 \times 10^{-0.0233t}$

    b. Per. = 2.2, $B = \tfrac{2\pi}{2.2} = \tfrac{\pi}{1.1}$; $C = \tfrac{1}{2}(50 + 10) = 30$; $D = 1.1$

c. $y = 30 + 20 \times 10^{-0.0233t} x \cos \frac{\pi}{1.1}(t - 1.1)$

d.

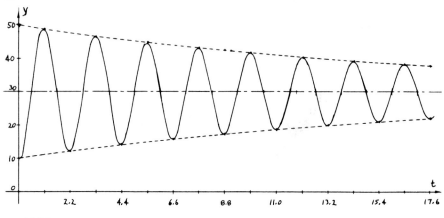

e. 44.36 cm

Exercise 2-13, pages 112-114;   Chapter Review and Test

Review   Problems

R1. a.   i. −0.3623

ii. 37°

iii.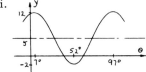

b.   i. −6

ii. 4.217

iii. 1.517 and 8.483

iv.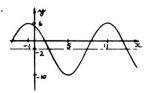

c.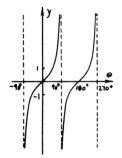

d.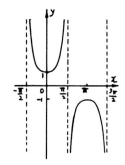

e.   i. $\frac{1}{2}$

   ii. −1

   iii. −1

   iv. $\frac{-1}{2}$

   v. $5\frac{\sqrt{3}}{2}$

   vi. −1

g.   i. $3\frac{\pi}{2}$ radian

   ii. 150°

   iii. 180°

   iv. $\frac{4\pi}{3}$

f.   i. $\frac{\pi}{6}$

   ii. $\frac{\pi}{6} + 2\pi n$ or $\frac{5\pi}{6} + 2\pi n$

   iii. $\frac{\pi}{4}$

   iv. π

   v. $\pi + 2\pi n$

   vi. $\frac{\pi}{3}$

R2.   a. $y = -10 + 35 \cos 9(\theta - 3°)$

    b. $y = 17 + 2 \cos \frac{\pi}{50} (x + 15)$

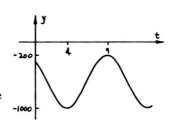

R3. *Porpoising Problem*

a. Graph.

b. Let t = no. of minutes.
Let y = no. of meters.
$y = -600 + 400 \cos \frac{\pi}{5} (t - 9)$

c. Submarine was *not safe* at $t = 0$ since it was only about 276 meters down, not below 300.

d. between 0.15 min and 7.85 min

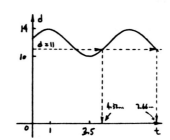

Chapter 2 Test

T1. Graph.
    Objectives: 1, 3

T2. Let d = no. of feet
    Let t = no. of s
    $d = 12 + 2 \cos \frac{2\pi}{5} (t - 1)$
    Objectives: 2, 3

T3. 10.38 ft
    Objectives: 1, 3

T4. 3.3 s
    Objectives: 1, 3

T5. 14.48° or 14°29'
    Objectives: 3, review concept

T6. 0.2527 rad
    Objective: review concept

T7. a. 9°
    Objective: review concept

    b. 13.25 ft
    Objective: review concept

    c. 0.29 s
    Objectives: 1, 3, new concept

CHAPTER 3.   Properties of Trigonometric and Circular Functions

Exercise 3-1, pages 121-122;   Three Properties of Trigonometric Functions

Answers for Problems 1 through 26 are contained in the problems.

27. $\sin x \csc x$, $\cos x \sec x$, $\tan x \cot x$, $\cos^2 x + \sin^2 x$, $\csc^2 x - \cot^2 x$, and $\sec^2 x - \tan^2 x$

29. $\sin x = \sin x$

$\tan x = \pm \dfrac{1}{\sqrt{1 - \sin^2 x}}$

$\sec x = \pm \dfrac{1}{\sqrt{1 - \sin^2 x}}$

$\cos x = \pm \sqrt{1 - \sin^2 x}$

$\cot x = \pm \dfrac{\sqrt{1 - \sin^2 x}}{\sin x}$

$\csc x = \dfrac{1}{\sin x}$

31. $\dfrac{\sqrt{3}}{2}$

33. $150°$

35.   *Triangle Problem*
Approximately 19.3 m
Approximately 40.0°

Exercise 3-2, pages 126-129;   Trigonometric Identities and Equations

Answers for Problems 1 through 34 are contained in the problems.

37. -1 39. π

41.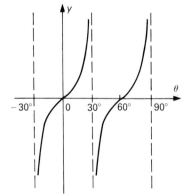

Exercise 3-3, pages 136-141;   Properties Involving Functions of More Than One Argument

1. $\cos (60° + 90°) = -\dfrac{\sqrt{3}}{2}$

$\cos 60° + \cos 90° = \dfrac{1}{2}$

3. $\tan(60° - 90°) = -\dfrac{\sqrt{3}}{3}$

   $\tan 60° - \tan 90°$ is undefined.

5. $\sec(60° + 90°) = -\dfrac{2}{\sqrt{3}}$

   $\sec 60° + \sec 90°$ is undefined.

7. a. Both expressions equal $\dfrac{\sqrt{3}}{2}$ b. Both expressions equal 0.

9. a. Both expressions equal $\dfrac{1}{2}$.   b. Both expressions equal 1.

11. a. Both expressions equal $\dfrac{\sqrt{3}}{3}$ b. Both are undefined.

17. *Computer Verification of Properties*

   For $y = \cos\left(\dfrac{\pi}{2} - x\right)$, use $B = -1$ and $D = 1.57079...$

   $y = \sin x$ and $y = \cos\left(\dfrac{\pi}{2} - x\right)$ are identical because the graph of one *overlays* the graph of the other.

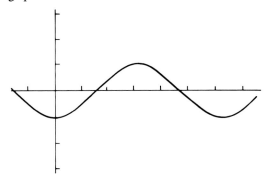

19. *Half-Cycle Displacement Problem #1*

   $\cos(x - \pi)$

   $= \cos x \cos \pi + \sin x \sin \pi$

   $= (\cos x)(-1) + (\sin x)(0)$

   $= -\cos x$

   $\therefore \cos(x - \pi) = -\cos x$, Q.E.D.

   Graphs are identical since one overlays the other.

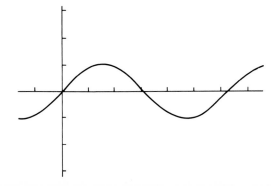

21. $\dfrac{-4\sqrt{3}-3}{10}$ 23. $\dfrac{-4-3\sqrt{3}}{10}$ 25. $\dfrac{25\sqrt{3}-48}{39}$

27. $\dfrac{\sqrt{6}+\sqrt{2}}{4}$ 29. $2-\sqrt{3}$ 31. $\sqrt{6}-\sqrt{2}$

33. $\frac{1}{4}(\sqrt{6}+\sqrt{2})$ 35. $2-\sqrt{3}$ 37. $\sqrt{6}-\sqrt{2}$

39. $\cos 15° \approx 0.9659278263$ 41. $\tan 15° \approx 0.2679491924$

43. $\cos 75° \approx 1.035276180$ 45. a. $S = \{-\dfrac{\pi}{30}+2\pi n, -11\dfrac{\pi}{30}+2\pi n\}$

  b. $S = \{49\dfrac{\pi}{30}, 59\dfrac{\pi}{30}\}$

47. a. $S = \{45° + 360n°, 135° + 360n°\}$
   b. $S = \{45°, 135°\}$

49. a. $S = \{\dfrac{\pi}{3}+\pi n\}$

  b. $S = \{\dfrac{\pi}{3}, 4\dfrac{\pi}{3}\}$

Answers for Problems 51 through 56 are contained in the problems.

57. $\cos A \cos B \cos C - \sin A \sin B \cos C - \sin A \cos B \sin C$
$$- \cos A \sin B \sin C$$

For Problems 59 through 62, see Section 3-4.

Exercise 3-4, pages 144-147; Multiple Argument Properties

1. *Computer Verification of Double-Argument Properties*

   The graph of $y = \cos 2x - \sin 2x$ *overlays* the graph of $y = \cos 2x$. The same holds for $y = 2 \sin x \cos x$ and $y = \sin 2x$. This is only a *verification* within the limits of accuracy of computer plotting, not a proof.

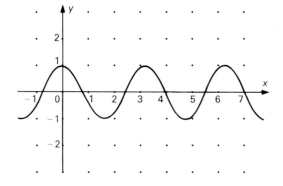

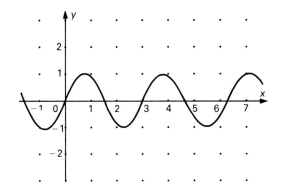

3. $\sin 2 (30°) = 2 \sin 30° \cos 30° = 2 \cdot \frac{1}{2} \cdot \frac{\sqrt{3}}{2} = \frac{\sqrt{3}}{2} = \sin 60°$

5. $\cos 2 (\frac{\pi}{4}) = \cos^2 \frac{\pi}{4} - \sin^2 \frac{\pi}{4} = \frac{1}{2} - \frac{1}{2} = 0 = \cos \frac{\pi}{2}$

7. $\tan 2 (60°) = \dfrac{2 \tan 60°}{1 - \tan^2 60°} = \dfrac{2\sqrt{3}}{1 - 3} = -\sqrt{3} = \tan 120°$

9. a. $\sin 2A = \frac{24}{25}$

   $\cos 2A = \frac{7}{25}$

   $\tan 2A = \frac{24}{7}$

   b. $2A = 73.73...°$

   $\sin 2A = 0.96$

   $\cos 2A = 0.28$

   $\tan 2A = 3.4285...$

   c. $\frac{24}{25} = 0.96; \frac{7}{25} = 0.28;$

   $\frac{24}{7} = 3.4285...$

11. a. $\sin 2A = \frac{-24}{25}$

   $\cos 2A = \frac{7}{25}$

   $\tan 2A = \frac{-24}{7}$

   b. $2A = 646.26...°$

   $\sin 2A = -0.96$

   $\cos 2A = 0.28$

   $\tan 2A = -3.4285...$

   c. $\frac{-24}{25} = -0.96; \frac{7}{25} = 0.28;$

   $\frac{-24}{7} = -3.4285...$

13. a. $\sin 2A = \frac{-12\sqrt{13}}{49}$

   $\cos 2A = \frac{23}{49}$

   $\tan 2A = \frac{-12\sqrt{13}}{23}$

   b. $2A = 297.94...°$

   $\sin 2A = 0.88299...$

   $\cos 2A = 0.46938...$

   $\tan 2A = -1.88115...$

15. a. $\sin 2A = \frac{4\sqrt{2}}{9}$

   $\cos 2A = \frac{7}{9}$

   $\tan 2A = \frac{4\sqrt{2}}{7}$

   b. $2A = 398.94...°$

   $\sin 2A = 0.62853...$

   $\cos 2A = 0.77777...$

   $\tan 2A = 0.80812...$

c. $\dfrac{-12\sqrt{13}}{49} = -\,0.88299...;$

$\dfrac{23}{49} = 0.46938...;$

$\dfrac{-12\sqrt{13}}{23} = 1.88115...$

c. $\dfrac{4\sqrt{2}}{9} = 0.62853...;$

$\dfrac{7}{9} = 0.77777...;$

$\dfrac{4\sqrt{2}}{7} = 0.80812...$

17. a. $S = \{\frac{\pi}{6} + \pi n,\ \frac{\pi}{3} + \pi n\}$

  b. $S = \{\frac{\pi}{6},\ \frac{\pi}{3},\ 7\frac{\pi}{6},\ 4\frac{\pi}{3}\}$

19. a. $S = \{90° + 180n°\}$

  b. $S = \{90°,\ 270°\}$

21. a. $S = \{\frac{\pi}{6} + (\frac{\pi}{2})n\}$

  b. $S = \{\frac{\pi}{6},\ \frac{2\pi}{3},\ \frac{7\pi}{6},\ \frac{5\pi}{3}\}$

23. *Computer Verification of Solutions*

For $4 \sin x \cos x = \sqrt{3}$, plot a horizontal line at $y = \sqrt{3} = 1.732...$. Then plot vertical lines at:

$x = \dfrac{\pi}{6} = 0.5235...$

$x = \dfrac{\pi}{3} = 1.0471...$

$x = \dfrac{7\pi}{6} = 3.665...$

$x = \dfrac{4\pi}{3} = 4.188...$

The results verify the solutions since the vertical lines cross the horizontal line *on* the graph.

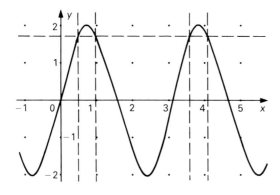

Answers for Problems 25 through 34 are in the text.

35. $\sin 3x = 3 \sin x - 4 \sin^3 x$

37. $\cos 4x = 8 \cos^4 x - 8 \cos^2 x + 1$

39. $\tan 14x = \dfrac{2 \tan 7x}{1 - \tan^2 7x}$

42. $\cos 6x = \cos^2 3x - \sin^2 3x$

43. $\cos 10x = 2 \cos^2 5x - 1$

45. $\cos x = 2 \cos^2 \frac{1}{2}x - 1$

49. $32.471...°$ See a dictionary!

51. $-\sqrt{3}$

For Problems 46 and 47, see Section 3-5.

Exercise 3-5, pages 151-155;   Half-Argument Properties

1. *Computer Verification of Half-Argument Properties*

The graph of $y = \cos \frac{1}{2} x$ overlays the graph of $y = \sqrt{\frac{1}{2}(1 + \cos x)}$ only for values x where $\cos \frac{1}{2} x$ is *non-negative*. For other values of x, the y-values are *opposites*. This happens because

$$\sqrt{\frac{1}{2}(1 + \cos x)} = |\cos \frac{1}{2} x|.$$

The same holds for $y = \sin \frac{1}{2} x$ and $y = \sqrt{\frac{1}{2}(1 - \cos x)}$.

For other values of x, plot

$$y = ABS \ (\cos \tfrac{x}{2}).$$

The title is "verification" since the computer confirms graphs only within the limits of accuracy of the plot.

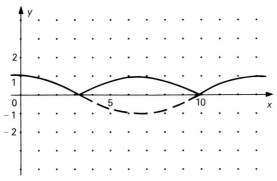

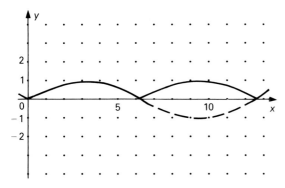

3. $\cos \frac{1}{2}(60°) = + \sqrt{\frac{1}{2}(1 + \cos 60°)} = \sqrt{\frac{1}{2}(1 + \frac{1}{2})} = \frac{\sqrt{3}}{2} = \cos 30°$

5. $\sin \frac{1}{2} \left(\frac{\pi}{2}\right) = + \sqrt{\frac{1}{2}(1 - \cos \frac{\pi}{2})} = \sqrt{\frac{1}{2}(1 - 0)} = \frac{\sqrt{2}}{2} = \sin \frac{\pi}{4}$

7. $\tan \frac{1}{2} \left(2\frac{\pi}{3}\right) = + \dfrac{1 - \cos 2\frac{\pi}{3}}{\sin 2\frac{\pi}{3}} = \dfrac{1 - (-\frac{1}{2})}{\frac{\sqrt{3}}{2}} = \sqrt{3} = \tan \frac{\pi}{3}$

9. $\cos \frac{1}{2} (420°) = - \sqrt{\frac{1}{2} (1 + \cos 420°)} = - \sqrt{\frac{1}{2} (1 + \frac{1}{2})} = -\frac{\sqrt{3}}{2} = \cos 210°$

11. $\sin \frac{1}{2}(-60°) = \sqrt{\frac{1}{2}(1 - \cos(-60°))} = -\sqrt{\frac{1}{2}(1 - \frac{1}{2})} = -\frac{1}{2} = \sin(-30°)$

13. a. $\sin \frac{1}{2}\theta = \frac{\sqrt{5}}{5}$

     $\cos \frac{1}{2}\theta = \frac{2\sqrt{5}}{5}$

     $\tan \frac{1}{2}\theta = \frac{1}{2}$

     b. $\frac{1}{2}\theta = 26.56...°$

     $\sin \frac{1}{2}\theta = 0.44721...$

     $\cos \frac{1}{2}\theta = 0.89442...$

     $\tan \frac{1}{2}\theta = 0.5$

     c. $\frac{\sqrt{5}}{5} = 0.44721...;$

     $\frac{2\sqrt{5}}{5} = 0.89442...;\ \frac{1}{2} = 0.5$

15   a. $\sin \frac{1}{2}\theta = \frac{2\sqrt{5}}{5}$

     $\cos \frac{1}{2}\theta = -\frac{\sqrt{5}}{5}$

     $\tan \frac{1}{2}\theta = -2$

     b. $\frac{1}{2}\theta = 116.56...°$

     $\sin \frac{1}{2}\theta = 0.89442...$

     $\cos \frac{1}{2}\theta = -0.44721...$

     $\tan \frac{1}{2}\theta = -2$

     c. $2\frac{\sqrt{5}}{5} = 0.89442...;$

     $-\sqrt{\frac{5}{5}} = -0.44721...;\ -2 = -2$

17. a. $\sin \frac{1}{2}\theta = -\frac{\sqrt{5}}{5}$

     $\cos \frac{1}{2}\theta = \frac{2\sqrt{5}}{5}$

     $\tan \frac{1}{2}\theta = -\frac{1}{2}$

     b. $\frac{1}{2}\theta = 333.43...°$

     $\sin \frac{1}{2}\theta = -0.44721...$

     $\cos \frac{1}{2}\theta = 0.89442...$

     $\tan \frac{1}{2}\theta = -0.5$

     c. $-\frac{\sqrt{5}}{5} = -0.44721...;$

     $\frac{2\sqrt{5}}{5} = 0.89442...;\ -\frac{1}{2} = -0.5$

19. a. $x = \frac{\pi}{3}, \frac{11\pi}{3}, \frac{13\pi}{3}, \frac{23\pi}{3}...$

     b. $x = \frac{\pi}{3}, \frac{5\pi}{3}, 7\pi, \frac{11\pi}{3}, \frac{13\pi}{3},...$

     c. See graph in problem 1 (first part).

     Actual replacement in part (a) should

     be:

     $|\cos \frac{1}{2}x| = \frac{\sqrt{3}}{2}$

23. $s = 0$

Answers for Problems 25 through 32 are in the problems.

33. $\tan \frac{1}{2}x = \frac{\pm \sin x}{1 + \cos x}$. For $x \varepsilon (0, \pi), \frac{1}{2}x \varepsilon (0, \frac{\pi}{2})$, so $\tan \frac{1}{2}x$ and $\sin x$ are both positive, and "+" should be used. For $x \varepsilon (\pi, 2\pi), \frac{1}{2}x \varepsilon (\frac{\pi}{2}, \pi)$, and so $\tan \frac{1}{2}x$ and $\sin$ x are both negative. Since $\tan \frac{1}{2}x$ and $\sin x$ have the *same* sign, the "+" must be used again to avoid a double negative. Similarly, for $x \varepsilon (2\pi, 3\pi)$ and for $x \varepsilon (3\pi, 4\pi)$, $\sin$ x and $\tan \frac{1}{2}x$ have the *same* sign. So the "+" must always be used. Note that $1 + \cos$ x is never negative, so the sign of $\tan \frac{1}{2}x$ will come out the same as that of $\sin x$.

For Problems 35 and 36, see Section 3-6.

37. $\sin 18° = \dfrac{\sqrt{5}-1}{4}$

    f.   The author and his students for several years sought a continuation of the pattern to $(\sqrt{7}-\sqrt{3})/4$, etc., but had been unable to relate the radical expression to the argument of the sine. In 1979, in response to a note in the Solution Manual for the First Edition of this text, Professor Ray Steiner of Bowling Green State University, and Professor E. Z. Chein of Penn State University presented a proof that the pattern *cannot* be generalized to $\sin(\pi/d) = (\sqrt{n-4})/4$, where n and d are both integers. You are invited to contact either professor or this author for details of the proof.

39. $\dfrac{\sqrt{3}}{2}$

Exercise 3-6, pages 160-163;   Sum and Product Properties

1. $\sin 65° + \sin 17°$

3. $\cos 102° + \cos 4°$

5. $\sin 7.9 + \sin 0.3$

7. $-\cos 11.8 + \cos 2.6$

9. $\sin 8x - \sin 2x$

11. $\cos 11x + \cos 3x$

13. $2\cos 29° \cos 17°$

15. $2\sin 38° \cos 16°$

17. $2\sin 3.4 \sin 1.0$

19. $-2\cos 4 \sin 2$

21. $2\sin 6x \cos 3x$

23. $2\sin 9x \sin x$

25. $S = \{0, \dfrac{\pi}{4}, \dfrac{3\pi}{4}, \pi, \dfrac{5\pi}{4}, \dfrac{7\pi}{4}\}$

27. $S = \{22.5°, 67.5°, 90°, 112.5°, 157.5°\}$

Answers for Problems 29 through 40 are in the problems.

41. $\dfrac{1}{4}\sin 3x + \dfrac{1}{4}\sin x$

43. $\dfrac{3}{4}\sin x - \dfrac{1}{4}\sin 3x$

45. $\dfrac{1}{8}\sin x + \dfrac{1}{16}\sin 3x - \dfrac{1}{16}\sin 5x$

47. $\sin x + \sin 7x = 2\sin 4x \cos 3x$

    Pattern: Sinusoid with varying sinusoidal axis.

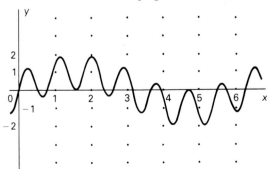

49. $\cos x \cos 8x = \dfrac{1}{2}\cos 9x + \dfrac{1}{2}\cos 7x$

    Pattern: Sinusoid with varying amplitude.

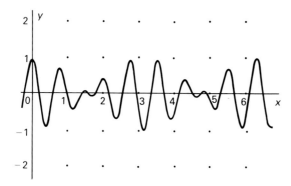

51. a. $\sin 2x \cos 3x = 2 \sin x \cos x (4 \cos^3 x - 3 \cos x)$

$= 8 \sin x \cos^4 x - 6 \sin x \cos^2 x$ (Other forms are possible).

b. $\sin 2x \cos 3x = \frac{1}{2} \sin 5x + \frac{1}{2} \sin (-x) = \frac{1}{2} \sin 5x - \frac{1}{2} \sin x$

c. The degree in part a equals the highest multiple in part b, which equals the sum of the multiples in the original expression, which equals 5.

53. See Section 3-7.

Exercise 3-7, page 166; Linear Combination of Cosine and Sine with Equal Arguments

1. a. $2 \cos (x - 60°)$
    b. $2 \cos (x - \frac{\pi}{3})$

3. a. $5\sqrt{2} \cos (x - 315°) = 5\sqrt{2} \cos (x + 45°)$
    b. $5\sqrt{2} \cos (x - \frac{7\pi}{4}) = 5\sqrt{2} \cos (x + \frac{\pi}{4})$

5. a. $13 \cos (x - 157.38°)$
    b. $13 \cos (x - 2.747)$

7. a. $17 \cos (3x - 208.07°)$
    b. $17 \cos (3x - 3.632)$

9. a. $4 \cos (x - 15°)$
    b. $4 \cos (x - 0.2618)$

11.

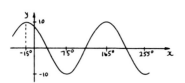

$$y = 5\sqrt{3} \cos 2x - 5 \sin 2x$$
$$= 10 \cos (2x + 30°)$$
$$= 10 \cos 2 (x + 15°)$$

13.

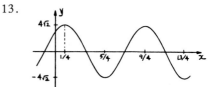

$$y = 4 \cos \pi x + 4 \sin \pi x$$
$$= 4\sqrt{2} \cos (\pi x - \frac{\pi}{4})$$
$$= 4\sqrt{2} \cos \pi(x - \frac{1}{4})$$

15. $S = \{124°, 344°\}$

17. $S = \{0.59, 4.98\}$

19. *Computer Verification of Property*

Plot: $y = 5 \sin x - 12 \cos x$

$y = 13 \cos (x - 2.747)$

The equations are identical since one graph overlays the other on the computer screen.

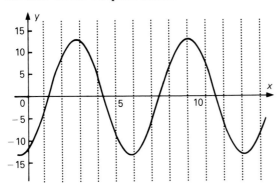

Exercise 3-8, pages 167-171; Simplification of Trigonometric Expressions

1. $\sin 2x = 2 \sin x \cos x$

2. $\sin^2 x = \frac{1}{2} (1 - \cos 2x)$

3. $\sin^2 x = 1 - \cos^2 x$

4. $\cos^2 x = 1 - \sin^2 x$

5. $\cos^2 x = \frac{1}{2}(1 + \cos 2x)$

6. $\cos 2x = 2 \cos^2 x - 1$

7. $\cos 2x = 1 - 2 \sin^2 x$

8. $\cos 2x = \cos^2 x - \sin^2 x$

9. $\tan 2x = \dfrac{2 \tan x}{1 - \tan^2 x}$

10. $\sin \frac{1}{2}x = \pm \sqrt{\frac{1}{2}(1 - \cos x)}$

11. $\cos \frac{1}{2}x = \pm \sqrt{\frac{1}{2}(1 + \cos x)}$

12. $\tan \frac{1}{2}x = \pm \sqrt{\dfrac{1 - \cos x}{1 + \cos x}}$

13. $\tan \frac{1}{2}x = \dfrac{1 - \cos x}{\sin x} = \dfrac{\sin x}{1 + \cos x}$

14. $\sin 3x = 3 \sin x - 4 \sin^3 x$
     (See Ex. 3-4, Prob. 33.)

15. $\cos 4x = 2 \cos^2 2x - 1$

16. $\cos 6x = 2 \cos^2 3x - 1$

17. $\sin x \cos x = \frac{1}{2} \sin 2x$

18. $\sin x \cos y = \frac{1}{2} \sin (x + y) + \frac{1}{2} \sin (x - y)$

19. $\cos x \cos y = \frac{1}{2} \cos (x + y) + \frac{1}{2} \cos (x - y)$

20. $\cos x + \cos y = 2 \cos \frac{1}{2}(x + y) \cos \frac{1}{2}(x - y)$

21. $\sin x + \sin y = 2 \sin \frac{1}{2}(x + y) \cos \frac{1}{2}(x - y)$

22. $\sin x + \cos x = \sqrt{2} \cos (x - \frac{\pi}{4}) = \sqrt{2} \cos (x - 45°)$

23. $\sin 3x \sin 7x = -\frac{1}{2} \cos 10x + \frac{1}{2} \cos 4x$

24. $\sin 3x + \sin 7x = 2 \sin 5x \cos 2x$

25. $\sqrt{3} \cos x - \sin x = 2 \cos (x + \frac{\pi}{6}) = 2 \cos (x + 30°)$

26. $-4 \cos x - 4 \sin x = 4\sqrt{2} \cos (x - 5\frac{\pi}{4}) = 4\sqrt{2} \cos (x - 225°)$

27. a. $\cos x \cos 37° + \sin x \sin 37°$
    b. $\cos x \cos y \cos z - \sin x \sin y \cos z - \sin x \cos y \sin z - \cos x \sin y \sin z$
    c. $4 \cos^3 x - 3 \cos x$

29. a. $\frac{1}{2} \sin 2x$

    b. $\frac{1}{2}(1 + \cos 2x)$

    c. $\frac{1}{4} \sin 3x + \frac{1}{4} \sin x$

    d. $\frac{3}{8} - \frac{1}{2} \cos 2x + \frac{1}{8} \cos 4x$

31. $\pm \frac{\pi}{6} + 2\pi n$

33. $-45° + 180n°$

35. $\frac{2\pi}{3}$

37. $30°$

39. $34.8°$
    11.5 ft

Exercise 3-9, pages 175-178;   General Trigonometric Equations

1. $S = \{120°, 300°\}$

3. $S = \{103°, 343°\}$

5. $S \{60°, -60°, 120°, -120°\}$

7. $S = \{90° + 180n°, 45° + 360n°, 135° + 360n°\}$

9. $S = \{2\frac{\pi}{3} + \pi n\}$

11. $S = \{0°, -30°, -150°\}$

13. $S = \{\frac{\pi}{3}, 5\frac{\pi}{3}\}$

15. $S = \emptyset$

17. $S = \{\frac{\pi}{3}, -\frac{\pi}{3}, -\pi\}$

19. $S = \{-90°, 0°\}$

21. $S = \{\frac{\pi}{6}, 7\frac{\pi}{6}, \frac{\pi}{3}, 4\frac{\pi}{3}\}$

23. $S = \{15°, -30°, -210°\}$

25. $S = \{178°, 358°, 28°, 208°\}$

27. $S = \{150°, 75°, -45°\}$

29. $S = \{22\frac{1}{2}°, -67\frac{1}{2}°, -22\frac{1}{2}°, 67\frac{1}{2}°\}$

31. $S = \{2\pi, 4\frac{\pi}{3}\}$

33. $S = \{16°, 34°, 52°, 70°, 88°\}$

35. $S = \{0, 2\pi, 4\pi, 3\frac{\pi}{2}, 7\frac{\pi}{2}\}$

37. $S = \{30°, -150°, -30°, 150°\}$

39. $S = \{\text{real numbers}\}$

41. $S = \{30° \ 58', 210° \ 58', 135°, 315°\}$

43. $S = \{25° \ 20', 228° \ 24'\}$

45. $S = \{0, 3.1416, 0.3398, 2.8018\}$

47. $S = \{0.6662, 2.475\}$

49. $S = \{5.435, 3.990\}$

51. $S = \{40°, 220°, 160°, 340°\}$

53. $S = \{2.150\}$

55. *Computer Check of Solutions*

   Problem 51: $3 + 4 \cos 2\,(\theta - 10°) = 5$

```
]RUN
FUNCTION IS:

  1 DEF  FN Y(X) = 3 + 4 * COS (PI / 90 * (X - 10))

USE THIS FUNCTION? Y/N Y
MENU:
1    SPECIFY INDIVIDUAL DATA.
2    SPECIFY RANGE OF DATA.
3    QUIT.
WHICH?   1
HOW MANY DATA POINTS?   4
TYPE X VALUE NUMBER 1:   40
TYPE X VALUE NUMBER 2:   220
TYPE X VALUE NUMBER 3:   160
TYPE X VALUE NUMBER 4:   340


X        F(X)
-----    --------------------
  40     5
 220     5
 160     5
 340     4.99999999
```

Exercise 3-10, pages 179-181;   Chapter Review and Test

Review Problems

R1. a. $\tan x = \dfrac{\sin x}{\cos x}$, $\cot x = \dfrac{\cos x}{\sin x}$

   b. $\tan x = \dfrac{\sec x}{\csc x}$, $\cot x = \dfrac{\csc x}{\sec x}$

   c. $\sin x \csc x = 1$, $\cos x \sec x = 1$, $\tan x \cot x = 1$

   d. $\sin^2 x = 1 - \cos^2 x$, $\tan^2 x = \sec^2 x - 1$, $\csc^2 x = 1 + \cot^2 x$

R2. $\sin(-x) = -\sin x$, $\cos(-x) = \cos x$, $\tan(-x) = -\tan x$,
   $\cot(-x) = -\cot x$, $\sec(-x) = \sec x$, $\csc(-x) = -\csc x$.

R3. a. $\sin(x + y) = \sin x \cos y + \cos x \sin y$

   b. $\cos(x + y) = \cos x \cos y - \sin x \sin y$

   c. $\sin(x - y) = \sin x \cos y - \cos x \sin y$

   d. $\cos(x - y) = \cos x \cos y + \sin x \sin y$

   e. $\tan(x + y) = \dfrac{\tan x + \tan y}{1 - \tan x \tan y}$

   f. $\tan(x - y) = \dfrac{\tan x - \tan y}{1 + \tan x \tan y}$

   g. $\cos(90° - \theta) = \sin \theta$

h. $\cot\left(\frac{\pi}{2} - x\right) = \tan x$

i. $\sec\left(\frac{\pi}{2} - x\right) = \csc x$

R4.   a. $\sin 2x = 2 \sin x \cos x$

e. $\cos \frac{1}{2}x = \pm\sqrt{\frac{1}{2}(1 + \cos x)}$

b.   i. $\cos 2x = \cos^2 x - \sin^2 x$

f.   i. $\tan \frac{1}{2}x = \dfrac{1 - \cos x}{\sin x}$

ii. $\cos 2x = 1 - 2 \sin^2 x$

ii. $\tan \frac{1}{2}x = \dfrac{\sin x}{1 + \cos x}$

iii. $\cos 2x = 2 \cos^2 x - 1$

iii. $\tan \frac{1}{2}x = \pm\sqrt{\dfrac{1 - \cos x}{1 + \cos x}}$

c. $\tan 2x = \dfrac{2 \tan x}{1 - \tan^2 x}$

d. $\sin \frac{1}{2}x = \pm\sqrt{\frac{1}{2}(1 - \cos x)}$

R5.   a.   i. $\sin x \sin y = -\frac{1}{2} \cos (x + y) + \frac{1}{2} \cos (x - y)$

ii. $\cos x \cos y = \frac{1}{2} \cos (x + y) + \frac{1}{2} \cos (x - y)$

iii. $\sin x \cos y = \frac{1}{2} \sin (x + y) + \frac{1}{2} \sin (x - y)$

iv. $\cos x \sin y = \frac{1}{2} \sin (x + y) - \frac{1}{2} \sin (x - y)$

b.   i. $\sin x + \sin y = 2 \sin \frac{1}{2}(x + y) \cos \frac{1}{2}(x - y)$

ii. $\cos x + \cos y = 2 \cos \frac{1}{2}(x + y) \cos \frac{1}{2}(x - y)$

iii. $\sin x - \sin y = 2 \cos \frac{1}{2}(x + y) \sin \frac{1}{2}(x - y)$

iv. $\cos x - \cos y = -2 \sin \frac{1}{2}(x + y) \sin \frac{1}{2}(x - y)$

R6. $5 \cos x - 7 \sin x = \sqrt{74} \cos (x + 54° \, 28')$

Chapter 3 Test

T1.   a. $S = \{\frac{\pi}{2}\}$

b. $S = \{-18.5° + 90n°\}$

c. $S = \{\pi + 2\pi n, \frac{\pi}{3} + 2\pi n\}$

d. $S = \{x: -\pi < x < \pi, \text{ and } x \neq \frac{\pi}{2}, -\frac{\pi}{2}, 0\}$

e. $S = \{0°, 60°, 120°, 180°, 240°, 300°, 360°\}$

f. $S = \{-143°, 37°\}$

T2.   a.   Objectives: 4, 5, 7

b.   Objectives: 1, 7

c.   Objectives: 1, 5, 7

T3.   a. $\cos 15° = \dfrac{\sqrt{6} + \sqrt{2}}{4}$

b. $\sin \frac{\pi}{8} = \frac{1}{2}\sqrt{2 - \sqrt{2}}$

T4. a. $2 \cos^2 x \cos^2 y - 4 \cos x \cos y \sin x \sin y + \sin^2 x \sin^2 y - 1$
Objectives: 3, 4, 7

   b. $2 \sin 45.5° \cos 12.5°$
Objectives: 5, 7

   c. $\sin^2 x \cos x = \frac{1}{4} \cos x - \frac{1}{4} \cos 3x$
Objectives: 2, 4, 7

   d. $\cos 38x = \cos^2 19x - \sin^2 19x = 2 \cos^2 19x - 1 = 1 - 2 \sin^2 19x$
$\cos 38x = \pm \sqrt{\frac{1}{2}(1 + \cos 76x)}$
Objectives: 4, 7

   e. $\sin 37° \cos 53° + \cos 37° \sin 53° = 1$
Objectives: 3, 7

   f. $\cos 23° + \sin 23° = \sqrt{2} \cos 22°$
Objectives: 2, 6, 7

CHAPTER 4. Composition of Ordinates, Rotary Motion, and Inverse Functions

Exercise 4-1, pages 186-187; Composition of Ordinates

Note: The following graphs were plotted by the computer programs of Exercise 4-2.

1.
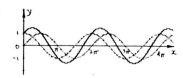

3.
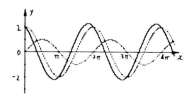

5.

7.
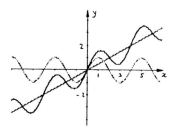

9.
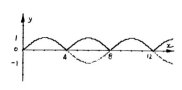

11.
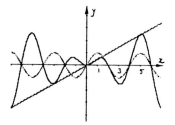

13.
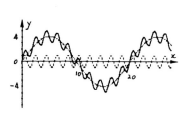

15.
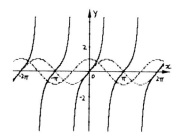

17.

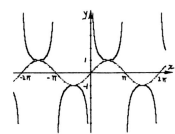

19.

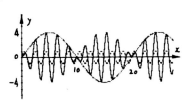

21. *Identity Problem*

Prove: $\cos x \sec^2 x = \cos x + \sin x \tan x$

Proof: $\cos x + \dfrac{\sin x \cdot \sin x}{\cos x}$

$= \dfrac{\cos^2 x + \sin^2 x}{\cos x}$

$= \dfrac{1}{\cos x}$

$= \sec x$

$= (\cos x \cdot \sec x) \cdot \sec x$

$= \cos x \sec^2 x$

$\therefore \cos x \sec^2 x = \cos x + \sin x \tan x$, Q.E.D.

23. $s = \{-\dfrac{2}{3}, 0, \dfrac{2}{3}\}$

25. $\dfrac{1}{2}$

27. 36°

Exercise 4-2, pages 189-192;   **Composition of Ordinates by Computer Graphics**

1.

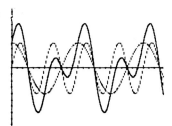

3.

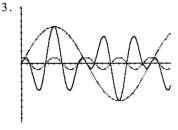

5.

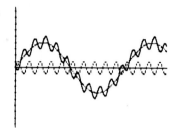

7.

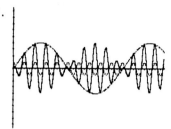

9.

11.

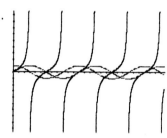

13. *Variable Phase Displacement Problem*

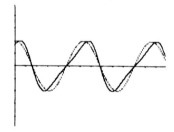

15. *Biorhythm Problem*

a.

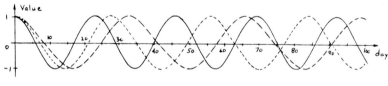

—————— Physical

- - - - - - - - Emotional

—— —— —— —— Intellectual

b. All three cycles are near their low points between about 11 and 18 days. So your performance would be poorest then.

c. All three cycles are near the time-axis around 76 to 77 days.

d. The period of the composite graph is the *least common multiple* of the periods of the individual graphs. Since 23, 28, and 33 are relatively prime, their LCM is $23 \times 28 \times 33 = 21{,}252$ days. So the next time all three biorhythms will be at a high point will be in about 58.2 years. So a person would experience this phenomenon only once or twice in a lifetime.

e.

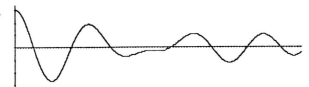

17.

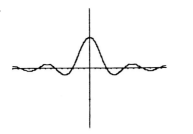

19. *Identity Problem*

Prove: $y = \cos x + 12 \sin x$ is a sinusoid of amplitude 13

Proof: By the linear combination property, the sum of two sinusoids with equal periods is a sinusoid with that same period.

Amplitude $= \sqrt{5^2 + 12^2}$

$\qquad = \sqrt{169}$

$\qquad = 13,$ \qquad\qquad Q.E.D.

Phase Displacement: $D = \cos^{-1}\frac{5}{13} = \sin^{-1}\frac{12}{13}$

$\therefore$ D 67.38...°

21. $-\frac{1}{\sqrt{3}}$

23. 1440°/s

Exercise 4-3, pages 193-195; Properties Verified by Computer Graphing

1.

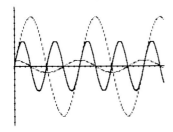

a. $A = 4, P = 6$

b. $y = 4 \sin \left(\frac{\pi}{3}\right)x$

c. $\quad 8 \sin \left(\frac{\pi}{6}\right) x \cos \left(\frac{\pi}{6}\right)x$

$= 8 \left(\frac{1}{2} \sin 2\left(\frac{\pi}{6}\right)x \right)$

$= 4 \sin \left(\frac{\pi}{3}\right)x,$ Q.E.D.

3.

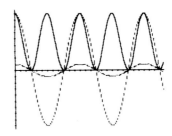

a. $A = 4.5, P = 6, V = 4.5$

b. $y = 4.5 + 4.5 \cos \left(\frac{\pi}{3}\right)x$

c. $\quad 9 \cos^2 \left(\frac{\pi}{6}\right)x$

$= 9 \left(\frac{1}{2} (1 + \cos 2\left(\frac{\pi}{6}\right)x)\right)$

$= 4.5 + 4.5 \cos \left(\frac{\pi}{3}\right)x$

5.

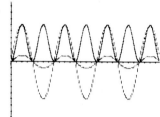

7.

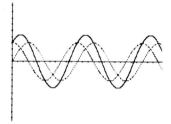

a. $A = 3, P = 4, V = 3$

b. $y = 3 - 3 \cos (\frac{\pi}{2})x$

c. $6 \sin^2 (\frac{\pi}{4})x$

$= 6(\frac{1}{2}(1 - \cos 2(\frac{\pi}{4})x))$

$= 3 - 3 \cos (\frac{\pi}{2})x$, Q.E.D.

a. $A \approx 4.2, P = 12, D = 1.5$

b. $y = 4.2 \cos (\frac{\pi}{6})(x - 1.5)$

c. $C = \sqrt{9 + 9} \approx 4.2$

$D = \cos^{-1}(\frac{3}{\sqrt{18}}) / (\frac{\pi}{6}) = 1.5$

$\therefore y = 4.2 \cos (\frac{\pi}{6}) (x - 1.5)$

9.

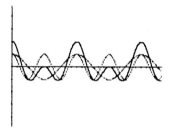

a. $A \approx 8.6, P = 20, D \approx 7.0$

b. $y = 8.6 \cos (\frac{\pi}{10}) (x - 7.0)$

c. $C = \sqrt{25 + 49} \approx 8.6$

$D = \cos^{-1}(-\frac{5}{\sqrt{74}}) / (\frac{\pi}{10}) \approx 7.0$

$\therefore y = 8.6 \cos (\frac{\pi}{10}) (x - 7.0)$

11. a.

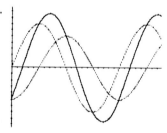

d.

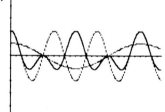

b. High points:

(12, 2), (18, 0), (0, 2), (6, 0)

c. $\cos (\frac{\pi}{3})x + \cos (\frac{\pi}{6})x$

$= 2 \cos (\frac{\pi}{4})x \cos (\frac{\pi}{12})x$

The two composed graphs are the same, as can be seen from the high points listed in part (b).

13. a.

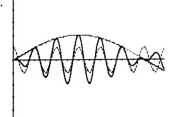
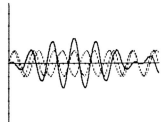

                                                      d.

b. Graph is a sinusoid whose amplitude varies sinusoidally.

c. $2 \sin (\frac{\pi}{12})x \cos \pi x = \sin (13\frac{\pi}{12})x - \sin (11\frac{\pi}{12})x$

d. Periods: $2\pi (\frac{13\pi}{12}) = \frac{24}{13} \approx 1.846$

                   $2\pi (\frac{11\pi}{12}) = \frac{24}{11} \approx 2.182$

    Graph above.

e. A product of two sinusoids with much different periods equals a sum of two sinusoids with nearly equal periods.

15. *Rotating Motion Problem*

    This question can be answered two ways. If you consider "moving" to be a *linear* velocity, you will be moving *three times* as fast at 6 feet from the center as at 2 feet. If you consider "moving" to be an *angular* velocity, you will be moving just as "fast" at 6 feet as at 2 feet.

17. $\frac{1}{2}$

21. About 6 radians in a complete rev

Exercise 4-4, pages 200-209; Angular Velocity

1. *Ship's Propeller Problem*

    a. 300π rad/min at both places

    b. Tip: 1200π ft/min

       Center: 0 ft/min

3. *David and Goliath Problem*

    15 rad/s

5. *Mower Cord Problem*

    a. 6π rad/s

    b. 1.2π ft/s

    c. 6π rad/s

7. *Pulley Problem No. 1*

    a. 4π rad/s

    b. 12π cm/s

    c. 12π cm/s

    d. 1.6π rad/s

    e. 48 rpm

9. *Gear Problem No. 1*

    a. 100 cm/s

    b. $\frac{20}{3}$ rad/s

    c. $\frac{20}{3}$ rad/s

11. *Cockroach Problem*

    a. $2\frac{\pi}{3}$ rad

    b. $8\frac{\pi}{3}$ cm

    c. $4\frac{\pi}{3}$ rad/s

    d. $16\frac{\pi}{3}$ cm/s

13. *Bicycle Problem*

    40 rad/s

15. *Three Gear Problem*

    a. 20 $\frac{\pi}{3}$ rad/s

    b. 260 $\frac{\pi}{3}$ mm/s $\approx$ 272 mm/s

    c. 272 mm/s

    d. 260 $\frac{\pi}{9}$ rad/s

    e. 908 mm/s

17. *Truck Problem*

    a. 600π rad/min

    b. 1800π in./min

    c. 180π rad/min

    d. 10 mph

19. *Clock Hands Problem*

    1.05 in./min

21. *Projector Problem No. 1*

    a.   i.   3.75 rad/s

        ii. $\frac{15}{(8\pi)}$ rev/s

        iii.   215°/s

    b. $\frac{5}{3}$ rad/s

    c. $\frac{100}{3}$ cm/s

    d. 0 cm/s, $\frac{5}{3}$ rad/s

23. *Earth's Rotation Problem No. 1*

    a. $\frac{\pi}{12}$ rad/hr

    b. 1047 mph

    c. 0 mph

    d. 907 mph

    e. By launching to the east, spacecraft is already going 907 mph.

25. *Record Player Problem No. 1*

    a. 1000 $\frac{\pi}{3}$ in./min

    b. 200π in./min

    c. $\frac{1}{6}$ in.

27. *Angular Velocity and Sinusoids*

    a. 0.1 rev/s $\frac{\pi}{5}$ rad/s

    b. $d = 6 + 7 \cos \frac{\pi}{5}(t - 3)$

    c. B is the angular velocity.

31. About 1.36 cm

Exercise 4-5, pages 215-217; Inverse Circular Function Graphs

1.

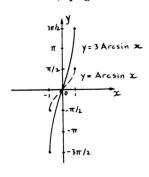

3.

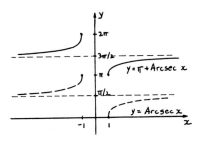

5.

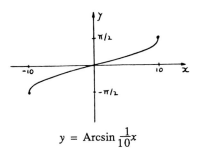

7.

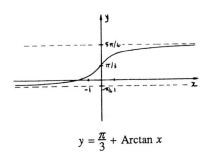

$$y = \frac{\pi}{3} + \text{Arctan } x$$

9.

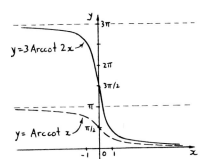

$$y = \text{Arcsin } \frac{1}{10}x$$

11.

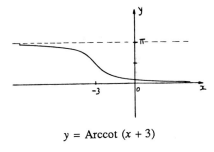

$$y = \text{Arccot } (x + 3)$$

13.

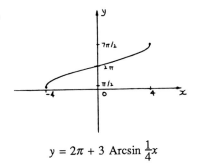

$$y = 2\pi + 3 \text{ Arcsin } \frac{1}{4}x$$

15.

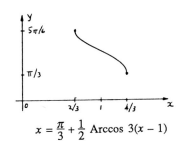

$$x = \frac{\pi}{3} + \frac{1}{2} \text{ Arccos } 3(x - 1)$$

17. *Inverse of a Linear Function*

   a. Slope = 3, y–int. = 2

   b. $y = \frac{1}{3}x - \frac{2}{3}$

   d. The graphs are *reflections* of each other through the line $y = x$.

   e. $f(f^{-1}(x)) = 3(\frac{1}{3}x - \frac{2}{3}) + 2 = x - 2 + 2 = x$

   ∴ $f(f^{-1}(x)) = x$, Q.E.D.

21. *Computer Graphics Problem 1*

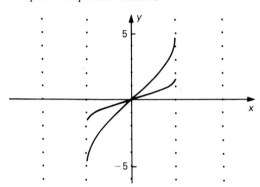

25. $\theta = $ Arcsin $0.7 = 44.42700...°$

   sin $\theta = 0.7$

   You get back the 0.7 you started with!

27. *Rotary Motion Problem*

   a. 0.0003810762... rad/hr

   b. About 53,700 mph

Exercise 4-6, pages 220-222; Exact Values of Inverse Functions

1. $\frac{\pi}{6}$	3. $\frac{\pi}{2}$	5. $\frac{\pi}{4}$	7. $\frac{\pi}{6}$	9. $\frac{\pi}{3}$
11. $\frac{\pi}{4}$	13. $-\frac{\pi}{3}$	15. π	17. $-\frac{\pi}{4}$	19. $3\frac{\pi}{4}$
21. $3\frac{\pi}{4}$	23. $-\frac{\pi}{4}$	25. $\frac{3}{4}$	27. $\frac{5}{13}$	29. $\frac{15}{17}$
31. $\frac{3}{2}$	33. -1	35. $\sqrt{10}$	37. 5	39. no value
41. $\frac{\pi}{6}$	43. $-\frac{\pi}{4}$	45. $5\frac{\pi}{6}$	47. $\frac{\pi}{6}$	

Exercise 4-7, pages 224-226;   Properties of Inverse Circular Functions

1. Arcsec $x = $ Arctan $\sqrt{x^2 - 1}$, for $x \geq 1$; or

π + Arctan $\sqrt{x^2 - 1}$, for $x \leq -1$

3. Arccos $x = \frac{\pi}{2}$ − Arcsin x 5. Arcsec $x = $ Arccos $(\frac{1}{x})$

7. $-\frac{7}{25}$ 9. $-\frac{336}{625}$ 11. $\frac{\sqrt{2}}{2}$ 13. $\frac{2(\sqrt{30} - 1)}{15}$ 15. $\frac{11}{13}$

17. 2

19. *Function of an Inverse Function Property*

a. Let $y = f(x)$.

Then $x = f^{-1}(y)$ by the definition of f^{-1}

$\quad\quad = f^{-1}(f(x))$ substituting $f(x)$ for y

$\therefore f^{-1}(f(x)) = x$ by transitivity and symmetry

20. *Cofunction Properties Problem*

a. Let $y = $ Cos^{-1} x.

Then $x = \cos y$ and $y \in [0, \pi]$.

$x = \sin (\frac{\pi}{2 - y})$ by the cofunction property.

$\therefore \frac{\pi}{2} - y = \sin^{-1} x$ by the definition of sin^{-1}.

Since $0 \leq y \leq \pi$, it follows that $-\frac{\pi}{2} \leq \frac{\pi}{2} - y \leq \frac{\pi}{2}$,

which is the range of the Sin^{-1} *function.*

$\therefore \frac{\pi}{2} - y = $ Sin^{-1} x, from which $y = \frac{\pi}{2} - $ Sin^{-1} x, Q.E.D.

21. *Reciprocal Properties Problem*

a. Let $y = $ Arctan x.

Then $x = \tan y$, and $y \in$ QI or QIV.

$\frac{1}{x} = \cot y$ by the reciprocal property.

$\therefore y = $ arccot $\frac{1}{x}$ by the definition of arccot.

If $x < 0$, then Arccot $(\frac{1}{x})$ is in QII, but y is

in QIV (see sketch).

So for $x < 0$, Arctan $x = $ (Arccot $\frac{1}{x}$) − π

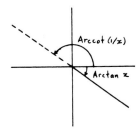

23. *Computer Graphics Problem*

The following is the output of PLOT INVERSE, which should look like your graph.

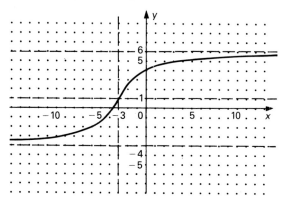

25. $x = \frac{1}{6}, \frac{1}{2}, \frac{5}{6}, \frac{3}{2}$

27. 13 rad/s

29. $y = \arccos x$:

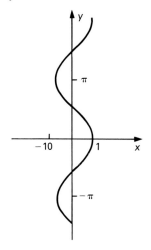

Exercise 4-8, pages 229-233; Real-World Applications of Inverse Circular Functions

3. *Spaceship Problem*

a. $d = 550 + 450 \cos \frac{\pi}{50} t$

b. $t = \frac{50}{\pi} \arccos \frac{d - 550}{450}$

c. 39.18, 60.82, and 139.18 minutes

d. 60.82 minutes, or just over an hour

5. *Tunnel Problem*

a. $y = 100 + 150 \cos \frac{\pi}{700}(x - 512.6)$

b. $x = 512.6 + \frac{700}{\pi} \arccos \frac{y - 100}{150}$

c. 1025.2 meters long

d. 374.8 meters long

e. Tunnel is 950.6 m

Bridge is 449.4 m

7. $y = \text{Arcsin } x$

9. Both equal 45.57299...°.

11. $3 \sin 24x - 3 \sin 2x$

15. 109.5648...°

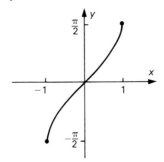

Exercise 4-9, pages 234-237; Chapter Review and Test
Review Problems

R1.

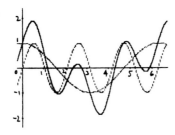

R2.

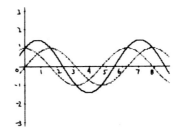

b. Amplitude ≈ 1.4, period $= 2\pi$, phase displacement $= \frac{\pi}{4}$

c. $y = \sqrt{2} \cos (x - \frac{\pi}{4})$, which agrees with the above.

R3. a. $2\frac{\pi}{3}$ rad/s

b. i. 20π cm/s

ii.   0 cm/s

R4. a. 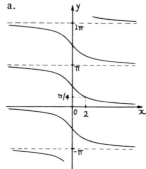   b. 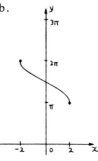   c.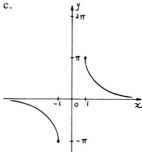

R5. a. i. $-\frac{\pi}{6}$ b. i.   Arccsc x

      ii. $2\frac{\pi}{3}$ ii. $\frac{\pi}{2}$

     iii. $-\frac{\pi}{4}$ iii. $\text{Sin}^{-1} x$

     iv. $\frac{1}{3}$ iv. $2x\sqrt{1-x^2}$

R6. a. $x = 3 + \frac{5}{\pi}\arctan\frac{y-6}{2}$ b.   1.106, 6.106, 11.106

Chapter Test

T1. a. $3\frac{\pi}{4}$ b. $5\frac{\pi}{6}$ c. $\pm\frac{\pi}{3} + 2\frac{\pi}{n}$ d.   undefined.   e. $\frac{5}{2}$

     Objective: 5

T2. a. 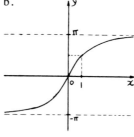   b.   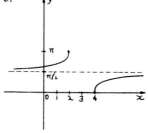   c.

     Objective: 4

T3. Let $y = $ Arcsin x. Then $x = \sin y$.
     From sketch, $v = x$, $r = 1$, $u = \sqrt{1-x^2}$.

     $\therefore \tan y = \dfrac{x}{\sqrt{1-x^2}}$, where $\pm$ is taken

         care of by the sign of x in Quadrants I and IV.

     $\therefore y = $ Arctan $\dfrac{x}{\sqrt{1-x^2}}$, where "Arctan" can be

         used because the ranges of both Arctan and Arcsin are Quadrants I and IV.

     Objectives: 2, 5

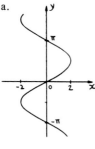
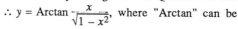

T4. Top: $x = 80 + \dfrac{250}{\pi} \arccos \dfrac{y + 100}{60}$

Bottom: $x = 80 + \dfrac{250}{\pi} \arccos \dfrac{y + 100}{60}$

Objective: 5

T5. a. Horizontal tunnel enters formation at $x = 163.3$, and emerges from formation at $x = 191.7$.

∴ Tunnel goes 28.4 meters through formation.

b. Horizontal tunnel *misses* the top of the formation. So tunnel enters the formation from the bottom at $x = 283.4$, then emerges through the bottom at $x = 376.6$.

∴ Length $= 93.2$ meters.

Objectives: 2, 5, 6

T6. a. 4π rad/s   b. 40π cm/s
      Objective: 3   Objective: 3

c. 10π rad/s   d. 39.6 km/h
      Objective: 3   Objective: 3

T7.

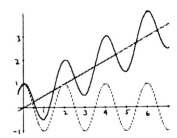

Exercise 5-1, pages 243-244;   Right Triangle Review

1. $m\angle C = 56°$

    $a \approx 17.7$

    $b \approx 9.92$

5. $m\angle Y \approx 50.48° \approx 50°29'$

    $m\angle Z \approx 39.52° \approx 39°31'$

    $z \approx 22.27$

3. $m\angle L = 42°28'$

    $l \approx 2.339$

    $n \approx 2.556$

7. $m\angle R \approx 77.98° \approx 77°59'$

    $m\angle S \approx 12.02° \approx 12°01'$

    $r \approx 46.3$

9.

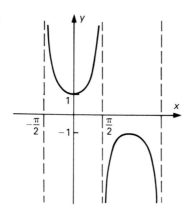

Exercise 5-2, pages 248-249;   Oblique Triangles—Law of Cosines

1. $a \approx 3.978$

7. $m\angle A \approx 28.96° \approx 28°57'$

11. no such triangle

15. *Accurate Drawing Problem No. 1*

3. $r \approx 4.682$

9. $m\angle T \approx 134.62° \approx 134°37'$

13. $m\angle O = 90°$

5. $e \approx 49.20$

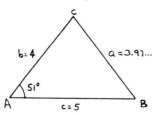

17. $\dfrac{2}{\sqrt{3}}$

19. $S = \{-46°, -166°\}$

21. 38.66... rad/s

    No more than 369 rpm

436

Exercise 5-3, pages 251-252; Area of a Triangle

1. 5.443
7. 23.66
3. 6.1
11. $\frac{231}{520}$
5. 23.66
13. 157.2

Exercise 5-4, pages 255-257; Oblique Triangles—Law of Sines

1. a. $b \approx 5.229$
   b. $c \approx 10.08$

3. a. $h \approx 249.9$
   b. $s \approx 183.6$

5. a. $a \approx 9.321$
   b. $p \approx 4.911$

7. a. $a \approx 214.7$
   b. $l \approx 215.3$

9. *Law of Sines for Angles Problem*

   a. $m\angle A = 33.122...°$

   b. $m\angle C = 51.317...°$ (apparently)

   c. $m\angle C = 128.682...°$ (actually)

   d. $51.317...°$ is the measure of the *reference angle* for C.

      $\therefore m\angle C = 180° - 51.317...° = 128.682...°$

   e. Knowing $\sin C = 0.78062...$ does not tell whether C is acute or obtuse. Knowing $\cos C = -0.625$, a *negative* number, tells that C is *obtuse*.

11. $S = \{45°, 225°\}$

13. $\frac{\pi}{360}$ rad/min

15.

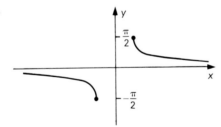

Exercise 5-5, pages 260-262; The Ambiguous Case

1. $c \approx 5.315$ or 1.317
7. $s \approx 5.52$
3. $c \approx 7.79$
9. $m\angle C \approx 23.00°$ or $157.00°$
5. No values of C
11. $m\angle z = 43.15°$

13. *Accurate Drawing Problem No. 1*

a.

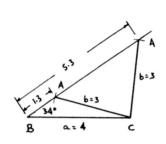

b.

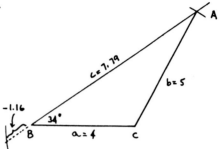

c.

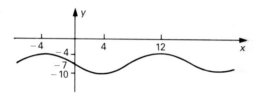

17.

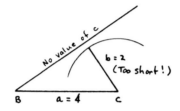

19. $\dfrac{3\pi}{4}$

21. 3.9 cm

23. $f(\theta) = \sqrt{58} \, \cos{(2\theta - 23.19859...°)}$
    Phase displacement is about 11.6°.

Exercise 5-6, pages 264-267;   General Solution of Triangles

Case		a	b	c	A	B	C	Area
1.	SAS	3	4	4.177	42° 59'	65° 21'	71° 40'	5.695
3.	SAS	30	60	34.74	20° 25'	135° 45'	23° 50'	363.7
5.	SAS	100	210	266.0	20° 12'	46° 28'	113° 20'	9641
7.	SSS	8	9	7	58° 25'	73° 24'	48° 11'	26.83
9.	SSS	3	6	4	26° 23'	117° 17'	36° 20'	5.333
11.	SSS	3	9	4	No such triangle			
13.	ASA	502.5	121.5	400	143° 10'	8° 20'	28° 30'	14567
15.	ASA	15.78	36.76	50	11° 30'	27° 40'	140° 50'	183.2
17.	AAS	6	6.507	6.190	56° 20'	64° 30'	59° 10'	16.76
19.	SSA	7	5	11.15	25° 50'	18° 08'	136° 02'	12.15

21.	SSA	5	7	10.26	25° 50'	37° 36'	116° 34'	15.65
	or:	5	7	2.339	25° 50'	142° 24'	11° 46'	3.567
23.	SSA	5	7		126° 40'	No such triangle		
25.	SSA	7	5	2.751	126° 40'	34° 57'	18° 23'	5.517
27.	SSA	3	5	4.000	36° 52.19386'	90°	53° 08'	6.000

31. $S = \{0 + 2\pi n\}$

33.

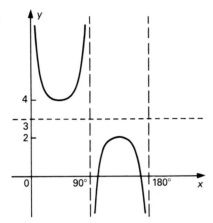

Exercise 5-7, pages 272-273;   Vectors

1. $|\vec{a} + \vec{b}| \approx 14.66$; $\theta \approx 45°50'$
    $|\vec{a} - \vec{b}| \approx 11.18$; $\theta \approx 70°13'$

3. $|\vec{a} + \vec{b}| \approx 11.69$; $\theta \approx 150°0'$
    $|\vec{a} - \vec{b}| \approx 28.73$; $\theta \approx 11°45'$

5. a. $\vec{r} = 13.55$ at 20.3°
    b. 20.3° + 180° = 200.3°
    c. Graph.

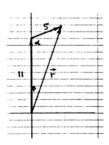

7. a. $\vec{r} = 8.61$ at 123.8°
    b. 123.8° + 180° = 303.8°
    c. Graph.

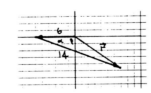

9. a. $1 - \sin^2 x$

    b. $\frac{1}{2}(1 + \cos 2x)$

    c. $\dfrac{1}{\sec^2 x}$

11. 6090 cm^2

13. $383\frac{1}{3}$ rad/min

Exercise 5-8, pages 278-280; Vectors—Resolution into Components

1. $6.038\,\vec{i} - 5.248\,\vec{j}$

3. $-6.134\,\vec{i} + 14.45\,\vec{j}$

5. a. $-12.8\,\vec{i} + 54.4\,\vec{j}$

    b. 55.86 at 103.26°

7. 70 miles at 41.8°

9. 167.8 mph at 304.1°

11. a.

     b.

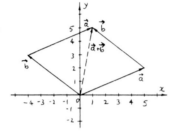

13.

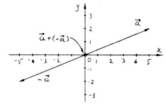

$|\vec{a} + (-\vec{a})| = 0$, so the vector is called the *zero* vector. It has *no* direction.

   c. From diagram,
   $\vec{a} + \vec{b} = \vec{b} + \vec{a}$

15. For each real number c, the product $c\,\vec{a}$ is a *unique vector*, which means that {vectors} is closed under multiplication by a scalar. The zero vector is necessary to insure closure since c could equal zero.

17. $S = \{\dfrac{7\pi}{6}, \dfrac{11\pi}{6}\}$

19. 58.5927...° or 121.4072...°

Exercise 5-9, pages 281-292; Real-World Triangle Problems

1. *Flagpole Problem*

    17.19 m

3. *Raindrop Vector Problem*

    a. 71° 34'

    b. 126.5 km/h

5. *Swimming Problem 1*

    Velocity = 5.8 km/h at 59° to heading

7. *Mountain Height Problem*

    445.7 m

9. *Missile Problem*

    a. 0.6327 km

    b. 0.1265 km/s = 455.5 km/h

    c. 53° 07'

11. *Oil Well Problem 1*

    a. 3042 feet

    b. 27.51 feet

    c. 132 feet deeper

13. *Oil Well Problem 3*

    a. 383.7 feet

    b. 1338 feet

15. *Stump Force Problem*

    a. Force is 439.5 pounds. They can pull up the stump.

    b. Angle $= 54°\ 54'$

17. *Velocity Components Problem*

    a. 38 km/h west

    b. 33 km/h north

19. *Canal Barge Problem*

Yank must pull with a force of about *66 pounds*, and the resultant force is about *111 pounds*.

21. *Ship's Velocity Problem*

25.14 knots at $166°\ 29'$

23. *Detour Problem*

    a. 8.69 km further.

    b. 607.5 km^2

24. *Surveying Problem 1*

    a. $133°\ 21'$

    b. 6838 m^2

25. *Surveying Problem 2*

    a. 4476 m^2

    b. 137.5 m

    c. $42°\ 57'$; $58°\ 03'$

27. *Ivan Problem 1*

16.52 km

29. *Ivan Problem 3*

    a. $111°\ 48'$

    b. 16.25 km^2

31. *CB Radio Problem*

Between 4.13 km and 9.44 km

33. a. Torpedoes can be fired from $279°\ 53'$ through $36°\ 07'$.

    b. Short-range torpedoes will never reach the target's path.

35. $S = \{0° + 45n°\}$

37.

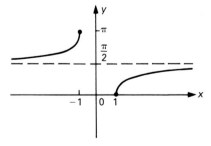

39. $4\frac{4}{9}$

Exercise 5-10, pages 293-295; Chapter Review and Test

Review Problems

R1. a. $m\angle Z = 34° \ 23'$

   $m\angle X = 55° \ 37'$

   $x = 12.1$ cm

b. $m\angle J = 50° \ 06'$

   $b = 12.19$ km

   $j = 14.58$ km

R2. a. $f = 25.78$

   $m\angle U = 18° \ 00'$

   $m\angle N = 16° \ 40'$

b. $m\angle M = 120° \ 00'$

   $m\angle Y = 32° \ 12'$

   $m\angle G = 27° \ 48'$

   c.   i. $b = 480.5$ cm

      $s = 475.0$ cm

   ii. 23.30 cm or 10.99 cm

R3.   Area $= 51.76$

R4. $|\vec{a} - \vec{b}| = 15.98$

   Angle $= 3° \ 45'$

R5. a. $\theta = 7° \ 36'$

   b. 3027 lb

Chapter 5 Test

T1. a. 254.9 km/h

   b. 22.56 km/h

   c. 2777 sq units

   Objectives: 2c, 3, 4, 5

T3. 4° 10'

   Objectives: 2b, 4, 5

T2. a. 84.2 km/h

   b. 87.2 km/h

   Objectives: 1b, 4, 5

CHAPTER 6. Mathematical Applications of Trigonometric and Circular Functions

Exercise 6-1, pages 301-303; Polar Coordinates

1,
3,
5,
7.

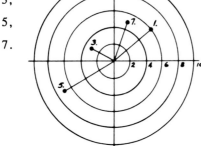

Examples of ordered pairs, Problems 1 through 8:

1. (6, 400°), (–6, 220°) 3. (3, 510°), (–3, –30°)

5. (7, 210°), (–7, 390°) 7. (5, 70°), (–5, –110°)

9. $r = 1 + 2 \sin \theta$ 11. $r = 5 + 4 \cos \theta$

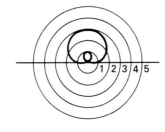

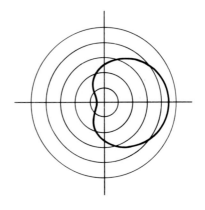

13. $r = 1 + \sin \theta$

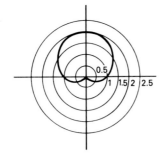

15. *Limaçon Conclusions Problem*
In $r = c + a \cos (\theta - d)$, if $a > c$, then r will sometimes be *negative*. In this case, the limaçon will have a loop.

443

17. $r = \cos \theta$

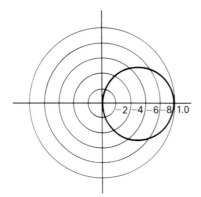

19. $r = \tan \theta$

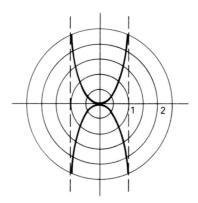

21. $r = \csc \theta$

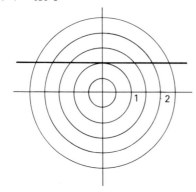

23. *Sine and Cosine Polar Graphs Problem*

   Conjecture: $r = \sin \theta$ and $r = \cos \theta$ have graphs that are *circles*. See Problem 8 in Exercise 6-2, and Problem 23 in Exercise 6-3.

25.

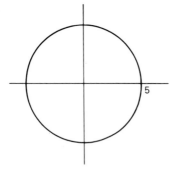

$r = 5$

Graph is a *circle* of radius 5 units, centered at the pole.

27. *Triangle and Line Problem*
   a. $r = 7 \sec \theta$
   b. This verifies that a line in polar coordinates has the form $r = k \sec \theta$, where k is a constant.

29. Prove: $\sec x \cos \tan^2 x = \sec^2 x - 1$
   Proof: $\sec x \cos x \tan^2 x$
   $= 1 \cdot \tan^2 x$
   $= \sec^2 x - 1$
   $\therefore \sec x \cos x \tan^2 x = \sec^2 x - 1$,
      Q.E.D.

Exercise 6-2, pages 305-309; Polar Graphs by Computer

1. $r = \cos \theta$

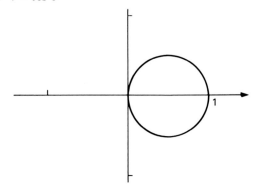

3. $r = \tan \theta$

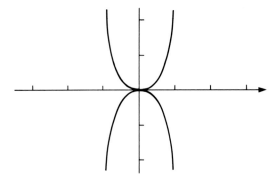

5. $r = \csc \theta$

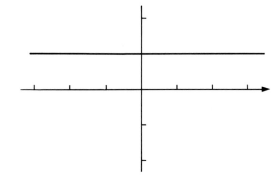

7. *Polar Equations of Lines Problem*

   a.   i. $r = 3 \sec \theta$

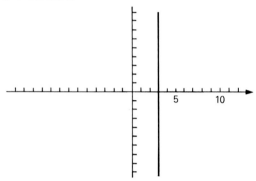

      ii. $r = 3 \sec (\theta - 60°)$

        Use these lines in PLOT POLAR.

        1 DEF FNR(T) $= \dfrac{3}{\cos} (T - \dfrac{PI}{3})$

        210 IF COS $(T - \dfrac{PI}{3}) = 0$ THEN 295

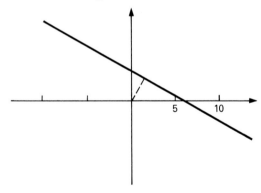

   b. Each line is 3 units from the pole.

   c. If the argument is $(\theta - 60°)$ instead of θ, the graph is rotated 60° counterclockwise about the origin.

   d. $r = 3 \csc \theta$

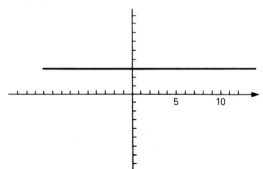

11. *Conic Sections Problem*

   a. $r = \dfrac{10}{(5 + 3 \cos \theta)}$

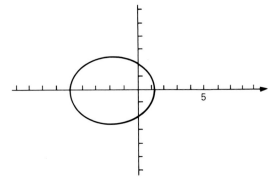

   b. $r = \dfrac{10}{(3 + 5 \cos \theta)}$

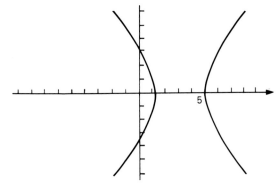

   c. $r = \dfrac{10}{(4 + 4 \cos \theta)}$

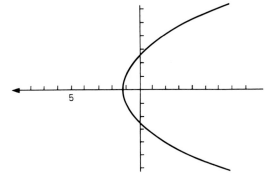

   d. Part (a): Ellipse
       Part (b): Hyperbola
       Part (c): Parabola

   e. If the limaçon has *no* loop, the conic is an *ellipse*. If the limaçon *has* a loop, the conic is a *hyperbola*. If the limaçon is a cardioid, the conic is a *parabola*.

13. $r = 9 \cos \left(\frac{\theta}{2}\right)$

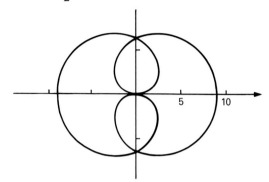

15. $r = 3 \csc \theta + 5$

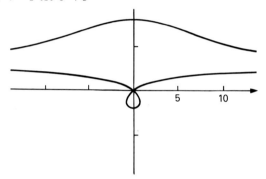

23. 32.4 cm
     196.5 cm^2

Exercise 6-3, pages 311-314;   Polar-Cartesian Transformations

1. a. $x^2 + y^2 - 8x = 0$
    b. circle

3. a. $3x^2 - y^2 - 12x + 9 = 0$
    b. hyperbola

5. a. $11x^2 + 36y^2 - 110x - 121 = 0$
    b. ellipse

7. a. $y^2 + 4x - 4 = 0$
    b. parabola

9. $x^4 + y^4 + 2x^2y^2 - 2x^2y - 2y^3 - x^2 = 0$

11. $x^3 + xy^2 - y^2 = 0$

13. $y^2 = x^3$

15. $r = \sec \theta \tan \theta$

17. $r = 5$

19. $r = -2 \cos \theta$

25. About 4800 lb

27. $S = \{77°, 137°\}$

Exercise 6-4, pages 319-322; Systems of Polar Equations

1. *Polar Coordinates of the Same Point Problem*

a.

b.

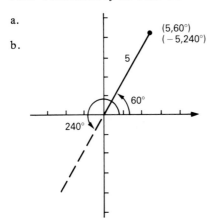

(5,60°)
(−5,240°)

5

60°

240°

c. $5 = 5\,(-1)n$ and $\theta = 60° + 180n°$
    $n = 4$: $r = 5$ and $\theta = 60° + 720°$, which coincides with (5, 60°)
    $n = -3$: $r = -5$ and $\theta = 60° - 540°$, which coincides with (−5, 240°)

3. a. $r = 8 \cos \theta$
    $r = 5$

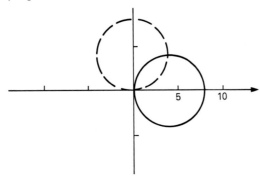

5   10

b. (0, 0°), $(4\sqrt{2}, 45°)$

5. a. $r = 10 \cos \theta$
        $r = 5$

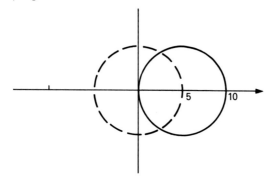

    b. $(5, 60°)$, $(5, -60°)$

7. a. $r = 4 + 4 \cos \theta$
        $r = 4 - 4 \sin \theta$

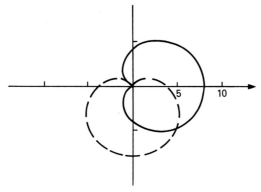

    b. $(0, 0°)$, $(1.17..., 45°)$, $(6.82..., -45°)$

9. a. $r = 8 + 6 \cos \theta$
        $r = 5$

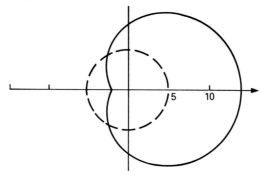

    b. $(5, 120°)$, $(5, -120°)$

11. a. $r = \dfrac{20}{8 + 6 \cos \theta}$

   $r = 5$

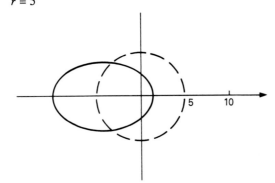

   b. $(5, 131.81...°), (5, -131.81...°)$

13. a. $r = 1 + 7 \sin \theta$

   $r = 4$

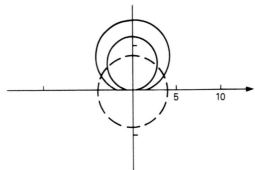

   b. $(4, 25.37...°), (4, 154.62...°), (4, 45.58...°) \; (4, 134.41...°)$

15. a. $r = 5 + 3 \cos \theta$

   $r = 4 - 6 \cos \theta$

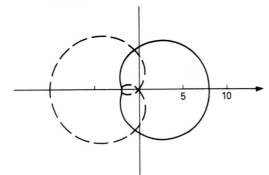

   b. $(4.66..., 96.37...°), (4.66..., -96.37...°), (-2, 0°)$

17. a. $r = 6 + 4 \cos \theta$
$\quad\quad r = 2 - 4 \cos \theta$

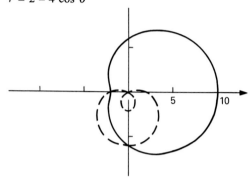

b. (2, 180°), (6, –90°)

19. a. $r = 4 + 6 \cos \theta$
$\quad\quad r = -2 + 6 \sin \theta$

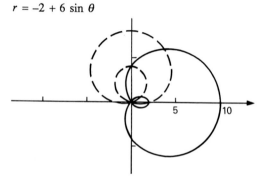

b. (0, 0°), (4, 90°), (2, 0°), (7.12..., 58.63...°), (1.12..., 31.33...°)

21. *Limaçon and Rose Problem*
$\quad\quad r = 5 + 3 \cos \theta$
$\quad\quad r = 8 \cos 2\theta$

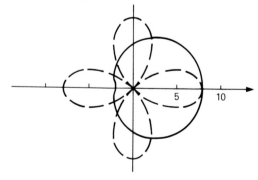

(8, 0°), (2.5625, 144.34...°), (2.5625, –144.34...°),
(3.38..., –122.46...°), (3.38..., 122.46...°),
(6.04..., –69.55...°), (6.04..., 69.55...°)

23. *Spiral and Line Problem*

(0, 0), $(0.5 + n\frac{\pi}{2}$, where n is an integer

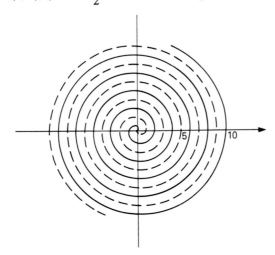

25. *Spaceship and Meteorite Problem*

(2.91..., 61.47...°) and (2.91..., –61.47...°) are *simultaneous* solutions of the two equations, meaning the meteorite *will* collide with the spaceship.

Exercise 6-5, pages 327-330; Imaginary and Complex Numbers

1. a. $4i$
   b. $4i$

3. a. $3i\sqrt{2}$
   b. $4.24...i$

5. a. $i\sqrt{7}$
   b. $2.64...i$

7. i

9. $-i$

11. -1

13. 1

15. 1

17. i

19. -1

21. 0

23.

25.

27.

29.

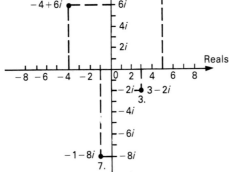

31. 5

33. 13

39.

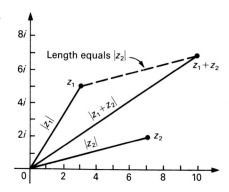

a. Length of lines equal absolute values of numbers.

b. Length = $|z_2|$. See graph.

c. $|z_1 + z_2| \leq |z_1| + |z_2|$ because each is the length of the side of a triangle, and no side of a triangle can be longer than the sum of the other two lengths.

41.

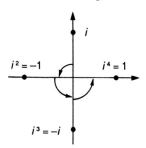

43. $z = \frac{\sqrt{2}}{2}(1 + i)$, $z^2 = (\frac{\sqrt{2}}{2}(1 + i))^2 = \frac{2}{4}(1 + 2i + i^2) = \frac{1}{2}(1 + 2i - 1) = i$.

So $\frac{\sqrt{2}}{2}(1 + i) = \sqrt{i}$, Q.E.D.

45. 0.003 inch

47. $r = \cos 2\theta$

Four-leaved rose

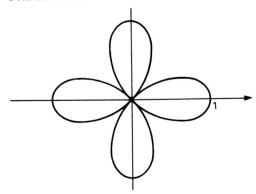

49. *Complex Conjugate Problem*

The number and its conjugate are a + bi and a – bi, where *a* and *b* are real numbers and
$i^2 = -1$

$\therefore (a + bi)(a - bi)$

$= a^2 - b^2 i^2$

$= a^2 + b^2,$

which is a real number by closure under multiplication and addition, Q.E.D.

Exercise 6-6, pages 335-337; Complex Numbers in Polar Form

1. $\sqrt{2}$ cis 45°   3. $\sqrt{2}$ cis 135°   5. 2 cis 60°   7. 2 cis 330°

9. 5 cis 306° 52'   11. 5 cis 216° 52'   13. cis 0°

15. cis 270°   17. $-3 + 3\sqrt{3}$ i   19. $-5\sqrt{2} - 5\sqrt{2}$ i

21. –5   23. –3i   25. 6.632 + 4.474i

27. a. 15 cis 83°   b. $\frac{3}{5}$ cis 11°   c. 9 cis 24°   d. 125 cis 108°

29. a. 8 cis 289°   b. 2 cis 187°   c. 16 cis 116°   d. 8 cis 153°

31. 3 cis 40°   33. 2 cis 20°

    3 cis 160°   2 cis 110°

    3 cis 280°   2 cis 200°

                                             2 cis 290°

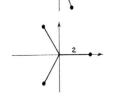

35. cis 45°   37. 2 cis 0°

    cis 225°   2 cis 120°

                                             2 cis 240°

39.   cis 30°

   cis 90°

   cis 150°

   cis 210°

   cis 270°

   cis 330°

41. $\cos 3\theta = \cos^3 \theta - 3 \cos \theta \sin^2 \theta$

   $\sin 3\theta = 3 \cos^2 \theta \sin \theta - \sin^3 \theta$

43.   a. $-8 = 8$ cis 180°

   $\sqrt[3]{-8} = 2$ cis 60°, 2 cis 180°, or 2 cis 300°

   b.   2 cis 180° = -2

   c. $64 = 64$ cis 0°, so $\sqrt[6]{64} = 2$ cis 0°, 2 cis 60°, 2 cis 120°, 2 cis 180°,

   2 cis 240°, or 2 cis 300

   d. $2 = 2$ cis 0°, and $-2 = 2$ cis 180°, both of which are cube roots of 64.

   e.   The numbers underlined in part c, above, are cube roots of -8. The others are *not* cube roots of -8.

44. $(-8)^{\sqrt{3}} = [8 \text{ cis } (180° + 360n°)]^{\sqrt{3}} = 8^{\sqrt{3}} \text{ cis } \sqrt{3}(180 + 360n)°$

   Infinite number of values: Each time n increases by 1, θ increases by $360\sqrt{3}°$. Since $360\sqrt{3}n$ is *irrational* except for $n = 0$, it is never an integer multiple of 360°. Therefore, no two values can be coterminal.

   None real: Since $\sqrt{3}(180 + 360n)°$ is *irrational* for all integer values of n, it is never an integer multiple of 180°. Therefore, the number never lies along the real axis.

45.   About 285 lb

49. $r = 3 + \sin \theta$

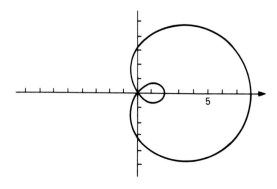

Exercise 6-7, pages 340-342; Complex Numbers for Vectors

1. $-1.742 + 3.709\ i$ 3. $-6.247 - 2.733\ i$ 5. $3.167 - 0.556\ i$

7. 4.098 cis 115.2°   9. 6.819 cis 203.6°   11. 3.215 cis 350.0°

13. *Pirate Problem*

   a. (92, 125)   b.   156 cis 54°

15. *Neutron Problem*

   a. Displacement = 42.30 cis 35° 32'

   b. Since horizontal displacement is only 34.42 cm and the shielding is 35 cm thick, the neutron is still in the shielding.

17. *Identity Problem*

   a. $1 + \tan2\ x = \sec2\ x$

   b. $\tan\ x\ = \dfrac{\sin\ x}{\cos\ x}$

   c. $\csc\ x = \dfrac{1}{\sin\ x}$

   d. $\cos\ (A + B) = \cos A\ \cos B - \sin A\ \sin B$

   e. $\sin\ 2a = 2\ \sin\ A\ \cos\ A$

   f. $\tan \frac{1}{2}A\ = \dfrac{\sin\ A}{1 + \cos\ A} = \dfrac{1 - \cos\ A}{\sin\ A}$

   g. $\sin\ A + \sin\ B = 2\ \sin\ \frac{1}{2}\ (A + B)\ \cos\ \frac{1}{2}\ (A- B)$

   h. $\sec\ x = \csc\ (\frac{\pi}{2} - x)$ or $\sec\ \theta = \csc\ (90° - \theta)$

   i. $\cot\ (-x) = -\ \cot\ x$

   j. $A\ \cos\ \theta + B\ \sin\ \theta = C\ \cos\ (\theta - D)$,

   where $C = \sqrt{A^2 + B^2}$ and

   $D = \arccos\ (\frac{A}{C})$ and $D = \arcsin\ (\frac{B}{C})$.

19. $y^2 + 2x - 1 = 0$

   Parabola

Exercise 6-8, pages 344-346; Introduction to Power Series

1. a. $f(0.2) \approx 1.2214000$ b. $f(0.2) \approx 1.2214027$

   c. $f(0.2) \approx 1.2214028$

2. Since the seventh term contributes nothing to the first 6 decimal places, $f(0.2)$ should be accurate to 6 *decimal places* if you use only the first six terms.

3. $f(1) \approx 2.71828$

4.

m	$(1 + \frac{1}{m})^m$
10	2.59374
100	2.70481
10,000	2.71815
100,000	2.71827

5. As m gets larger, $(1 + \frac{1}{m})^m$ gets closer to $f(1)$.

∴ $e ≈ 2.71828$

6. $e^{0.2} ≈ 2.71818^{0.2} ≈ 1.22140 ≈ f(0.2)$

7. $f(x) = e^x$

8. $g(x) = 1 - \frac{x^2}{2!} + \frac{x^4}{4!} - \frac{x^6}{6} + \frac{x^8}{8!} - \frac{x^{10}}{10!} + \frac{x^{12}}{12!} \cdots$

9. g is an even function since all terms have even degree.

10. $g(0.2) ≈ 0.9801$

11. $g(-0.2) ≈ 0.9801$ since g is an even function.

12. $h(x) = x - \frac{x^3}{3!} + \frac{x^5}{5!} - \frac{x^7}{7} + \frac{x^9}{9!} - \frac{x^{11}}{11!} + \frac{x^{13}}{13!} - \cdots$

13. h is an *odd* function since all terms have odd degree.

14. $h(0.2) ≈ 0.1987$

15. $h(-0.2) ≈ -0.1987$ since h is an odd function

16. $g(x) = \cos x$ and $h(x) = \sin x$

17. $g(0) = 1 = \cos 0$, and $h(0) = 0 = \sin 0$

Exercise 6-9, pages 350-354; Taylor Series for Sine, Cosine, and Exponential Functions

1.

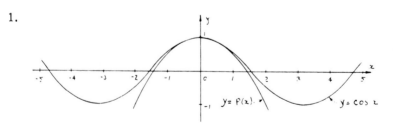

Graphs are close together for $-0.8 < x < 0.8$.

3.

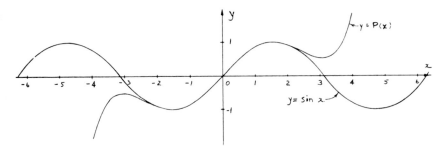

Graphs are close together for $-2 < x < 2$.

4. $\sin 0.3 \approx 0.29552$ 5. $\cos 0.3 \approx 0.95534$

6. $e^{0.3} \approx 1.34986$ 10. $\sin 25° \approx 0.42262$

15. e^{3i} 17. $3e^{2i}$ 19. $\sqrt{2}\, e^{i\frac{\pi}{4}}$ 21. $2e^{-i\frac{\pi}{6}}$ 23. $e^{i\frac{\pi}{2}}$

26. $e^{i\pi} = \cos \pi + i \sin \pi = -1 + 0i = -1$

     $\therefore e^{i\pi} = -1$, Q.E.D.

27. $i^i \approx 0.2079$

30.

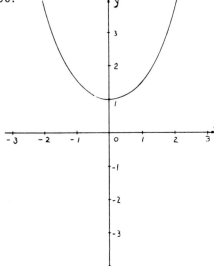

$y = \cosh x$

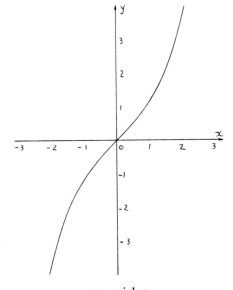

$y = \sinh x$

31. $\tanh x = \dfrac{\sin x}{\cosh x}$ $\operatorname{sech} x = \dfrac{1}{\cosh x}$

      $\coth x = \dfrac{\cosh x}{\sinh x}$ $\operatorname{csch} x = \dfrac{1}{\sinh x}$

32. a.

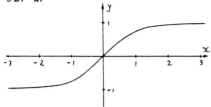

$$y = \tanh x$$

b.

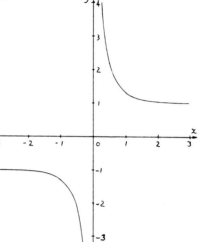

$$y = \coth x$$

c.

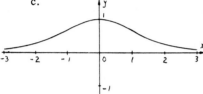

$$y = \text{sech } x$$

d.

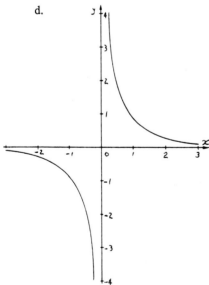

$$y = \text{csch } x$$

Exercise 6-10, pages 354-358;   Chapter Review and Test
Review Problems

R1. a.

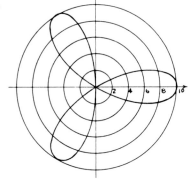

$$r = 10 \cos 3\theta$$

b.

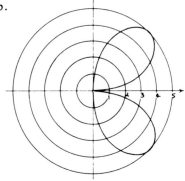

$$r = 10(\cos \theta \cdot |\sin \theta|)$$

c.

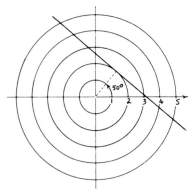

$$r = 2 \sec (\theta - 50°)$$

d.

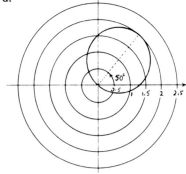

$$r = 2 \cos (\theta - 50°)$$

e.

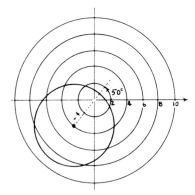

$$r^2 + 8r (\theta - 50°) - 9 = 0$$

R2. a. $(x^2 + y^2)^3 = 4x^2y^2$ b. $r = 6 \cos \theta$

R4. a. $10i$

    b. $\dfrac{3\sqrt{3}}{2} - \dfrac{3}{2} i$

    c. $-16\sqrt{2} + 16\sqrt{2}i$

    d. $1.532 + 1.286i$, $-1.879 + 0.6840i$, $0.3473 - 1.970i$

R5. Force ≈ 1034 cis $156°$ 09'

R6. a. $\sin 0.06 \approx 0.0599640065$

    b. $\cos (ix)$ $= 1 - \dfrac{(ix)^2}{2!} + \dfrac{(ix)^4}{4!} - \dfrac{(ix)^6}{6!} + \ldots$

                $= 1 + \dfrac{x^2}{2!} + \dfrac{x^4}{4!} + \dfrac{x^6}{6!} = \cosh x$

                $= \cosh x$

        $\therefore \cos (ix) = \cosh x$, Q.E.D.

    c. $\cos i = \cosh 1 = \frac{1}{2}(e^1 + e^{-1}) \approx 1.543$, which is a *real* number, *greater than 1*.

Chapter Test

T1. $\overrightarrow{v} = a\,(\emptyset \text{ cis } (\emptyset) - 90°)$.

    Objectives: 4, and review of Section 2-11

T2. Objectives: 3, 4, and review of Section 3-3

T3. Objectives: 4, and review of Sections 3-1 and 3-8

T4. Objective: 1

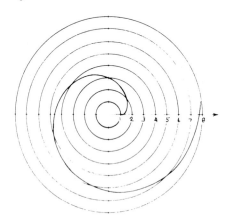

T5. a. 0.458258 rad

  b. 1° 38'

  Objectives: Review of Sections 1-5 and 1-6, and real-world app.

T6. a. $f(x) = x - \dfrac{x^3}{3} + \dfrac{x^5}{5} - \dfrac{x^7}{7} + \dfrac{x^9}{9} - \dfrac{x^{11}}{11} + \dfrac{x^{13}}{13} - \cdots$

  b. $f(0.3) \approx 0.2915$.   c. Arctan $0.3 \approx 0.2915$

  d. $f(x)$ = Arctan x. $f(0)$ = Arctan $0 = 0$, f and Arctan are *odd*.

  Objectives: 5, new situation

T7. a. (6, 90°) satisfies first equation but not second one.

  b. (2, 16, −163.739...°)